In Time of War
Growing up During the Nazi Occupation
and its Aftermath

Anna R. Dadlez

In Time of War
Growing up During the Nazi Occupation
and its Aftermath

Published by The John Paul II Catholic University of Lublin

Lublin 2006

IN MEMORY OF

Jadzia Dadlez

and other youthful members of the Home Army (AK)
killed in the Warsaw Uprising (August – October 1944).

"Thus the gallant resistance of the Poles to German occupation, which had never faltered and had rightly won the admiration of the democratic world, had ended with the obliteration of their capital and the establishment, not of the freedom for which they fought, but of an imposed government which gave the heroes of resistance a choice between exile, outlawry or capitulation to the puppets of a foreign power."

Hugh Seton-Watson, *The East European Revolution*

"The word Holocaust suggests to most people the tragedy the Jews experienced under the Germans during World War II ... Yet, by excluding others from inclusion in the Holocaust, the horrors that Poles, other Slavs, and Gypsies endured at the hands of the Nazis are often ignored, if not forgotten ... From the historical point of view, no reasonable student of World War II can deny that Hitler's policy toward Poles was also genocidal and that about as many Polish Christians as Polish Jews died as a result of Nazi terror. Without detracting from the particularity of the Jewish tragedy ... it is time to speak about the forgotten Holocausts of World War II."

Richard C. Lukas, *The Forgotten Holocaust*

Contents

Foreword

Anna Dadlez's remarkable novel is novel in many respects. It is novel conceptually, it is novel in its historical accuracy, it is novel in the author's not pushing any political agenda.

The sensitive description of life during two hostile occupations by two Great Powers with opposing ideologies but similar methods of control and domination in divided wartime Poland focuses, most originally, on the impact of war on children and their psychological and intellectual evolution and secondly, on the lives of women in times of political terror and economic hardships.

Dadlez subscribes to the current interpretation of the history of wartime Poland averring that not only Jews but also Christians were victimized by the Nazis and their supporters. She rightly stresses the significance of the Polish independence and punishment of Polish collaborators with the Nazis. However, she is aware of the reality that not all inhabitants of wartime Poland shared the moral and cultural values and the patriotism of the author's world. That world was proud of the historic traditions of the "Borderland of Western Civilization." It was proud of the Polish constitution that antedated the last Partition of Poland in the last decade of the eighteenth century. It was proud of the Polish scientific and cultural contributions to Western Civilization. It was proud of Poland's Catholic heritage.

That Poland, however, reconstituted as it was at the end of World War I was unable to withstand the crises of the inter-war years. Located between Nazi Germany and Bolshevik Russia it had to accommodate itself to the realities of international politics. With territories occupied and coveted by both Germany and Russia, for some Poles collaboration with the Nazis was preferable to surrender to the communists. Few were those who foresaw the Soviet takeover with the acquiescence of an ally who declared war on Germany in 1939 because of Hitler's invasion of Poland and who endorsed the United States' proclaimed goal of making the world safe for democracy.

The most remarkable feature of Dadlez's collective recollections is the awareness of the children, parents, relatives and friends that "life must go on." And it is precisely because the novel is dedicated to recalling the life experiences of real people during uncertain and perilous times that the survival and, then, the eventual revival of the fundamental human and cultural values that were shared by a significant segment of Polish society could transcend the tragedies and miseries of war and oppression.

The resurgence of an independent Poland, member of NATO and the European Union, is indeed encouraging. But the recollections of the survivors should serve as a lesson of the unpredictability of how the lives of decent, peace loving, people can be affected, even transformed, by forces and rivalries – internal and external – over which they have at best only marginal control.

Stephen Fischer-Galati
Distinguished University Professor,
Emeritus (University of Colorado)
and Editor of East European Quarterly
and East European Monographs

Introduction

I grew up in Poland and in the Soviet Union during World War II, and the experience is still with me. The Soviet impact on Poland during this period was enormous, and it was an impact that I experienced personally as a deportee to the USSR. However, the effects of the Nazi occupation were equally disastrous and far-reaching. (It is worth remembering that for some twenty-two months both Hitler and Stalin were good friends, loyally collaborating in the destruction of Poland. This honeymoon ended with the German attack on the USSR, which forced the Soviet Union into the camp of the allies.) I did not experience the German occupation personally, at least not for long. Rather, I saw it through the eyes of my husband's family, friends, and acquaintances, most of whom were still children at the time of the Nazi occupation of Poland. Some of these experiences I related to my students. Some of them I recollected when I felt in need of inspiration. Any member of the Polish expatriate community heard such stories, or told them, or passed them on to others. These were personal stories about particular experiences. They are not the stuff of history texts but a part of the fabric of individual lives that collectively become history.

It was only about three years ago that I decided to amass and retell these stories. After some consideration, I also decided to present them in fictional form. There were several reasons for my decision. First, I believed that it was important to present particular, human, examples rather than mere broad outlines. This is better expressed in fiction. It is also something that can make a subject more accessible to students, which I have found time and again in my teaching. Some of the stories related to me involved childhood experiences, and fiction seemed the most effective means of retaining that perspective. Finally, the deeply personal nature of the experiences which were related to me were more readily expressible in this form. It is, after all, literature rather than history that Aristotle associates with the universal. It is poetry that captures the essence of the human experience. The novel I have written is one in which fact and fiction closely coincide.

My methods involved the traditional research of the professional academic, as is consistent with my background and training.[1] These stood me in good stead in providing an adequate historical backdrop against which to consider the new information I received, and in enabling me to evaluate the information critically. My methods went beyond traditional approaches in embracing personal narratives of wartime experience. In the course of my research interviews, I visited various people in Poland and talked to some in the United States and Canada. My memory also went back to my sojourn in England in the late 1940s when young members of the AK, the Polish Underground army, became my friends. Despite the terrifying news from our country, then under Soviet rule, nearly all of them returned, as did Nina in the novel. "We must build Poland again," they told me. "But you cannot build it abroad. Our place is there, Russians or no Russians." I can sincerely say that if it were not for the loss of my father and experience in Kazakhstan, and my mother's and my pathological fear of the Soviets, I might have followed their example.

Those stories have been with me all the time, but in order to write about them and to be more intimately connected with them, I decided to interview the survivors, as many as I could find in the United States, Canada, and Poland. There is hardly any story in the book that was not related to me as a personal experience. We know that the memories of elderly persons may play tricks; it is also true that the persons involved might not have understood the broader ramifications of the political scene at the time of their youth. (Although there is no denying that children grow into adults very quickly in times of war, it is still undeniable that their psychological awareness of and reaction to danger are different.) Yet the basic experiences of these individuals – their fears and hopes – survived, and apart from the circumstances found an echo in my own life under Soviet rule. They will also be understood in any society torn by war and suffering under a foreign hostile occupation, where personal and national issues blend to become indistinguishable.

---

[1]   I earned my Ph.D. in political science, history, and economics, with a concentration on Eastern Europe, from Syracuse University's Maxwell School in 1973.

Author's Note

The issue of 'globalism' which is becoming fashionable nowadays implies communication, and meaningful communication requires knowledge of what other people think and why. To understand others we must know their past experiences for, to paraphrase Marx, the environment in which people live affects their consciousness and their behavior. However, because of our country's superpower status, the outside world has become much more familiar with our way of life than we are with theirs, despite inaccurate media representations.[2] Since we are better known to them than they are to us, it is our duty, if we are really interested in 'globalism,' to learn about other countries, their past and their present.

The present experience of American youth does not, thankfully, include foreign and hostile occupation. It is natural that, for them, the most important things in life do not revolve around questions of food and shelter, efforts to avoid arrest, interrogations, and even the possibility of collaboration with the enemy. For the young people of Warsaw during World War II on the other hand, the problems of our youngsters would appear trivial, unreal, having nothing to do with solving what they considered real-life dilemmas. In comparison to the lives of Americans with their almost unlimited array of options, the Varsovians under the Nazi occupation had very few choices open to them, but each choice affected their very existence. Consequently, life was always dangerous but, in a way, much simpler.

This book describes the experiences of three Polish girls and a boy (a street urchin), their faithful assistant and advisor, in Warsaw and other parts of Poland during the years 1939-1945. These include the desperate defense of the city, its hostile occupation, and the two uprisings. It presents that part of the Second World War which is not familiar in the West. Although the Jewish Ghetto uprising of 1943 described in this work has found a relatively adequate exposure in the American media, the Polish anti-Nazi uprising of 1944, which left hundreds of thousands dead and the capital a heap of rubble, has not received equal attention. The historical background of the story has been painstakingly researched, and frequent references are given to the sources. For the rest, the author drew on her own experiences as a Polish teenager, "an enemy of the people," who was deported to Soviet Kazakhstan.[3]

---

[2]   Carl Berstein, "The Idiot Culture," *New Republic*, 1992.

[3]   The topic was touched upon in my book *Journey from Innocence* (NY: Columbia University Press, 1998).

In the work, an emphasis is placed on the role of children during a hostile foreign occupation anywhere. This aspect of war has not, to my knowledge, been adequately presented in historical publications or in historical fiction. Focused on are: the pressures of growing up in a hurry; responsibilities shared with adults; the reaction of young people, whose concept of death has been hitherto very unclear and vague, to mass killings and the possibility of their own early demise; and, at least among some, the inner struggle between abject submission and defiance. There are also examples of helpless rage which, among the young, may lead to irrational, perhaps even criminal behavior. Contrasted with this is another kind of courage, a psychologically balanced courage based on reason and endurance. Here the importance of religious beliefs and friendship cannot be overestimated.

The portrayal of women, mothers, sisters, and grandmothers, as well as female acquaintances faced with political and economic terror and, in some cases, involved in the Resistance, is also recorded.

To those who detect in the work a 'feminist' flavor, the author admits freely that it was her intention to make it so. Her own life experience convinced her that characters such as those portrayed did indeed exist in war-torn Poland, and probably in other parts of the world. Another possible reservation of a would be critic might have to do with the absence of romantic entanglements. But we are talking about the 1940s. In Poland, and I believe elsewhere at that time, children were not expected to exhibit sexual sophistication. Sex was presented as something one dealt with when one grew up. But even among older people, interest in sex declined markedly during the struggle for survival in the environment engendered by war. "You think that we, the young Serb communists, thought about sex when we were held in the Secret State Police prisons?" asked Professor N. Popovic in his political economy class during my years at Syracuse University in the 1970s. "Well if you do, you are wrong. When your life hangs by a thread, what you think about is survival, family, God... Aphrodite has a very low priority under such conditions." I am convinced that this dictum applies to war-torn parts of the world today.

Although the story deals with human tragedy and suffering, efforts have been made to present the troubles of main characters with humor, when possible. Humor, as many psychiatrists state, is intimately connected with one's ability to live through shattering events. It can act as a defense mechanism, occasionally allowing one to relax, gather one's wits, and go on.

Finally, I would like to stress that the book is not about heroes. It exposes, I hope, significant human frailties and peculiarities which are universal. The occasional emergence of true human brotherhood, even among people who are on different sides of a calamitous conflict, is also, I believe, an integral part of any war.

Chapter One
Childhood: Pre-War Warsaw

When little Krystyna arrived, Mrs. Nowak, a neighbor of the Ilski family, congratulated the parents in a manner markedly less enthusiastic than that she had exhibited on two previous occasions. "Three girls in a row, one after the other. How... nice" she remarked to their mother in somewhat dubious tones. "But wouldn't you like to have a boy? A boy to carry on the family name, to be the protector of his sisters?"

"We are quite happy with our female gang," Mother retorted, laughing. "My husband calls them our three musketeers. If it is a question of the family name, they can always keep it when they marry. I sincerely hope that a male protector will not be necessary. Surely at times like these, they must learn to stand on their own feet." Here Mrs. Nowak was in full agreement. "With this awful Hitler screaming his head off about Germany's right to rule the world, and his counterpart in Russia demanding similar powers, our poor Polish children may indeed have to fend for themselves. God grant that all this does not end in a war," was her pious comment.

That was in 1930s Warsaw, the capital of Poland. Although political and military conflicts loomed on the horizon, for the three Ilski girls life proceeded peacefully, with each of them pursuing different interests. "It is uncanny how different our children are," Mother confided to Mrs. Nowak a few years after Krysia's arrival. "The eldest of our 'three Musketeers,' seems to be a romantic type, inclined toward literature, music, and art. Nina, on the other hand, is a very down-to-earth, rational individual, a sceptic disinclined to take anything for granted. Little Krysia defies description. A five-year-old introvert, a quiet child who, because she has two older sisters, has quickly developed her mental capacities. She often amazes us with her comments."

The above described differences often came up in discussions on various topics which seemed to divide the family into camps. One of the issues constantly raised by Nina was the unfortunate circumstance of her name. "Why was it decided to call me Nina?" she demanded of her grandmother, who moved in with the family when mother had resumed her work at the university. "At least Kinga was a princess and gave a salt mine to Poland,[4] and Krystyna was a famous queen of Sweden, teacher told us. But Nina? Was there any Nina anywhere who did anything worthwhile, for example, by commanding a guerilla detachment like Emilia Plater?"[5] Grandmother admitted that she was unaware of a warrior by the name of Nina. "But the name is very nice," she argued, "Mrs. Nowak says that it reminds her of the sound from a harp." But Nina was not convinced. "Harp, indeed. You should have given the name to Kinga, she would have welcomed it. As for me, I am going to adopt the name Emilia when I am confirmed. I have fixed it up with father already."

What made things worse for Nina was the new French song that became popular in pre-war Poland, entitled *Ninon*, and translated into "Smile to me Nina" in Polish. You could hear it on the radio, in picture houses, on the streets. Nina took it personally. "Smile to me Nina, smile to me Nina" she repeated angrily. "How absolutely sickening! Can anyone tell me why on earth she should smile when she does not feel like it?" Grandmother tried to say that it was nice for a girl to smile, it was polite and it made people happy. In the discussion that ensued, mother and Kinga sided with grandmother but father supported Nina. "An artificial smile is worse than no smile at all," he insisted. As usual when disagreements arose little Krysia sat quietly and listened attentively, her eyes following each of the speakers. When asked what she thought, she declined to commit herself in a hurry. "I have to think about it," she declared. "I will tell you tomorrow."

---

[4]   A legend had it that a Hungarian princess, Kinga, was aware of the lack of salt mines in Poland. On accepting the hand of a Polish Prince in marriage – and inspired by the tales of her old nanny – she threw her engagement ring into one of the salt mines in Hungary. On coming to Poland, Kinga asked her new countrymen to dig in a place she indicated. After digging for some days they came to huge deposits of salt, and in the first salt crystal which was extracted, Kinga's engagement ring was found.

[5]   Emilia Plater was a colonel in the anti-Russian uprising of 1830.

War Rumors

But the hit *Ninon*, like others of the kind, was slowly replaced by more military tunes. Toward the end of the 1930s, no child in Poland was ignorant of the Nazi menace, although it was downplayed by parents. While in school, teachers endeavored to talk to the children about the grievous situation without frightening them. There were hopeful signs of treaties. Assurances were given to Poland by her allies, Britain and France. Kinga, who was almost fourteen, informed her younger sisters that there was nothing to fear. "There is not the least danger to Poland," she lectured twelve-year-old Nina and five-year-old Krysia. "Mr. Hitler and Mr. Stalin would never pick a quarrel with our country."

"But people pick quarrels sometimes," Nina pointed out. "Didn't Mr. Sawicki get drunk last Saturday and attack Mr. Drozd? Aren't Germany and the Soviet Union much bigger than we are?"

"That makes no difference at all," responded Kinga loftily. "They may be as huge as they like. We are not afraid of them!"

"Mr. Drozd might not have been afraid of Mr. Sawicki, but he got thrashed all the same," pursued Nina doggedly. This made Kinga angry. "What kind of a patriot are you to talk like that?" she shouted. "Don't you know what real superiority means? It is with us, not with them. There is not going to be war, do you hear? Rachela says so and she knows. She is fifteen."

It was perhaps natural that Kinga, at fourteen, was grandmother's object of special attention. "The oldest daughter in a family is often treated as if her role consisted of helping to raise the younger children," she told mother. "This should not be so in our case. Kinga is an exceptionally sensitive child; she has a poetic nature and a heightened sense of etiquette; she is entering womanhood. No special demands should be placed on her, please. I am here to take care of things." Take care of things grandmother did, while mother did the shopping on her way home from work and Jozia, the custodian, came weekly to do general cleaning and the laundry. Their father, an architect, was working as a draftsman because of the endemic unemployment for the people in his profession.

Neither a sense of etiquette nor consideration for girls entering womanhood seemed to be on Mr. Hitler's agenda. On September 1, 1939, Nazi Germany attacked Poland. Soon after, the Soviet Union invaded from the east.[6] Those developments

---

[6] "The outbreak of war was made possible by a secret protocol of the 'Pact of Non-Aggression' ... signed in Moscow on 23 August 1939." It was followed by a "'German-Soviet Treaty of Friendship' of 28 September 1939, which also provided for the joint action against the expected Polish Resistance," see Norman Davies, *Heart of Europe* (Cambridge: Oxford University Press, 1966), pp. 64-66.

took only a few weeks but they wrenched changes in the Ilski household that would not otherwise have occurred for years.

It was Kinga who suddenly became an adult when she was saying good-bye to her father, as he left to join the Polish army. "You are the eldest," he told her. "Mother will be overwhelmed, and grandma is elderly so it is up to you to care for them all. Nina will help." To this Kinga listened with mixed feelings. Something in her cried out against this unexpected awesome responsibility. Was mother going to leave them as well? Why should she, Kinga, be considered head of the family? Was she not a sensitive girl whose interests lay in the pursuit of music and art? Didn't grandmother promise her such a future? Wasn't she too young and inexperienced to care for her family? But of course she did not say it, and her heart went out to this parent of hers who stood there so anxious and pathetic. She pulled herself together and trying not to show her panic, assured him with confidence she would do what he had asked, no problem.

It seemed that this good-bye started a whole series of awful events. The very first days of bombing demanded from her fortitude hitherto wholly unimaginable. She was terrified of the bombs which kept dropping from the German planes, and the very sound of sirens filled her with such panic that only the memory of her father and consideration for her family kept her from screaming at the top of her voice and running, running down the deserted streets toward who knew what. Since no other member of her family manifested such propensities, Kinga told herself that she was a weirdo, a coward, undeserving of her father's trust. In Nina's vocabulary such a girl was scornfully called "*niezdara*" or a bungler, and Kinga fought with all her strength the notion of appearing such a weakling. "If I manage to get through these alarms without disgracing myself," she thought, "I will probably remain immune to horrors for life. Didn't Adam Asnyk write: 'Raz w zyciu winien kazdy z Was alpejskiej palmy zdobyc kwiecie' (If only once in life, each of you should obtain the bloom of the alpine palm?) In school we discussed this poem and the teacher explained that the author believed that an act of will and determination in difficult circumstances (i.e., the act of striving toward a lofty, perhaps unobtainable ideal – the alpine palm) would make a person able to face future adversities bravely. Well this is my act of will. I am not going to scream or cry. If I manage this every time the sirens wail, I shall be brave all my life. I don't think that there could be anything worse than that awful sound of oncoming Nazi bombers and the waiting for their diabolical cargo to fall on us," she thought. But Kinga did not know how wrong she was.

On her way back from school (there were still schools open in Warsaw, although attendance had dropped significantly) Kinga used to pass a newly built house with a small garden. On that fatal day, there were agitated people around it talking about the direct artillery hit it had taken and trying to decide if there could still be somebody alive under the ruins. "Thank God it is not our house," Kinga thought, hurrying on. Her relief was mixed with a feeling of shame at finding anything to be happy about in such circumstances. The very next moment, she came across the body of her grandmother lying on the sidewalk. "Some of the bricks were blown away by the blast and reached the pedestrians," a policeman informed the people around. "Do you know this lady? She was hit by a part of the balcony just as she left that grocery store. Can you identify her?" Kinga stepped out and gave the required information as if in a dream. She could not believe that grandmother was really dead. She could not be dead with such a peaceful expression on her face despite the wound and the blood. Kinga had never seen a dead person in real life although she did see them in movies, but movies were quite different. In movies there was no dust in the air, no odor of cement, no odor of blood – if it was blood that she smelled. The behavior of the people in movies was different. A plump lady grabbed her and nearly suffocating her in her arms repeating, "you poor darling, you poor, poor darling." It was then that the sense of reality hit her like a ton of bricks. Not only was her dear grandmother dead, not only was she not coming back, but it was her duty to inform mother and the kids of this terrible tragedy. Oh how pitiless life has become. How good it would have been to be here with grandmother at the time and to have died with her!

The Faltering Defense

After grandmother's burial (at night, in an unfamiliar corner of the cemetery, with a young priest who was in a great hurry to attend to other bereaved relatives), mother changed in a way that the girls found difficult to describe. "She looks the same," whispered Krysia to Nina one night when Kinga was doing her homework and mother was sitting in the kitchen gazing at a window covered by black cloth in order to discourage the Nazi bombers from targeting any sign of human habitation. "What is it that makes her so changed?" Nina thought for a while. "It is the grief that does it," she finally said. "Father's departure was the first thing and now grandmother … and it is all this worry that the war is going badly."

"Kinga has changed also," whispered the little girl unhappily. "She does not sleep at night. I don't even want to talk to her any more. She seems so distracted. Tell me Nina, are you… are you going to change also?" she asked in a terrified whisper. "Not I," Nina answered with an assurance that surprised herself. "Somebody in this family must be above change. We will manage, don't you worry Krysia. I'll see to it. Do you want a drink of water before bed?"

"No, thank you. Thank you dear, dear Nina," was the grateful reply. "Thank you for being the same."

"No problem," replied the second musketeer.

Although Nina firmly decided that she would not change, things around her changed continually from bad to worse. There was no news of father, and terrible rumors about the decimated army now fighting on two fronts, against the Nazis and against the Soviets, was reported on the radio by speakers who all seemed to have lumps in their throats. Hopes of foreign intervention, so readily promised by the Allies, were not fulfilled and Nina, for one, did not believe that help was coming. The bombing continued; the food supplies ran short. Kinga believed that "we should attend school as long as possible," to which Nina turned a deaf ear. "Going to school at a time when the whole city seems to collapse around us can only seem proper to females like Kinga," she grumbled. "Doesn't she know that the school will be gone in a matter of days, even if the bombs don't touch the building? With the defeat of Poland (here Nina looked around, for mother forbade them to talk about it) we will have a hard time finding food, let alone worrying about education. The winter will come shortly. We haven't sufficient supplies of food and fuel, and the stores are either closed or empty."

Nina tried to remember grandmother's stories about the first World War, when she bribed a Russian soldier with her ruby ring to free great uncle Edward. But would a ring be helpful in getting food in occupied Warsaw? Nina did not know but decided to take inventory of all the saleable things the family possessed. If it comes to the worst, she reasoned, a German soldier might be just as much attracted to a piece of jewelry as was the Russian. The Germans would have food. She decided to make a list of what jewels there were and to hide them. The stories of searches so prominent in Polish war literature came to her mind in all their impressive colors. People hiding weapons in forests; women stitching golden chains to the collars of their coats and putting diamonds in holes drilled in the heels of their shoes. Neither mother, still working, nor Kinga, assiduously attending courses several hours a day in a variety of locations, objected to her putting their valuables in the cellar among lumps of coal, but were of the opinion that it was unnecessary. On the whole, neither mother nor Kinga seemed to be interested in what Nina was doing, and appeared only mildly appreciative when she dragged home a sack of potatoes she had traded for her skirt in the suburbs, where there were still some farmers' markets. The fact that in order to not walk home skirtless, Nina had to tie her sweater around her hips, did not elicit any comments from the two older females either. Only little Krysia looked at Nina's strange attire with surprise and asked her questions.

"Well, I went to the farmer's market to find out how much food I could get for my watch," Nina embarked on her story sitting on the kitchen floor and inspecting the potatoes one by one. "These are nice firm spuds you could not find in any of the city stores that are still open," she exclaimed in a self congratulatory manner. "There was a woman with a cart full of potatoes and with her a little girl. When I went around the wagon trying to determine what was in the sacks, the kid (her name was Nanka, by the way) grabbed my old red pleated skirt, the one mother bought me years ago when Kinga got her shoes and you the blue dress, and started yelling that she wanted it. Her mother did not pay much attention at first, but when Nanka's howls kept increasing in volume – we can consider ourselves lucky that you do not throw such tantrums too often..." The narrative was interrupted by the vehement and assertive "I never, never throw tantrums," from the listener, "... her mother, embarrassed by the people looking in our direction, tried to hush her up. Then somebody cried that the artillery fire seemed to be aimed in our direction. 'I don't have money, only what is on the cart,' whispered the woman to me, 'and we have to leave. Last week they requisitioned my neighbor's horse... Would you accept payment in potatoes? You have another skirt under this one, don't you?' I almost burst out laughing. Who has heard of wearing two skirts at the same time? So I told her that I haven't, but not to worry, I could make one out of my sweater. I must say she did not look convinced and the deal would have probably fallen through if the little monster, seeing the hesitation of her mama, did not start emitting ear piercing shrieks. 'All right, then, take the whole sack for the skirt, but let me see how you look,' said the woman, and after inspecting my makeshift skirt and tightening the sleeves around my waist, she put the brat (now clutching her new acquisition) on the cart and drove away. She turned once and looking at me with a worried expression and called 'God be with you, hurry back to your mom, girl. I will try to be here again on Wednesday next week and will give you another sack of potatoes free.'"

Krysia was duly impressed. "Did the artillery shots come near?"

"I don't know if they did, for I grabbed the sack and ran. But you know I could not run for long, those potatoes were terribly heavy. I was carrying them on my back and the sweater kept sliding down on me and I did not have a safety pin or anything. I give you my word, if it weren't for grandma's lectures on young ladies behavior I would have given up on decency and walked on in my underwear!"

"You wouldn't!" breathed Krysia in shocked disbelief. "What would people have said?"

"Oh I would have, never fear," was the eager response, "and I would not be the only one either. Only this morning Mrs. Nowak was telling mother that five gentlemen appeared on Akademicka Street yesterday in broad daylight stark naked, without a stitch of clothing on except for the hats."

"Not nearly enough in this weather," commented Krysia after a long pause. "While Mrs. Nowak was understandably agitated," continued Nina, "Mother simply said 'poor men, they must have been from a mental institution.' I confess I do not understand what is happening to mom. She doesn't seem to react to anything any more. If Kinga goes that way also, you and I will be the only sane people in this family." Having expressed that sobering sentiment, Nina left eight potatoes in the kitchen and carried the rest to the cellar.

Krysia was left feeling very inadequate. She understood perfectly what Nina was saying; mother was behaving strangely. She would dress up and leave in the morning but she stayed out till late and came back tired, dispirited, and seemingly occupied with thoughts she did not share with her daughters. Krysia didn't know what to think. All she knew was that all this was not only very sad but boded ill for the future. Krysia once heard a description of a terrible storm given by their maid, Jozia. She remembered how a black cloud had appeared on the horizon of Jozia's village, and moved closer and closer and a terrible silence fell on the people and animals and they just waited. Krysia thought that something like this was happening to their city, that the dark cloud had already swallowed father and grandma and the people in the bombed houses, and that maybe it would want more.

She was greatly relieved when Nina, just back from the cellar, appeared her own unaltered daring self. She was carrying some onions and carrots. "While mother is looking for a job (the university was closed after suffering some damage) and Kinga is being enlightened, we, you and I, are going to cook," she announced. "What do you say to a vegetable soup fortified by buttermilk? And for the second course, bread with lard from Mrs. Nowak?"

"I say that would be very acceptable," replied Krysia already smiling. The black cloud was retreating before her indomitable big sister.

A New Home

In late September the war situation deteriorated further. There was no news from father, the Soviet Union was now occupying Eastern Poland, and Warsaw succumbed to the ultimate humiliation of negotiating with the enemy. The Nazi bombardment went on, however, day and night. Nina's precautionary covering of all the windows in order not to show light to the German bombers proved to be useless. A direct hit to their house collapsed the upper floors and showered with plaster and heavy dust the four females crouching under the cellar arch in the darkness below.

For a long time after that shattering crash only whispers were heard. Mother and Kinga prayed quietly, Krysia called on their departed grandmother to take them where there were no bombs, Nina's mind was furiously revolving around the crucial question: Will the cellar ceiling hold? It was mother who spoke first in a weak voice. "I believe that the upper floors are demolished but that we are relatively safe here. Thank God that we heard the siren and left the bedroom in time. Thank God that this house is so strong. The electricity is gone, I see, but if we uncover these small windows we may be able to breathe easier and see something, although it is not yet morning. We must find out what has happened to the other houses."

But they could not open the small window with a cracked pane nor the solid door to the yard. It seemed that they were in a kind of well with rubble surrounding them on all sides. Kinga tried to find the word which described her panic. Was it claustrophobia? Is it what you feel when you are confined in a small place without the possibility of getting out? Nina, however, was already busy removing pieces of glass from the window frame. "We could get out this way," she announced. "The opening is small but I think I may get through." It was then that a realization that not everything was right with the state of her pants came to her with a shock. They were wet, quite wet. To have this disgraceful incident happen to her, the family provider! "Just as well mother did not allow us to undress," she thought. "If I had a nightgown on, it would have been much worse." The shameful circumstance was later confided to mother after she had promised that she would never, never reveal it to anyone. "This would have never happened to Emilia Platter," was Nina's tearful comment, "or to Princess Kinga either, now would it mom?"

"It might," remarked her parent. "It has often happened to soldiers under fire. Some very brave persons had such accidents in moments of great danger. You have nothing to worry about Nina. You are in a good company." Meanwhile Krysia was eyeing the opening with great interest. "You are all too big," she announced. "I am the only one who can slide through. Perhaps if I undress and cover myself with Vaseline." But mother was adamant. "Nobody is trying to get through before we remove every piece of glass from the frame. I do not want wounds from broken glass on my hands. Then when it is safe to get through, we will wrap Krysia up..." It was only then that they all realized that they only had the clothes they wore, for the rest of their belongings remained on the inaccessible upper floors. But there was a piece of stiff cloth covering the heap of coal, and although Krysia protested weakly, she was wrapped in it before being pushed through the window. "Don't go far, stay close," called mother, "just look as far as Mrs. Nowak's house and the one on the corner. Can you see them?"

But before the little girl had time to answer, there was heard a sound of heavy steps and a masculine voice asked. "Is there anyone there? Are there any wounded?" They recognized the voice of Mr. Lis, a custodian from the nearby college and a member of the citizens' patrol who had complimented Nina on her work with the windows. "We are all right," called mother and Nina added "Krysia, show Mr. Lis to the door; it is terribly stuffy here and this window is very small. Can that door be opened?"

"No problem," came an encouraging reply soon after. "I will have to get help, but give me another pair of hands and we can remove the portion of wall that fell just behind it. But my, you were lucky, ladies, to escape unharmed. You won't be able to get to your apartment, though. From what I can see, the house is a huge heap of rubble. With you sitting right under it. My, my, how well those old houses were built. You don't find many of them nowadays."

The night air felt sweet when they emerged. Soon other persons appeared, tearful Mrs. Nowak among them. Her house escaped without damage but the corner one was in even worse shape than the Ilski's. "When I saw what happened to your home, I was sure that you and your three sweet angels were no longer with us," Mrs. Nowak lamented, at the same time taking big gulps from the bottle of liquor which Mr. Lis obligingly offered her. Nina, who was convulsed at being included in the angelic group, told herself that nothing was more efficacious in getting people back to normalcy than hearing nonsensical comments. Back to normal she was, having surreptitiously removed the offending garment and put it in the laundry basket. Water pipes seemed to be undamaged and after giving the cellar a thorough inspection, Nina decided that cold and unfriendly though it had seemed to her before, it was after all not a bad place in which to organize their new lives. Guerilla units often had to winter in forests, occupying shelters far inferior to what they had, she reminded herself. It was a shelter with running water, there was a heap of coal in one corner and a big basin and boxes full of washing detergent and soap in the other. Getting a stove for winter would be the main challenge and meanwhile, if they could get a primus, a small kerosene stove, it would do for cooking the potatoes and onions she had providentially stored here. There was also a bundle of the girls' clothing that grandmother was going to bestow on the St. Cecil's Society for the poor. "I do not think that grandmother would grudge us these old clothes in the present circumstances," mused Nina, going through the bundle and looking at each piece with great care. "Here, for instance, are Kinga's pyjamas which, with a little alteration, could become a garment I am in great need of just now. Here is a sweater which I hated, but will welcome in the coming winter. Those socks do not belong to us, they are dad's and how useful they will be for mother. No denying that none of us will win prizes for elegance after all this, but who cares? Certainly not mother, Krysia, and I, although I would not vouch for Kinga, who in the last year or two became disturbingly interested. Well if she does not like it, she can lump it. We can perhaps make Mrs. Nowak's blankets into winter coats. None of us knows much about sewing, but one can always learn. If we could only sweep the rubble from the floor and wash all that dust from our persons, life may become bearable."

One of the problems they did not anticipate was the quality of water they were getting. Never before had they seen water like that dripping now from the faucets: yellow, smelly, and totally undrinkable. Kinga, always inclined to be immaculate in her attire, was especially disgusted. "Now this is totally unacceptable," she wailed. "Why were we never told in school that water could be so horrible instead of spending our time reading about pure whispering streams, pristine mysterious lakes, and unsoiled mighty rivers? Weren't any of those writers ever bombed? One would have thought that in a siege laid to the city, water would be considered sacrosanct. Not to our Nazi friends, though, who would probably want to see all of us poisoned. Without intending to alarm you mom, I predict that within a week or two all of us will develop scurvy or whatever it is that people who do not wash get." But mother appeared more optimistic. "It may be only a temporary setback," she protested, "and even now, when you let it stand for a while – like the water in that pickle jar – the sediment collects at the bottom and the water itself becomes clear and clean. We are lucky to have running water at all, the other people…"

"Right you are mom," interrupted Nina. "We cannot demand perfection in the water we get. Do you know what swims in the liquid that the Karnickis get from their faucets? Apparently the sewer pipes flooded the water supply during the bombing. Imagine – you want to have a nice cup of tea, you fill the kettle and then you find in your cup…"

"Mom!" screamed Kinga at the top of her voice, "please, please tell her to be quiet. I do not want to hear it. It is horrible to bring such images to our minds just while we are eating Mrs. Nowak's sandwiches! Mom, please, tell her to stop." Mother intervened in a tired voice, "Really, you should not give us all the details regarding what your friends found in their water, Nina. It is far better to leave things to the imagination."

"I wish we could leave the Nazis and their bombs to the imagination," muttered the incorrigible Nina.

Hard reality stared them in the face. There was no stove, no hot plate, no heater. After going around the neighborhood Nina finally managed to acquire an old primus with some kerosene. A make-believe tea (made of dried cherries) could be obtained in a little corner store and the family had some tea in the cups supplied by Mr. Lis and Mrs. Nowak. The problem of constructing beds was beyond even Nina's versatility. The floor of the cellar was stone and very cold, and nobody seemed to have a spare bed at present. Finally Mr. Lis and another gentleman dragged some boards into the cellar and placed them on pieces of rubble, creating a platform on which all four could finally rest. It was not a very happy arrangement, the boards moved and slipped from their supports, and it was only after mother announced that any turning should be done by the four of them simultaneously, that the bed, although hard, became an acceptable and even appreciated alternative to sleeping on the floor. The old outhouse in the yard let them remember that civilization, as they knew it, was not totally out of their reach.

The Surrender

Soon after those events, the city surrendered on September 27, and the country, split into two occupation zones. In the beginning of October,[7] the population descended into a deep mourning. In Warsaw, hateful uniforms, hateful voices, hateful activities offended the residents' sight and hearing. On a walk with Krysia, the girls witnessed a scene that affected all three of them but especially depressed the youngest. A group of men in German uniforms were working a crane which was supposed to knock the figure of a Polish eagle from the top of one of the government buildings. The huge ball repeatedly hit the object and parts of the statue fell to the ground. That seemed to be too much for Krysia, who burst into tears crying, "they are killing our eagle, they are murdering our eagle!" In vain did the older girls reason with her about the impossibility of killing a bird made of stone. She was disconsolate for a long time and even when the sobs finally ceased, her whole body remained hot and trembling. The sisters wrapped her in blankets – which their neighbors kindly provided – and put her on the makeshift bed, Kinga lying down with her and trying to divert her attention from the scene they had witnessed by talking about other, more hopeful things. Nina ran to Mrs. Nowak for a thermometer, and when mother arrived she found the little girl sleeping fitfully with tears still glistening on her cheeks. "I do not understand this at all," whispered Kinga. "In general she is mature above her age. Here she is bemoaning the destruction of a statue as if it were alive. No matter what we did, it had no effect. Now she has worked herself into utter exhaustion and her temperature is up."

"It is this whole tragedy," responded mother quietly, "this violence and injustice, this ugliness. Grandmother's death, father's disappearance, Warsaw's defeat. For her, all that was related to this symbol of Poland's independence. Remember the verse all of you learned in kindergarten: 'Who are you? A young Pole. What is your sign? The White Eagle.' She fully realized what we have lost only when she saw the eagle removed and that horrible swastika put in its place."

"Oh, did they put swastika there?" cried the two girls, and Nina added in undertone, "The filthy swine. If only I had a gun."

---

[7] "The country inflicted over 50.00 casualties on the Wehrmacht and were still fighting hard when the entry of the Russians on 17 September sealed their fate... It could be argued that at this stage the Soviet terror in many ways exceeded that of the Nazis," Davies, *Heart of Europe*, p. 65, 67. Also, "According to a speech (October 31, 1939) reported in 'Prawda' of V. Molotov to the Supreme Soviet, 737 Soviet soldiers had lost their lives in the Polish campaign and 1,862 were wounded." Tadeusz Piotrowski, *Poland's Holocaust* (NC: McFarland and Co., 1998), p. 307.

Mother's attention was again focused on Krysia who, in her half conscious state, named some animals, which – she lamented – had failed to help the poor white bird. "Where was the rooster and the lion and others? Why did they allow all this to happen?" moaned the child. Only her parent guessed that the animals Krysia mentioned were symbols of France and Britain and that the questions she asked had been repeated in every Polish home, although in different ways. Where were Poland's allies?[8] "He is not lost, our bird," mother whispered to the sick girl. "There will come a time when he regains his strength – you will see." Krysia gradually calmed down and fell asleep.

Later, Mrs. Ilski turned to Nina and said quietly but with great seriousness, "I heard you mentioning a gun. This is not the way, certainly not for you. Put it out of your mind and don't let me hear it again. Promise?" With reluctance Nina said yes, but then she immediately accosted mother regarding the gender of the Polish eagle. "Why did you tell Krysia that the eagle was a he?" she asked heatedly. "Didn't Lech see a white mother eagle against the red sky?[9] Wasn't she coming with food for her eaglets? So what is this general obsession with making everything important masculine?" Krysia, who had awakened and was listening to the conversation with interest, remarked that it could have been a father eagle, since Mr. Sparrow in the story they had read to her was a very caring parent. The eagle could have been a good father coming home with food for his children. That made Nina even more irritable. "You are too clever by half," she exclaimed. "First those animals who are supposed to represent countries – if dad told you about them, why didn't I hear it? Now the lecture on bird fathers. What are you, an unrecognized genius zoologist just six years old?" But Krysia only smiled and announced that she was feeling much better. Mother, however, acknowledged that she was at fault calling the Polish eagle a he, since indeed it could have been a female bird that Lech saw and adopted as an emblem of his country; in fact, it was very likely. Nina received the explanation graciously and peace was restored in the family.

---

[8]   Although both Britain and France declared war on Germany on September 3, 1939, – as they were obliged to do according to the Polish-British-French treaty of spring 1939 – no help ever came to Poland or was even attempted. Not surprisingly, the period of war from the invasion of Poland up to the Nazi attack on France is called 'a phony war' in the West. It certainly was not phony for Poles. For Britain's overtures toward Germany from the beginning of World War II till the 1940 invasion of France. See Clive Pontin, *1940 Myth and Reality, The Truth about Britain's 'Finest Hour'* (Chicago, Ivan R. Dee, 1991).

[9]   An old legend has it that in prehistoric times, in the Carpathian Mountains, there lived three brothers named Lech, Czech, and Rus. While Czech and Rus went southward and eastward, respectively, to establish the countries of Czechs and Ruthenians, Lech traveled north. On a tree under which he rested, was a nest of white eaglets. Soon he saw a white bird against the red sky (it was sunset) which was coming home to feed the young birds. Lech said: "Here I will build my nest and for a symbol of it I choose the white eagle on a red ground." This is how Poland received her emblem.

The Ilski Family at Work

The fall of 1939 led to an early and severe winter. Mother managed to get some kind of job in the library which provided them with a ration card for one person. But although the work formally ended at five o'clock, she often came home much later, looking worried and depressed. Kinga attended the secret high school, (universities and high schools were closed to Poles under the German occupation) whose classes took place in different locations every several days. Nina, between primary and high school age, was too young to go with Kinga and too old for primary education. She would have to wait to join Kinga. Krysia became housebound; there were no pre-school facilities and besides, she developed an incessant cough which the old family doctor Dr. Stein (father of Kinga's friend, Rachela) diagnosed as 'walking pneumonia' and which had kept her in the cellar for many weeks now.

The longer the occupation lasted, the more it seemed to Nina that she had suddenly, and without so much as being asked, become the head of the family. Of course there were mother and Kinga. Lying on their common bed next to both of them Nina tried to analyze her feelings which – she had to admit – were not very complementary to either. What on earth had happened to that mother who, before the war, was so full of energy and joy, always teasing father about his seriousness, standing up against the opinions she disagreed with, encouraging the girls to think for themselves and not take anything for granted. That mother was gone and Nina thought with exasperation that now, after all they had suffered, her parent had begun to acquire the characteristics of a helpless female, a type she detested. For Mrs. Ilski now appeared helpless, no question about it. One would have reasonably expected, for instance, that if mother went out in the morning with an empty basket, there would be something in it on her return. But this was never the case. Mother and the basket would reappear late at night in the same state in which they left. Why did she come home so late? Besides, there was that strange ambivalent behavior of her parent, who looked as if she were trying to decide something of tremendous importance. Meanwhile there was very little food – unless Nina got something, that is – and no medication for Krysia and no extra blankets. Trying to be fair toward all the members of her family, Nina had to concede that her sister, at the mature age of fourteen, was no better. Kinga now attended classes at the "Flying College" and spent evenings using up the rest of the candles reading German essays and repeating German phrases ad nauseam, all of which had – according to Nina – nothing to do with their present predicaments. Mother actually encouraged her to do all this. "I fully understand Mr. Engels, although he was a German and a communist," Nina told Krysia, "when he said that food comes before art. For it is art that mother and Krysia are pursuing, or in other words the activities that are not absolutely vital, while getting food, the very thing that keeps us alive, is left to me. But how am I supposed to manage with only one ration book when everything is rationed? How long can I go on selling our valuables? I wish I could ask Mr. Engels about it." Krysia, huddling under the blankets in the cold cellar moved her head sadly in agreement.

The occupied city settled down to the grim reality. After a while, some relief came from Kinga who, after her classes, got a part time job at the bakery from which she sometimes obtained bread 'on the sly' – since she was not entitled to anything above the ration card.[10] Also neighbors and even strangers appeared at their door bearing gifts of food, blankets, and even an electric heater which at first seemed useless for lack of electricity, but which worked beautifully once Mr. Lis's nephew managed to repair the damaged electric lines. After going around the city in pursuit of food, and looking for the best deal she could get for her watch, Nina learned that a soup kitchen was opened by the Nuns of St. Cecil on Biala Street on Thursdays, and that she could get extra portions for her family, if she asked. She hated standing in line with so many miserable people, yet she was there every Thursday and every Thursday evening was rewarded for her labors by her family's delight with the soup. The truth was that the nuns made it almost a full meal, for the soup – apart from vegetables – also contained rice and noodles. "This is the best soup I have eaten in my life," Krysia repeated each Thursday, and mother and Kinga agreed. It was becoming clear to them, that while they could compare their present existence with what they had before the war, little Krysia was slowly forgetting "the good old times" and was thus spared the pain of reminiscences.

---

[10]   The first German decrees carrying the death penalty for trading in various foodstuffs were posted in December 1939. Later they became routine: "Poland became the killing-ground of Europe, the new Golgotha." Davies, *Heart of Europe*, p. 64.

An Unlikely Ally

It was in the soup kitchen that Nina met Jozek, a ten-year-old urchin. At first Nina, who was trying to get the process of acquiring the soup over as quickly as possible, did not pay much attention to the bedraggled boy. There were many similar youngsters roaming the streets of Warsaw nowadays. This boy, however, seemed different. First of all he brought a bucket with him, while most people, Nina included, brought with them far less capacious containers. He also appeared inclined to express his opinions freely to the people around him on any subject whatsoever. His conversations with the nun who was distributing the soup always followed an established pattern. To the question of how many people there were in his family, his reply never wavered: three adults and six children, four of them below the age of five, he would declare boldly. Mother dead, father held by the Russkies, aunt and uncle missing in action. He declared himself to be the single surviving member of his immediate family. He always got a huge portion of the soup although the young nun admonished him repeatedly not to 'exaggerate.'

It happened that on that particular Thursday nobody got any soup. The nuns, looking harassed and unhappy, explained that the authorities had rescinded permission to distribute food. They, the nuns, were trying to acquire a permit, but meanwhile the only free distribution was on Magistracka Street, in the other part of Warsaw. This was when Jozek came to express his disappointment in a loud and assertive voice. "I bet that the blasted Secret State Police is eating our soup," he declared boldly. "It is enough to look at that fat Goering to figure out where the food from Poland goes," he continued despite the discomfort of the gathered people, who after uneasily looking around started to shuffle away. "Just as well that I got some provisions stored for such emergency," he remarked companionably to Nina, who was trying to decide whether to risk the long walk to Magistracka Street or run home. "Hans gave me some only yesterday, actually."

"Who is Hans and how can you get food from him?" was Nina's question.

"Oh there are some normal people even among them," the boy replied sententiously. "Naturally he does not do it openly and nobody in his right mind would expect him to. He sneaks to their warehouse late at night – he works there you see – and goes in through the window that he unlocked when he was leaving work. He takes only things at the back of shelves, so that nobody notices the next morning. Clever chap, Hans, though German."

Nina's reaction to this revelation was mixed, suspended between moral indignation (the seventh commandment!!!!) and an inclination to be impressed. Wasn't it ingenious of Hans to devise such a clever way of pilfering food? But her upbringing prevailed and after a pause she told Jozek with great severity. "He is a thief and he is German and you should have nothing to do with him." But, curiosity getting the better of her, she added, "What, may I ask, do you give him for those stolen goods?"

"Scarves," was the unexpected reply. "I give him silk scarves for his friends and family. Females like to have scarves, you know. They do peculiar things with them, put them on their hairdo, or wind them around their throats, or..."

"Jozek," interrupted Nina, "where do you get those scarves from?" But Jozek suddenly remembered a pressing appointment and, after murmuring "see you next Thursday," left Nina alone and deep in thought. Was it really wrong to accept stolen goods from a German, whose country had devastated Poland? Didn't the Germans steal from us, our cities, our houses? Perhaps this boy believed that the food Hans gave him was really his own. It was obvious that Jozek had no family, that he was fending for himself. Perhaps without Hans he would have perished. This, of course, did not answer the scarf question. Nina decided that she would try and get that matter resolved next time. Meanwhile the rain intensified and she felt dampness penetrating through her shoes. "I will not go to Magistracka Street," she decided. "For all I know they may not have enough soup for the extra people. There are still some potatoes and margarine at home." She started walking toward home when she heard hasty steps behind her. It was Jozek, smiling broadly with a big can in his hand. "This is for you and your mom and sisters," he panted. "Do you know what it is? 'Fleisch' it says on the label, meaning first class pure meat! No bones, no cartilage no skin! Fat content moderate! Ready to eat, fit for Hitler himself!" Seeing her hesitating, he quickly added "I have got several of those. It is a present, actually." Then he put the can into the empty container she was holding and saying "See you next Thursday," ran away.

That left Nina even more uncertain about what to think. But she knew one thing; she knew that nothing on earth would have made her voluntarily deprive her family of the splendid bounty.

Next Thursday, the people waiting for soup were told that permission had been granted to the sisters to distribute soup for two weeks more. After that, no more 'handouts,' declared the authorities. All of those gathered received the news in silence; even Jozek did not say anything. The distribution coincided with heavy snow and Jozek led Nina to a doorway to wait out the storm. It was a secluded place, and one could sit on the wooden stairs. Here Jozek became even more talkative than usual as if a need to unburden himself had become pressing. "I did not lie when I was talking to that young nun the other day," he said. "Well, not entirely. I am the last of my 'nuclear' family, but it was only a small one, mom and me. So she had only half a right to chide me, actually."

"Where is your mother?" asked Nina. "In the graveyard," was the cheerful reply. "She is in the graveyard and sister Loretta told me to say Hail Mary for her every night. I do it every second week or so. There is no sense overdoing it." Soon Nina was in possession of Jozek's whole biography. He never knew his father. Some time previously he and his mother – who sometimes came to visit him in an orphanage – were involved in a serious bus accident. She died, he was unconscious for a long time. "When I woke up I was in a hospital," he reminisced, "a nice establishment but depressingly clean. It sort of spoils your appetite. Then I was taken back to the orphanage on Pilsudski's Street, you know, that huge building with a tower – no longer in operation, though. Not a bad place, considering the excessive number of females there. At first I could not remember anything, but later I did, a bit. They told me that mom was a brunette but I remember her as ginger haired like me. That was before she became platinum blonde with dark roots showing. Mom tried to become like the movie stars, Greta Garbo and such. She was fond of the pictures, our mom! No matter how hard up she was, she always found somebody to buy her a ticket."

"The food in the orphanage was third rate, though, till they got Sister Hermencia into the kitchen," the boy continued, shifting his position on the stairs, "and was she a treasure!!! She managed good meals every day, but Sundays were special. Her pies with raisins and cinnamon would have made her a millionaire in no time in New York! It helped that she had a new kitchen stove at her disposal and a refrigerator that a rich guy had bestowed on our institution. The refrigerator alone would make your eyes pop! A technological masterpiece! I was often in the kitchen, since Sister Hermencia chose me to help her on special occasions, having recognized my talents. 'When it comes to dough and pastry,' she would remark, 'you have either got it or you have not… and I say this to you, and may the good Lord forgive me if it goes to your head, I say that you Jozek have pierogi (dumplings) potential…' Her words, not mine, actually," he added modestly.

"So what happened to Sister Hermencia?" asked Nina, for whom culinary mysteries had little attraction. "Buried together with the refrigerator, actually," answered Jozek sadly. "It was not empty either. I figure that those Nazis have a lot to answer for!"

Broken Families

Meanwhile changes were occurring that affected all Varsovians in different ways. As usual in a war situation, the question of who died and who was, or at least could still be alive, was of primary importance. The people whose relatives had been killed during the war seemed to be able to cope with such tragedy better than those who had lost them at the hands of the new authorities. In time, executions occurred every several days.[11] The names of executed Poles appeared on lists eagerly displayed by the Germans on public buildings with the warning that a similar fate lay in store for those Poles who were also guilty of such crimes. Apart from the lists of hostages, who had just been in the wrong place at the wrong time, most references were to the shadowy organization of 'bandits' that the Reich promised to liquidate ruthlessly and soon. Families of such persons, among them Mrs. Nowak's sister-in-law and two nieces, could not even find consolation in the traditional palliative statement that "they had died defending their country," for such comfort was usually reserved for people in uniform, while the present victims were civilians. Their families tormented themselves with guilt, believing that they could have prevented the tragedy, if they had only acted differently.

"I knew that there was danger lurking somewhere in their vicinity," a tearful Mrs. Nowak said, sitting on a rickety stool in their cellar. "I felt it! I said to Misia, 'don't let them leave the house! We have been spared so far, let's not tempt the devil!' But it did not matter what I said, or what she said. We knew that Edek, my nephew, was involved in the Polish Scout movement and it stood to reason that the Nazis would not look kindly on it. Then it happened!" Here Mrs. Nowak burst into floods of tears, soon followed by sniffles from Kinga and Krysia. "It happened! They, the devils, came to arrest him and my brother, always impulsive and headstrong, actually told them that they had no right to look for the boy. To tell the Secret State Police (Geheime Staats Polizei, National Secret Police) that they had no right! If only he had not said it! Poor Misia, who studied the language of those fiends, attempted to tell them that her husband did not mean it, that his mental state was precarious because of the bombing. She did everything possible, but to no avail. They arrested both of them and when our loved ones said good-bye to us, I felt it was final. Sure enough, my little niece found the names of her father and brother on the poster put up on Zielna Street. It referred to my noble brother and his dear son as 'bandits'!"

---

[11] The "execution of the first hundred innocent civilians of Warsaw [occurred] in December 1939," see Wladyslaw Szpilman, *The Pianist*, (NY: Picador 2002), p. 44. Wladyslaw Szpilman was a survivor of the Warsaw Ghetto.

The last words were barely heard, and as Mrs. Nowak started sliding off the stool mother caught her in her arms and gently deposited her on the makeshift bed next to Krysia. "She has fainted, but she will be all right," mother whispered to Kinga. "She is coming to. Boil water and put sugar into it. She should have a hot drink as well as extra blankets. I am going to see to the younger Mrs. Nowak. You girls have to convince this lady that we all love her, that we consider her a member of our family, that we are all in this national catastrophe together."

After mother had left, there was little movement. Mrs. Nowak slept, although tears were still running down her face. Kinga busied herself with the kettle, Krysia snuggled close to their visitor covering both of them with bedding. Nina, who had been biting her knuckles throughout their neighbor's narrative, was now washing her bloody hands in the sink. "Are we too young to do anything about all this?" she whispered to Kinga. "Can we do nothing?" Kinga surprised her younger sister as she had never done before. "Our time will come," she answered. "Just you wait. We shall have our chance."

There were also men and women held by the Nazis as "suspicious" in prisons and camps, whose families went from one Nazi official to another, usually without finding out what the future held for them. Mr. Lis' young cousin was one of them and her family lived constantly between hope and despair.

The Ilski family belonged to the Poles whose relatives were listed as missing in war, and the word 'missing' created different images in the minds of different people. The missing persons could of course be dead as well, but they could be alive and unable to contact their families. The optimists tried to console themselves, hoping that their dear ones were among those who had crossed the borders to Hungary or Rumania in order to get to "our ally France," and help in the war effort. For there was a war going on, they tried to convince themselves and anybody who wanted to hear. Did not the two powers, France and Britain, declare war on Hitler on September 3, 1939? The fact that the allies showed no enthusiasm for helping Poland in its war, was put down to mitigating circumstances. "France and Britain wanted to help us but they were not prepared. Now that our brave boys and girls are there, in France, they will no doubt start a counteroffensive and show Hitler what is what."

There was still another possibility of danger to Poles, one which was as yet not wholly comprehended. The missing family members could have fallen into Soviet hands, and it was uncertain whether their fate would be similar to that of the people on this side of the border. The sentiment prevailed that, since Poland's treaty of non-aggression with the Soviet Union was relatively recent (reaffirmed in 1938), the Polish prisoners of war in the Soviet zone might perhaps be better off than their counterparts under Germany. As to the fate of the civilians, there circulated grim reports of terror and deportations to Siberia, but not many believed them. Surely nobody, but nobody, could be as bad as Germans, asserted Mr. Lis, and most Varsovians agreed. Only a few elderly people familiar with the Soviet system contradicted such opinions, claiming that both of Poland's enemies were equally bad.

The Ilski family discussed the fate of their missing husband and father every night, and every day Nina would run to the post office to find if there was a letter for them. But there were none, either from father or from their relatives in Lwow, in the Soviet zone. In her dreams, she frequently saw father coming toward her from a distance and when she was about to embrace him he invariably disappeared. In the dream she knew that it would happen, and in her frustration she tried to devise ways of holding on to him, all in vain. She would wake up in despair only to find that Kinga was crying in her sleep and mother was reading some papers by the light of the candle, papers that Nina suspected had some sinister significance. But neither she nor Kinga asked mother about them. Kinga's dreams were horrible, much worse than Nina's, for she saw their parent in prison and there was no way for him to escape. Nina had an inkling that Kinga did not tell her all the terrible things that befell father in her dreams and she did not press her to. Her own fears were so great that she could not cope with Kinga's. After consultation, both girls decided to keep those dreams from mother and Krysia and were praised for it by a nun who came to visit mother on some errand that she did not disclose. "You are both brave, big girls," she said. "You must believe me when I say that such dreams are simply a figment of your imagination and they in no way reflect reality. God willing, your father will come back to you. But you are right not to tell your mom. You should be her support and spare her as much as you can. Of course Krysia is too young for such sadness even when it is only in a dream."

Another visitor who appeared rather unexpectedly in their cellar was Dr. Stein, Rachela's father. He asked about Krysia's health, took her temperature and listened to her cough but then sat in one of the available stools and stayed there unmoving, looking around their habitat and occasionally poking the walls with his cane. He repeatedly asked about the soundness of the ceiling and was eagerly assured by Nina that a commission did inspect it, that they declared the walls strong enough but forbade anyone to try and enter the upper stories. The inspectors attached a huge sign to the balcony to this effect.

"Good, good," murmured the doctor and continued to sit. Mother was out as usual, and the girls did not know how to interpret this strange behavior. To Kinga, the physician brought back memories of visitors who came to see their parents before the war. She remembered her grandma's instruction that when "a visitor comes, no matter for how long, you have to serve tea and cake. Remember that simple hospitality creates a congenial atmosphere and facilitates conversation." Mindful of this, she shyly asked Dr. Stein if he would like a cup of the cherry tea and perhaps a piece of bread. He declined the bread but accepted the tea and sipping it from the chipped blue mug, a present from Jozek, continued to look distractedly at the ceiling and the walls. He seemed to have difficulty expressing what he wanted to say. After a long pause, Krysia broke the silence by asking about his daughter. She was all right and was going to join the classes attended by Kinga. The latter was overjoyed and begged to say 'hello.' Then, suddenly, the visitor said in a strangled voice: "You like Rachela, don't you? By the way, I call her Myszka." After the three of them answered with an enthusiastic 'yes' he told them that his daughter would visit them in the near future. Then he bade them, with a degree of severity that shocked them, not to bug their mother when she was late from work. "Your mom and I, we lost our country," he said. "You lost it too, but you do not understand the extent of it. If your mom stays late, she stays late and that is her business not anyone else's, understand? Do not bother her, understand? You have to listen to me, for I knew you before you were born." With these words he departed with the blue mug which, after shutting the door, he left on the outer sill of the cellar window.

They were left surprised and uneasy. Surely it was their business to ask why mother was late so often. Why should he, a family doctor, scold them for it? "I have always thought that it was the parents who blamed their children for being late," mused Nina. "Remember the row created by Mr. and Mrs. Sawicki when their daughter Lusia came late from her date with that student? She was to be home at ten p.m. and came back at eleven. You remember Mrs. Sawicki shouting that Lusia's dad had a weak heart and that he almost died thinking that Lusia was hit by a car?"

"I am not sure that he thought exactly that," interrupted Kinga knowingly, "I am not sure that it was exactly an accident he was afraid of, considering Lusia's loving nature..."

"Be it that as it may," continued Nina, "it seems to me grossly unfair that we can not ask our own mother why she stays out so long after working hours. We know that the library closes at six; don't we?" But Kinga seemed unwilling to pursue the theme and Krysia wanted to hear further details of Lusia's predicament.

Next day, mother's arrival earlier than usual brought some unexpected news. She was leaving her work in the library where she was cataloguing foreign books and was now planning to become a nurse. "You, a nurse?" exclaimed all three in amazement. Mother's experience with the noble profession of nursing was limited to a four-week course organized by major hospitals before the war and called "emergency medical assistance." In those classes, the participants attended to the would be victims of shells, bullets, etc. "Didn't you bandage poor Mr. Socha so tightly that you almost smothered him?" Nina reminded mother innocently. "For weeks after that he complained to father, whenever he met him, that his jaw never felt the same after your ministrations."

"Didn't he die soon after?" added Krysia. "I remember Granny saying that you all went to his funeral."

"For heaven's sake be quiet both of you," cried their mother. "It was an unimportant mistake! He was supposed to have a head wound and I was attempting to stop the bleeding. My bandaging might have been a little snug but it did him no harm, although your father liked to tease me about it. For your information, Krysia, it was his brother who died, not the gentleman I attended to. I may not be a highly proficient nurse but I will be all right. If nothing else, I can always empty bedpans."

The children were stunned. Their mother, an academician, employed in a job of this kind. "But mom, you have no experience or qualifications for hospital work," Kinga said quietly. "Why leave the translations which you can do so well and start on something entirely new? The pay will probably be much less too." Mrs. Ilski did not seem to have a convincing reply to this and she soon changed the subject by dropping another piece of news. "Dr. Stein will write me a recommendation to the General Hospital. I have talked to him about it. By the way, Rachela, or Myszka as he calls her, is going to stay with us for a while in a month or two. We have to prepare for her. Isn't it nice?"

This time the amazement of her children expressed itself in a long silence. "Are we to understand that you have invited her to live with us in this cellar?" Nina asked and the words came out with difficulty. "She, whose father's beautiful house was not bombed, who is always dressed like a model, who is probably used to luxuries? Are you sure that she knows how we live now?"

"Her father knows," was the curt answer, "and she does too. You should be aware that I did not issue the invitation lightly and neither was it accepted in such a way. Dr. Stein believes that his family may be in danger even greater than ours. They are Jewish and our occupiers have recently said and done things that cause us to believe the Jewish people may face some special persecution. The recent regulations pertain to their wearing a white band with a blue star of David and it bodes no good.[12] Dr. Stein is needed in the hospital, so he may be spared. But he is worried about his daughter and therefore I suggested that she come and live with us, if he thinks it advisable. She will not wear the band and nobody must know she is Jewish; we will say she is our cousin. Therefore nobody, absolutely nobody must know the truth."

---

[12]   Orders to this effect were issued in December 1939.

"You mean we have to lie?" asked Nina who saw in mother's instructions a staggering departure from the past, when family, school, and books urged them time and time again never to tell a lie. "Saying that Myszka is our cousin is a lie, but it is a noble lie," mother asserted. "You are old enough to understand that even a lie may be good. The older you get, the better you will understand it. Krysia, my darling, can you trust your mother in this?"

"I think I can but what would Sister Cecilia say?" responded the little girl uneasily. "She told us in kindergarten that God would not love us if we lie." Here mother suddenly became tearful, ('mushy' thought Nina). "You will ask her when you see her," she whispered huddling with her youngest. "She will tell you that God distinguishes between bad lies and good lies. All we are doing now is saying a good lie, for Dr. Stein and Myszka."

The three girls remained silent. Until now, they considered all Poles equally oppressed, Jews as well as Christians.[13] But this oppression was not spread evenly, for there were still complete families and undamaged homes in Warsaw. Dr. Stein's was one of them. When Nina looked at the houses that were still standing, she felt envious, although – she told herself – not badly envious, not envious enough to wish those people to lose their homes, just wishing that her family did not have to live in a cellar. Kinga confessed that she had similar thoughts when she observed well-dressed women and secretly bemoaned the fact that due to the bombing, the wardrobe of the Ilski family consisted of 'rags' which they would not have dared to offer to the poorhouse before the war. They found it hard to believe that some people could suffer not because their relatives were lost, or their houses bombed, not because they were hostages or 'bandits,' but because they had a rabbi rather then a priest to talk to them about religion in school. Now they had learned that Myszka, a grade above Kinga in high school, was among those in extra danger, and their hearts went out to her.

While Kinga and Krysia considered how to organize a friendly welcome, Nina speculated on how an extra person would affect their food rations. Later, in bed, she went through the day's happenings and concluded that apart from the terror

---

[13] "In the first year of the occupation and even later, the Polish population did not have the impression that the Jews were more oppressed than they. Quite the contrary. It was mainly the Poles who were arrested, tortured in Secret State Police prisons, executed, sent to concentration camps in Auschwitz, Buchenwald and Sachsenhausen. The Jews were more circumscribed in respect to the economy,... but the majority of the Polish people considered this to be the lesser of evils... . According to the estimate of Szymon Datner, long time director of the Jewish Historical Institute in Warsaw, for every Jew who died between 1939 and 1941, ten Poles were killed by the Nazis," Piotrowski, *Poland's Holocaust*, p. 115.

and deprivation that had been known to them for months now, there were other troubling issues involved in the occupation which required an reassessment of what she had accepted before as good and proper. It seemed quite a revelation to regard subterfuge as good, even noble, instead of abominable as they had been told before. But she comprehended, perhaps even more swiftly than her sisters, that circumstances could be responsible not only for a change in basic Christian morality, but also for the way one practiced it. "Of course there was no need for mother to explain the matter to me," she murmured to Kinga. "For I am mature enough to understand it perfectly. It was also not necessary for her to become so weepy. If there is ever a question of helping anybody against these nasty Germans, I would lie and lie and then tell God why. If you have problems with it, Kinga, I am willing to explain it to you. Just say the word," she offered condescendingly. But Kinga declined.

So now there was to be another member of the Ilski family, and Nina was still trying to evaluate the change. It was very nice for them all to have Myszka living there, but what about things like bedding, food, clothing? Coming from an undestroyed home – and do what she could, Nina felt pangs of envy about such people– Myszka would probably bring things with her. Extra blankets and perhaps an electric heater would be especially welcome and perhaps some provisions? But mother shattered those hopes by announcing that the girl would only be able to bring one suitcase. "One small suitcase, nothing more," she said firmly. "People who fled from the Germans, who were sprayed with bullets from Nazi planes, would not carry electric heaters with them, now would they? It is absolutely necessary that we regard her as a cousin and a refugee from Poznań. As such, she is coming next month. She is no longer Stein, she is Ilski to everybody. Is that clear?"

"All right, all right," Nina grumbled to herself. "No need to assume this tone and get excited. We accept the premise that the Jews may now be in greater danger than we are. I still don't understand why, and I wonder how on earth the Germans will identify them. But I know better than to ask just now. Mothers!"

This monumental change in their lives was accepted by the girls without much discussion. Even Nina resigned herself to include another mouth to feed in her efforts, and managed to convince Mrs. Nowak to part with an old rug which was to be useful in constructing a new bedding arrangement. Like other people affected by the war, they had learned that there were now forces which were operating beyond their control. What seemed normal before, was not so now. It became progressively clear that in post-war Warsaw, basic human rights had a very low value in the eyes of the Nazi authorities, and even those few rights began gradually to disappear while ever new reports of German atrocities came to their attention.

Worrying about unexplained absences of any member of the family became their everyday concern. Thus Krysia was brought to near hysteria on the occasion of Kinga's unforseen extra hour's work in the bakery. Mother was now working in a hospital, and her day seemed to be even longer than before. In order to avoid unnecessary anxiety she had established a timetable to which everybody should conform. She, Kinga, and Nina, must keep to the times indicated on a piece of paper nailed to the wall. In case of a lengthy and unexplained absence of her own – here her voice trembled a little – they had to inform Mr. Lis, who would know what to do. Krysia would leave the cellar only in the company of one of them. An extra lock on the door should be used, and uninvited strangers should not be allowed to enter. "What about 'Gosc w dom, Bog w dom?'[14] asked irrepressible Nina. "Is the famous Polish hospitality gone, then?"

"You know what I mean, Nina," mother said in a tired voice, and indeed Nina did know. Rumors had been circulating about some shady characters inquiring about unknown persons, and occasionally attempting to enter without being invited.

Now that they knew that Myszka had reasons to be even more fearful than they were – for they trusted mother implicitly although her reasons for believing this remained unknown – the fact that the girl was going to be under their protection made them feel compassionate and important. Krysia especially was greatly flattered. She promised to take care of Myszka when left alone with her and to offer her tea from the thermos that mother prepared for her youngest daughter every morning.

It was against Nina's nature, much though she was prepared to welcome the new arrival, to meekly accept mother's very incomplete explanations. "What about Dr. Stein?" she asked mother one evening before Myszka's arrival. "Is he still Stein or is he Ilski too? May I ask," she added in a sarcastic way that the family knew only too well, "how many new cousins can we expect in the near future?" Kinga bade her to be quiet in a whisper and Krysia looked rather anxious and unhappy but mother's answer was surprisingly controlled. "Dr. Stein is a very gifted physician who now, because of the huge number of patients, is greatly needed even by the Germans," she said. "He remains Stein. But he prefers that his daughter now assume another identity. It is his wish, and I agree with him completely. The important thing now is not to let her feel unwelcome and treat her as a member of the family. Nobody must know otherwise." But Nina would not give up. "If he is not in danger, why is she? It must not be nice for them to be separated, especially in view of what we

---

[14]   A saying traced to very early times in Polish history when a guest was welcomed with all the attention a divinity would have received.

can offer her here." But mother cut this remark short. "What we have here may be better for her than what she would experience in the ghetto, which for all we know may become a reality. He believes it and so do I. Now, may we have some peace and quiet for a change?"

For once, Nina was left speechless. She had never heard the word 'ghetto' and had no idea what it could mean. But something told her that mother's readiness to explain things was already exhausted. There was Kinga, of course, who might not know much either. If she did know what "ghetto" was, she would probably act condescendingly superior toward her younger sister. Rather than endure that, Nina decided to ask Jozek, a person surprisingly knowledgeable about the new reality and who, being two years younger, would not be patronizing.

Their First Christmas under the Occupation

Heating the cellar was one of the most important life necessities for the Ilski family. Although the electricity was still working, it had grown very expensive and the little electric heater Mrs. Ilski had purchased from the by-now extensive street market for an exorbitant price (her gold brooch) could never raise the temperature in the cellar over the freezing level. Surprisingly, it was Sister Cecilia, generally believed not to be equal to facing the practical problems of the occupation, who informed them of an 'amazing invention.' By utilizing a metal barrel, an equally solid pipe, and great quantities of saw-dust tightly packed, this device produced the effects of an economical and very efficient stove. Ignoring the fears of unadventurous adults, (you may all die from carbon monoxide, said the fearful Mrs. Nowak) Nina and Krysia repaired to the disclosed address. They found a young couple busily employed in hauling sacks of sawdust into a large shed where big metal barrels stood in a row.

"Supplies, especially of sawdust, are almost inexhaustible," commented the young woman cheerfully. "Because of the destruction of the city, the Germans reactivated several sawmills around Warsaw, and my dad, who is a construction man, told us about huge piles of sawdust available to basically anybody. Old oil drums, undamaged after the bombing of the refinery, are also on the market. The rest we provide," she added proudly.

After this introduction, she took them to a shed where they saw big sacks filled with sawdust. Next came the demonstration of the couple's invention. Sturdy metal barrels on legs were tightly packed with sawdust surrounding a pipe, with a handle protruding from the barrel. On the underside of the barrel, there was an open slit and a container for gathering the ash. Another pipe, much longer, was inserted into the cover of the barrel and extended outside through a ventilator. After removing the shorter pipe from the container to provide air flow from beneath, they lighted the lower layers of the sawdust. The fire slowly consumed the dust, exuding blessed heat all around. Any noxious gases would escape through the exhaust pipe.

Deeply impressed by this invention, Nina and Krysia immediately started negotiations for its purchase. Alas, the price was prohibitive. The young man complained about the difficulty of getting barrels of the right kind by bribing the Germans, and gloomily predicted that to keep Poles warm in winter was not what the Nazis wanted, so this business would not survive long. Looking uneasily at the two girls, the young woman seemed more amenable to negotiation. It was lucky that just then Krysia started coughing, her deep rasping cough. The couple looked at one another and without a word the woman went to get a glass of water. "Where do you live? How far from here?" asked the man. "But," stammered Nina "we cannot…" As soon as she uttered these words she became afraid that the wonderful fortune which his questions seemed to imply might after all pass them by, so she corrected herself saying, "we may not be able…"

"That's all right, he will survive and so will I," came from the woman who was back, patting Krysia affectionately. "Drink slowly my pet, and God be with you. Don't you worry about a thing. He will use our wheelbarrow to get it to your place."

So it happened that the 'wonderful invention' came to occupy an honored place in the cellar. On bringing it over, the kind man told Nina to come for sawdust whenever they were short of it. As to payment, he was nonchalant. "You are young, and will probably survive the war," he told them. "So will my wife, God willing," he added after briefly reflecting on his own dubious chances for survival. "So sometime, in a free Poland, you pay her back."

That first December following the beginning of the war was strange in the Ilski's household. It was as if their lives were suspended between two different worlds: the pre-September 1939 world was still recent, and the memory of the previous Christmas fresh; but at the same time, the stark reality of their lives would not let them forget even for a short time how radically the times had changed. Thus, they existed side by side; the terrible present and those enticing images from the past.

While the two older girls freely talked about the delights of Christmases past, Krysia's age prevented her from having equally accurate recollections of various occurrences which her sisters remembered; still, she contributed to their conversations with the little she knew. One of the notable events that stayed with her was the unexpected appearance in her bed at night of a large teddy bear, which St. Nicholas (the bishop who used to like giving presents to children when they were asleep) had left for her. Another was a somewhat blurred vision of candles on a tree, a magical tree with an angel at the top. The teddy bear, named Tytus, was a casualty of the bombing, and the candles they had in the cellar in no way resembled the Christmas candles. Krysia pestered her sisters to tell her more about 'the old Christmas' and never got enough of it. In contrast to them, she did not fully understand the shattering change that affected their lives and found it easier to pretend that nothing was very wrong.

Her sisters, however, began to question the usefulness of such reminiscences in their present circumstances. They knew that even the unintended comparison of the 'then' with 'now' brought tears to their and their mother's eyes, and were afraid that recollections of that time – both sweet and painful – might make her suffer even more. What was the use of living in the past, in wallowing in what Nina described as 'mushy sentimentalism'? She for one entertained serious doubts about the efficacy of such an approach. "We remember those wonderful days, we cry, we become unhappy and it all makes us weak, gets us desperate," she argued. "Perhaps we should forget about what has been, perhaps we should just struggle ahead without those disabling regrets." But Kinga would not go that far. "We cannot forget about Father and Grandmother, about our school and our country," she pointed out and Krysia added, "and about little Jesus and ... Tytus," the latter name being mentioned somewhat timidly and in an undertone.

Although the elder girls firmly believed that they were much too old to discuss questions of this sort with their depressed and harassed parent, a time came when Mrs. Ilski herself began talking about Christmas. She told Krysia in a sympathetic but not overly commiserating way that St. Nicholas would not be coming to Poland this year, because of war, but that he had made plans of to visit the country in the future. She also expressed confidence that her girls would manage to procure a branch of sorts which could very well act as a tree. In lieu of decorations – here she was obliged to stop for by no power of the imagination could she conjure up a source of decorations in their present circumstances. But to her relief, the children, including Nina, accepted those initial plans with enthusiasm. "Will do," announced the latter with confidence. "I am not yet sure how we shall manage the tree, but I have one or two plans as yet unspecified in my head. What about Wigilia, though? (A Christmas eve supper.) Kinga, can you get some extra bread from that bakery of yours?"

"I can and I shall," was the confident reply. Mrs. Ilski added that Mrs. Nowak would come to Wigilia with traditional barszcz (beetroot soup) fortified with potatoes, while Sister Cecilia would bring 'oplatek' and tell Krysia what it was supposed to signify. (Oplatek is a wafer symbolizing human brotherhood, affection and forgiveness. It is traditionally shared by the people present at the Wigilia.) "Christmas is Christmas, wherever and whenever you are," she added. "It is a very important time of the year, especially for Krysia who was still small last year. We will talk about what we had and what it meant to us, and if we cry a little, it does not matter, does it?" The girls agreed that it did not, Nina surrendering her previous convictions with great haste.

Despite all the surrounding gloom, the Ilski family went to bed that night in much better spirits than those of the last few months. It was a relief to them to know that this December they were not going to shun thinking and talking about what the past meant to them, for although such reminiscences often made them cry, they were precious and a part of themselves, and did not undermine their resolve and courage.

Indeed, it came to pass that the Christmas of 1939, although sad, was not unduly sorrowful. There was no general feeling of hopelessness and despair, the expectation of which had made Nina so adamant in her initial reaction to the celebration of Wigilia. The great plus was that they were no longer cold, for the new stove, under the careful scrutiny of Mr. Lis, was performing beyond expectations. It was hardly believable that a simple contraption could have such beneficial effects on those who were not lucky enough to obtain other means of getting warmth.

There was also food of sorts for the great night of Wigilia. Nina brought more soup than usual from the soup kitchen, and the good nuns saw to it that the soup that day was much richer. More noodles, rice and even occasional onions and turnips could be seen in it. Mrs. Nowak brought the long expected barszcz, Mr. Lis a cake made of carrots and honey, and Kinga got an extra portion of bread from work. Because of such bounty, it did not matter much when Kinga began listing the traditional twelve dishes, all meatless and all exquisite, which the Ilski family had had on the previous Christmas. The rest of the company contributed by talking about various Wigilia specialities in different parts of Poland.

There was also a tree – well, really a branch which stood in the corner adorned with pieces of ribbons and balls of cotton wool which mother brought from the hospital (it was unsterilized cotton wool, not suitable for the patients). The makeshift table (an old door on wooden supports constructed by Mr. Lis) was, according to custom, covered with straw (Christ was born in a manger) and covered with white tablecloth lent by Mrs. Nowak. But the most important were oplatki, the wafers brought by Sister Cecilia. They, according to centuries of tradition, were to be shared by all the people gathered at the table to reaffirm the idea of universal human brotherhood.

They sat at the table only after Kinga, who for a long time now had been in the yard observing the sky, rushed in shouting that the first star had in fact appeared in the sky, an announcement which Nina and Krysia did not fail to verify. When it came to sharing the oplatek, Sister Cecilia told them a story of how Wigilias often brought together people who had been enemies for years and years, people of different races, cultures, and degrees of wealth. Looking sternly at the children, she insisted that to share oplatek without forgiving one's enemies would be contrary to the welcoming of the birth of the Savior.

"Just as well we do not have to share the oplatek with... you know who," Nina whispered to Kinga. "I do not think I would be equal to it, would you?" Kinga agreed that to do this would be unconscionable, but she was not sure whether the oplatek itself did not mean forgiveness in general, even including the Nazis. "Better not ask Sister Cecilia," she advised her younger sister. "For what happens if she says that this is what our religion requires? Can we touch the oplatek feeling as we do about THEM?" Krysia, who was listening intently to all that was said, including the whispered conversation among the older girls, came up with what she believed to be a compromise. "We eat the oplatek and tell little Jesus that we will forgive the Germans and the Russians when they get out of Poland," she proposed. The adults let the comment go, although Sister Cecilia did not look too happy about it.

To the delight of the children, especially Krysia, Mr. Lis told them that his granddad, a farmer, used to take oplatek to the farm animals, for they too were God's creatures. "Granddad firmly believed that animals could speak that night. So his kids spent hours talking to the animals in the barn."

"And?" cried the girls. "Well, my father swore that although the cows and horses seemed indifferent, the little goat called Zuzia did in fact answer his pleasantries and wish him a merry Christmas and a happy New Year, in her own language."

By mutual consent, there was no talk about presents, although the three girls each received a small pre-war chocolate bar somehow obtained by Mrs. Nowak and Mr. Lis. It was in the middle of their cries of appreciation that there came a soft noise outside, followed by faint scratching at the door. For a while nobody spoke. "Whoever is there must be admitted," Mrs. Nowak said solemnly. "It is well known that nobody can be turned away during Wigilia. This is why we always leave a place for the unknown visitor at the table. An old legend says that on this holy night, anything can happen. A visitor could be Christ in disguise."

"It is all right, the door is not locked. Come in please," cried Mrs. Ilski. But nobody came in, and when she opened the door all they could see was the empty yard with the star-studded sky above.

Chapter Two
Myszka

In the new year, Myszka arrived to a warm welcome. In a way, she was as puzzled by the arrangements her father insisted on as were the Ilski girls. She admitted that she was not going to ask questions because her dad told her not to do it and mother immediately commented on the wisdom of such an approach. Myszka had with her a suitcase (exactly as mother predicted) and a small radio which received a lot of attention. Her new bed, made from large soap boxes covered with an old rug, was viewed humorously. "I shall imagine that it is a magic carpet and that it will take me to a magic land," she fantasized to the delight of her audience. "There may be a place on the carpet for one of you too."

"Oh," cried Krysia "may I? I am the smallest and will not be too heavy! Please Myszka, please!"

"We will go there and each of us will tell the rest what she saw in the magic land," promised the newcomer. "Each of us will have a story to tell." This idea was accepted enthusiastically by the rest of the family. "You tell me what you have seen in there and I will write about it," commented Kinga. "I may even attempt to write it all in verse if... if I have an inspiration."

"There may be lovely orchards and crystal streams, palaces and mysterious lakes. Perhaps big friendly forests with beautiful wild animals who will welcome us," whispered the little girl, her eyes huge and mysterious. "Perhaps there will be a little elephant called Mizio, like the one we saw in the circus and Myszka and Kinga will write about all this and Nina will draw pictures. Won't you draw pictures Nina?"

"When I have time," Nina answered cautiously, although she was greatly flattered by her proposed involvement in the magic carpet adventures. "I may not like to brag about it," she thought, "but my pictures were highly praised in school." Mother now joined the others in pressing her to take part in "a joint project" involving trips to a magic land, as told, written and illustrated by the four of them. "I could try to illustrate the stories although I am not sure about Mizio," Nina finally conceded and was immediately encouraged by Krysia to trust in her genius. Mother promised to bring discarded sheets of paper from the hospital – they were used only on one side – and Myszka would get a variety of paints and colored chalks from her father. The finished stories with pictures were to be pinned together and kept by Krysia in her 'desk,' i.e., a cardboard box. When that night the little girl whispered to Myszka, "I know now that you are our cousin," her older sisters agreed wholeheartedly.

Nina's worries as to whether mother would know how to register their 'cousin' and fill out all the forms pertaining to their family were communicated to Kinga. In response to her sister's remarks about "mother's lamentable impracticality," (witness the inevitably empty basket she carried with her) Kinga made a non-committal reply and when further pressed by Nina "to look into things before mom lands us all in jail" retorted with a degree of irritation that "things are not always what they seem." That left Nina flabbergasted. "Well, if my sister says that an empty receptacle (except for occasional silly papers) is not what it seems, all I can say is that I am glad of her illusions," Nina commented to herself. "Although I could ask what an empty basket really is for, I refrain from doing so because I know when my older sister is in a mood. But I am glad that at least one of us sees to it that some provisions are what they seem – like the eggs I brought yesterday… I am very glad indeed."

But before long Nina herself was forced to amend her opinions listening to mother's exchange with Mrs. Nowak after the latter had met Myszka. "Poor child, what has happened to her parents?" inquired Mrs. Nowak on her visit to the cellar when Kinga and Myszka were out with Krysia. "To be an orphan at that age," she continued mournfully after receiving mother's explanation. "How sad! But you know dear, Myszka carries a strong resemblance to your family! I would recognize it anywhere! Those dark curls! She must have inherited them from your husband's side of the family."

"You are absolutely right," cried mother with enthusiasm. "My husband's aunt – quite a beauty in her time – dark eyes, dark hair, an eagle profile… part Armenian, you know."

"They are very handsome people," noted Mrs. Nowak, "handsome but very unfortunate. When you think how those horrible Turks treated the poor Armenians… . Give my love to your young cousin, dear."

"If somebody told me a year ago that mother would be such a skillful fibber, I would never have believed it," thought Nina, scrubbing potatoes. "But is it really necessary to fool Mrs. Nowak? Perhaps it is. Eagle profile, indeed! Great aunt Julia looked like a china doll and her hair was blonde! Just as well that our family album was lost. But mother's performance – wow! Impressive is the word!"

In May came the shattering news about the fall of Paris. The German victory was proclaimed on posters, on the radio, and in newspapers. For Poles, who often considered France their second motherland, it was a terrible blow.

The Ghetto

The ghetto issue emerged with a new intensity in the fall of 1940 when the only Polish newspaper edited by Germans started printing attacks on Jews as 'social parasites and agents of infectious diseases.' These, according to the authorities, were the reasons for their separation from the 'aryan' part of the town. Aware of the information, which Mrs. Ilski described as 'filth,' Nina decided to have a chat about it with Jozek. They met at the new soup kitchen, this time on Pasteur Street, pronounced 'much inferior' by the boy. "What kind of a soup is it?" he grumbled. "A lot of greenery floating in a suspicious looking broth, probably artificially colored. Not a sign of noodles. I shudder to think what Sister Hermencia would say to it!" Upon being asked about the ghetto, he pointed his finger to the northeast. "It is over there," he said. "This is where the people who go to synagogue are supposed to be. It is sort of reserved for them." To Nina's further inquiries as to why Jews should live in that particular quarter of Warsaw, Jozek was less forthcoming, "Don't know exactly why, but will find out. One of these days, I will go there to have a look around. One has to examine one's scope, if you take my meaning. Actually," he continued, "I may be Jewish myself, for all I know. On my dad's side, that is. Mom could not qualify, though, for did she love pork chops!" Nina was losing patience. "I asked you if you knew why the Jews are being separated from us, right? I do not think that they would be better off there. I do not think that eating or not eating pork has anything to do with it."

"Well, some eat pork and some don't," was a conciliatory reply. "Anyhow there is very little of it now. But I am going to investigate in case they have a really superior soup kitchen there. Nothing ventured nothing gained," he concluded philosophically.

Yet for a long time there was no news from Jozek. He missed a session in the soup kitchen and Nina began to feel uneasy. Suppose they kept him in that ghetto because he got there under false pretenses? Or maybe he could get there but could not leave? All she knew about this new project was that it had been organized by the Nazis and, therefore, it meant harassment at best, despite the existence of the Jewish Council which had been created by Germans to deal with the Jewish community administration. This was announced on the radio but mother called it hogwash. Jozek was sometimes too open in his remarks about the authorities and perhaps he had gotten in trouble. But it was no use expecting bad things to happen before they actually did, she told herself, remembering Sister Cecilia's visit.

This philosophy proved correct, for Jozek materialized a week later, although not in his usual good spirits and looking somewhat thinner than she remembered. After they received their soup portion and left the other people behind, he began to speak about his experiences. "A bad place," he announced. "A very bad place. Badder than any other in Warsaw. No soup kitchen of any kind. Plenty of police, some German, some Jewish. You can get in, I did, no problem, but when you try to get out – ooo – you really have to look sharp.[15] 'Get back where you belong, schnell,' they shouted. "Zurück, zurück."

"How do the people look?" Nina enquired anxiously.

"Some are still O.K., in fact very elegant and there are rich restaurants. But some are desperately poor, dressed worse than I," and he looked mournfully at his split shoes and tattered trousers, "and they are starving.[16] The guards carry big clubs. One of them, a cross-eyed one, tried to hit me with it. He missed, but it was close!!! And me an orphan," he added in an aggrieved tone. "What would Mother Superior say to it?" Here Jozek descended into the depths of self pity, seeing which Nina offered him her handkerchief which he used with prolonged and thunderous sound effects. Urged to continue, he began again:

"It was evening, just about six o'clock, and I heard some dogs that they brought to guard the ghetto at night. So I decided to stay the night and try again the next morning. I tell you I would not have half minded some soup and a roof over my head." It appeared that he had been lucky enough to be allowed to join a Jewish family, a woman with three children, one of them a baby. It was the baby that captivated him, and occupied most of his narrative. "After I was given two blintzes (not what you would called sustenance, if you take my meaning Nina, but very welcome under the circumstances) I tried to explain to the lady why I was there, but could not, for the baby was very fractious and roared right into her ear, rendering the poor mother half deaf. So, I volunteered to hold him and I walked with him and sang a hymn we had learned at school. Would you believe it, he calmed down, snuggled against me and listened! A religiously inclined kid, and clever! I stayed the night with them and he slept with me good as gold! Then the same thing happened in the morning when I gave him 'Kiedy ranne wstaja zorze' (a religious song) – appropriate because of the time of the day, you understand – and did he appreciate it! I told his mother that based on my experience with religious vocations, I would not be surprised if he grew up to be a famous rabbi!"

---

[15] Warsaw ghetto gates were closed in November 1940.

[16] In Szpilman's *The Pianist*, comments describing savage brutality and despicable behavior are reserved for the Jewish police in the Ghetto and for the members of the Jewish Council, pp. 65-74, 90, 107, 114. He also describes the huge economic inequality existing in the Ghetto, pp. 67, 83, 91. Among other writers, Wladyslaw Bartoszewski's *The Warsaw Ghetto* (MA: Beacon Press, 1987) gives a shattering picture of the Ghetto seen from the unique perspective of a liaison between the Polish Underground and the Jewish leadership within the Ghetto.

Jozek refreshed himself with a few spoons of soup and continued haltingly, by now his self assurance and cockiness gone. "When I was leaving, the lady kissed me and little Icek pulled my hair, but it was affectionate like. He laughed and we all laughed also... I keep thinking about them. They still had some food but... There are already those who do not have any..." He turned away rubbing his eyes with Nina's handkerchief, now soaked through.

Both of them sat on the church steps in deep silence. "So this is why Dr. Stein wanted Myszka to live with us and change her name," thought Nina, "so that she would not be there. If it weren't for those fiendish Nazis, Jozek, who had no family of his own, could have become a friend to that family, could have enjoyed that little Icek and his kindly mother. But as it is now, he could not even visit them. Couldn't they get out at all?" she asked "After all, you did, didn't you?" After helping himself to more soup Jozek reverted to his old cocky self. "I did, due entirely to my powers of invention, actually," he responded in a dignified voice "and invention it was, I am telling you. Next day, after I saw that the cross-eyed one was no longer there, I went to a fat one (he also had a club but looked less fierce) and told him that my aunt wanted me to go to the Aryan side to retrieve her diamonds. 'Where are the diamonds?' asks he. 'In a bombed building on Marshall Street,' say I, bold as brass. Actually there is a bombed building on that street scheduled for demolition as very unsafe, so I had figured that he would not be likely to try to get inside it, not with his weight. To make it all more believable I said that I knew in which room the diamonds were, and that being skinny I would try to get there through the balcony. But here I goofed, for that house never had a balcony, and if they were to check..."

"Go on, go on," Nina urged impatiently. "Well, I soon suffered another near heart attack when he and another who joined him asked me for my aunt's name. What was I to say? I said Brumberg, for this is the name of that big department store close to our soup kitchen, you know, the one with the five big windows. Are you with me Nina?" he was now coming to the climax of his story and was obviously enjoying himself. After savoring her breathless "Yes, yes, so?" Jozek took a deep breath, pretended to re-lace his shoe and after stirring his soup and commenting on its inadequacy condescended to continue. "Where was I? Well, they said they would check on it and I should stay in the police cubicle and not to move. One step out of it and I was dead..."

"God," whispered Nina. "Holy Mary of Czestochowa."

"I stayed there wondering what I would say if a strange lady rejected me as her nephew. Which would be only natural under the circumstances... But then I remembered how Sister Teresa had told us that Jesus was Jewish, and since I was among the Jews, I said one Hail Mary to His mother, to be on the safe side. It worked out," he ended triumphantly, "it worked out beautifully. They came back and told me that there were dozens of Brumberg people in the ghetto, and they were not going to bother to find my aunt. That I should go to that bombed building, find the diamonds and bring them directly to them, and they would see to it that my aunt got them. Fat chance!!!"

He received Nina's heartfelt congratulations with dignified equanimity.

Life Goes On

Despite all the anxieties connected with Myszka's stay, Nina had to admit that her arrival could only be seen in a positive light. Food problems were somewhat ameliorated by mother's ingenious use of the family ration cards and Nina's spreading acquaintance with suburban farmers, who often let her have produce at prices below what they were in the city. Also, although contact between Dr. Stein and his daughter was limited to a minimum, he managed to send her some goodies from time to time, and she loyally shared them with her new family. Dr. Stein was not yet in the ghetto, mother informed them. He was needed in the hospitals outside, but there was every possibility that this freedom would not last long. "Your dad is quite a hero," mother told Myszka one night. "With his skills, he probably could be excused from living in the ghetto. But he does not want it, for apart from having to beg those nasty Germans for permission to stay where he now is, he wants to help the ghetto people who may need him even more." Remembering Jozek's description of what he had seen, Nina was sure that Dr. Stein's assistance would be greatly needed there.

Since nobody seemed to know why the Nazis decided to put the Jewish population of Warsaw behind walls, opinions attempting to interpret the official mind varied. While some expected that unidentified horrors were yet to come, others took a far more optimistic view of the situation and saw it as temporary. Myszka, belonged to the latter. "Perhaps this is only a short term arrangement," she suggested hopefully. "Perhaps Mr. Hitler wants to have all the Jews together to find out if they would like to leave, if they have relations in other countries. Many of us do, you know. For instance I have an aunt in Sweden. I would not mind going to Sweden with dad, although I would miss you." She could not finish her ruminations for Krysia's arms wound tightly around her neck and emotional appeals not to go to Sweden or anywhere else were made by the little girl over and over again. This was strongly seconded by the other girls. Mother however said nothing, and after kissing each of them departed with her basket.

Things became more settled when Myszka joined Kinga in attending classes at the 'Flying College' and Nina graduated to the generally recognized position of family provision manager. More and more often she thought with longing about the time when she would be old enough to join them. "All the time I am worrying about food and fuel," she confided to Jozek, "and trying to get the best price for the things we still have to sell, (like the bargain salt pork, cabbage, and flour I got for mom's earrings). I wish that I could spend time reading and discussing things, as Myszka and Kinga do at their secret classes. Of course, they do repeat what they have learned at home, but I wish I could get it all first hand, not second. Well it will not be long now, for I am much older. But what is going to happen to us all when I start my classes, is anyone's guess. Who could survive on rationed brown bread and beetroot jam? We will probably all starve to death," she finished in self-congratulatory manner.

The scholarly and artistic aspect of their existence was in full swing that second winter. Myszka and Kinga had expanded their knowledge of Polish literature and history, while at the same time, perfecting their German. They had promised mother that on coming home they would try to repeat what they had learned to the younger girls. The magic carpet stories were now copied on sheets of hospital paper and decorated by Nina. Myszka's radio provided music, although the most beloved songs were no longer heard on the radio. Those were the tunes the older girls had sung at their scout meetings before the war. One of them, entitled "Wszystko co nasze Polsce oddamy" (We will give all we have to Poland), precipitated a visit from Mrs. Sawicki, a lady now evicted from her beautiful villa at the corner and staying with her relatives across the road. The words of the song prompted Mrs. Sawicki's intervention at ten p.m. "Dear Mrs. Ilski," she addressed mother ingratiatingly after hugging each of them separately. "You will not think me an interfering person if I tell you that the singing of such emotional songs may get you into deep trouble, very deep trouble indeed. With those words about Poland, you know, and the association with the scouts, which the present authorities have condemned (latest on the radio), your girls must not indulge." But mother did not see it in this light. "I am glad that the girls in my family show such artistic tendencies," she said easily, "surely it is important to enjoy music."

"Oh, but I am for it also," argued their visitor. "The world of music and song fascinates me deeply. I am all for nice nonaggressive musical compositions along the lines of 'Smile at me' (here Nina gave an exaggerated shudder) or 'Tell her of my love, little flowers.' (Kwiatki powiedzcie jej.) Surely there is no need for politics, no need at all."

"We cannot stop what we like to do simply because they – you know who – are here temporarily," mother announced quietly but assertively, causing Mrs. Sawicki to dash toward an open window in order to close it. "We all need some refuge from all this around us, this oppression, this ugliness. It cannot last forever." But the visitor was already at the door. "Please understand that my remarks were meant well," she whispered before exiting. "As to oppressiveness and ugliness they are now drawing closer… Number 16 on the street next to ours has been rented by the new officials, uniformed,… possibly connected with investigatory agencies. Be alert, Renata, for heaven's sake, be alert!" With this, she firmly closed the door behind her.

The question now before them was to evaluate what such neighbors, as described by her, would do to them and the people living on their street. Mother did not seem especially perturbed, although she cautioned the girls to be prepared for a casual encounter with the Germans. "Any remarks by them, if they come, should appear to be incomprehensible to you, although I know that Myszka and Kinga are now very proficient in the language. Simply look as if you did not understand what they mean. Should you be addressed in Polish, which is rather unlikely, answer in a non-committal manner and go your way. Do not let yourselves be drawn into a discussion, but do not appear flustered. All this is simply precautionary. I do not believe that our new neighbors will bother us, although it may be wise not to call their attention to us by loud singing. We will have another lock on the door. After sunset, the door has to be securely locked, especially when I am not here. But please remember that even among them, there are decent people."

Not all of the girls agreed. "Decent people indeed!" Nina started her opposition but was prevented from fully expressing her opinion by Myszka's suddenly bursting into tears. "Oh God, oh God," she moaned her shoulders shaking, "what if they see me and recognize me as a Jew? What if they order me into the ghetto and perhaps kill you all as well?[17] Knowing that they are just on the next street, I will never feel safe. What if Ms. Sawicki is right and they are indeed the Secret State Police?" [Nazi police.]

In vain did all of them try to calm her down. While Krysia asserted that, "Jewish is beautiful" mother explained that thousands of Aryans had features and hair similar to Myszka's. "You know that Poland was a multiethnic commonwealth; there is no physical type that corresponds to a non-Jewish person. All those supposed racial characteristics are an exaggeration. And the same applies to Germans. Look at their VIP's, Goebbels for instance. He looks positively Middle-Eastern. Besides, our underground courts – and there is such a thing although I am not going to talk about it now, so don't press me Nina – have imposed severe punishment for the criminals who report on Jews and others to the Germans to get favors from them.[18] There is really no reason to be anxious, darling."

---

[17] Of all the countries occupied by Germans, only in Poland was there a policy of capital punishment for helping Jews. It was imposed on the Pole involved, his/her family, and often their acquaintances. See examples of such Bekanntmachung (notice) in Bartoszewski, *The Warsaw Ghetto*, pp. 37, 110, 11.

[18] "The Underground authorities followed up their warnings about blackmailing Jews... by executing the culprits and publicizing these executions in the Polish clandestine press," Richard C. Lukas, *The Forgotten Holocaust, the Poles under German Occupation, 1939-1944* (KY: The University Press of Kentucky, 1986), p. 119. For a more comprehensive description of the underground courts see Stefan Korbonski, *Fighting Warsaw*, (Minerva Press, 1956), pp. 124-135. Stefan Karbonski was the last Chief of the Polish Wartime Underground.

Although such arguments did have some effect, and Myszka was amused by having a master of Nazi propaganda and the right hand of Hitler looking non-Aryan, she still insisted that she must do something to change her appearance. "What if I were to dye my hair blonde?" she inquired. "Wouldn't it make me look more Aryan?"

Against Krysia's vehement objections (Myszka with yellow hair would not be Myszka) mother and the older girls were inclined to approve the hair coloring, if that was what Myszka really wanted. Nina immediately volunteered to get a dye by telling a soup kitchen acquaintance, who had been a hair dresser, that she wanted a dye for her aunt. By her own account, the lady claimed to be superior to other beauticians in culture and expertise, but was now obliged to stand in line for soup by the calamity which she described as 'low class barbarism.' "I did not treat the hair only in my sophisticated premises at Biala Street," Nina imitated the lady's confidential outpourings. "I treated their souls, I treated their entire being… Young as you are my dear, you have to know the meaning of elegance, the meaning of panache… Panache is what counts in a woman. Be a woman, my dear, a WOMAN… ." Encouraged by her audience's appreciation, Nina proceeded to tell them what her own approach would be in asking the lady to recommend a first class product. "My aunt – a woman of the world in the full meaning of the word," she announced in simpering accents while rehearsing her role "not at all passé, if you take my meaning, and by no means devoid of aspirations, believes – and here I venture to agree – that in the area of feminine aspirations, blonde women, especially those possessing panache… ."

"Honestly Nina," mother interrupted, sounding displeased, "it is not nice poking fun at people. Is it not enough that we unfortunately have to depart from the truth on occasion, without making a habit of it?" But the girls giggled like crazy and Nina was highly satisfied with the reaction she had received.

Soon after the agreement was reached, Kinga focused on another obstacle. Many people had seen Myszka with dark hair, she pointed out. How would they explain to them the change in her appearance? "I do not mind the college people," Myszka responded. "They all know I am Jewish, and they would not ask me questions. The problem, if there is one, would be with the neighbors, Mrs. Nowak, Mr. Lis and the latest visitor."

"I believe that we are safe there," Ms. Ilski remarked. "If they comment on the change we will tell them that you wanted to look like Veronica Lake. But chances are they would not be inquisitive, certainly not Mr. Lis and Ms. Nowak. Mrs. Sawicki is so short-sighted that she could not distinguish between you and Kinga. So if you are determined, we can proceed."

Thus Myszka changed from a brunette to a blonde and this alteration in her appearance gave her courage to go outside and even to meet the new neighbors.

After that major alteration in their friend's appearance, the three of them who took part in the process had yellow fingers for weeks. They looked at the fact with satisfaction, for it seemed to prove the veracity of Nina's soup kitchen acquaintance, who claimed the dye was a product of great superiority. Of course washing arrangements in the cellar were a great nuisance, despite the easy availability of water which after several months of the occupation, the authorities allowed to run warm for a few hours every week. The outside toilet was also a great bonus in their lives and any complaint about its distance from the house was immediately countered by mother with "Remember how the people who hide from the Germans live in forests and caves. At least we have water and soap."

"Well, the Germans are allowing soap on the market because they are afraid that there will be a wave of sicknesses which may spread to them," Nina remarked. "It does not mean that they want us to be free of germs! No way!"

Maintenance of relative hygiene was easier when mother started working in the hospital and had access to showers there, and through the good services of Ms. Nowak, whose bathroom was available to all of them weekly. Still it was decided that taking full advantage of the offer would not be fair to the lady, (warm water and soap were expensive) and the ablutions in the bathroom were limited to two girls once a week. Not to deplete the lady's supply of towels, they created their own. Used torn towels were available to the hospital staff, and mother duly brought some home. After boiling them and cutting off the damaged parts, Kinga patiently stitched the sides creating a number of small but absorbent pieces of cloth. Nightly sponge baths became routine, but did not really satisfy anybody.

"Necessity is the mother of invention," Nina announced one afternoon when all of them (except mother) were home. "For a time now I had my eye on a big barrel that stands in front of that ruined store on the corner. It was originally put there to catch rain water, but there are no gutters now and it is wasted. I do not believe that anyone would grudge us that barrel. Why don't we appropriate it and use it in lieu of a bathtub?" It was a bold and intriguing proposition, but not without pitfalls. The barrel obviously had belonged to somebody at one time and it looked heavy. Nina readily overcame the moral objections and pronounced herself fit for the physical effort involved in the project. "Look here," she cried exposing her thin forearms. "Did you ever see such muscles? This is what carrying sacks of potatoes does to you. I believe that I could now satisfy even that unpleasant gym instructress who always complained that we were all flabby. Imagine that, even today, one of us could luxuriate submerged up to her neck in warm water in that deep wonderful barrel. Of course it would have to be throughly washed from inside out, but it would be worth it! But mind, if we decide to do it, we had better do it before mother arrives!" On this there was no disagreement. Mother, surprisingly advanced on some issues, tended to be stubborn elsewhere.

The deed was done. When Mrs. Ilski arrived late in the evening (as a hospital worker, she had a pass for walking the streets of Warsaw after the curfew), a big barrel occupied a corner in the cellar and disheveled but happy girls were ready with their story. "This barrel is so huge that you can have two ways of washing in it," Kinga instructed her parent. "You can attach a hose to the faucet and have a kind of a shower in it, or you can fill it with warm water and be covered altogether. Of course you have to scoop out the dirty water afterwards but it is no big thing."

"But how on earth did you get it here?" asked mother eyeing the proportions of the barrel. "We rolled it, all three of us," responded Myszka joyfully, "and you should have heard the noise. It was earth shaking. People were running out of their houses. Mrs. Sawicki actually thought that it was an artillery assault. We had to send Krysia to calm her down."

"I did explain to her what we needed the barrel for," proud of her responsible task, Krysia elucidated her role. "I said, 'dear Mrs. Sawicki, the noise is due to my sisters' rolling the barrel through the street, it has nothing to do with bombs.' But she became more at ease when that nice young man confirmed what I had said."

"For there was a young man involved also," Kinga jumped in impatiently, "and he offered us help. Imagine my horror, mom, when Nina proceeded to tell him in detail what we needed the barrel for, and actually invited him to come to us one day and bathe himself! Myszka went white at the suggestion, I can tell you. But Nina was impervious to tact and delicacy. She added that she would see to it that there would be a partition and he would have full privacy! I thought I would just die from embarrassment and so did Myszka! It was too much, it really was! Mom, please speak to her!"

"Are you so silly and sensitive, Kinga, that the very mention of a man in a bath brings a blush to your cheeks?" Nina retorted heatedly. "He might have been deprived of a bathroom in the same way we are! What would you say if you were locked up in a toilet with a strange man for twenty-four hours? This is what happened to Jozek's acquaintance." Aware of the impression she was making, Nina continued happily. "There was a bomb raid, and the people in the store dispersed in panic. Two of them, male and female, rushed to a toilet, believing that was the safest place in the store, and I am sure Mrs. Nowak told us likewise. Well, the bathroom was not damaged but the whole building collapsed around them and they could not get out. The floor of the toilet was flooded and their feet were killing them, so they took turns sitting on the toilet seat. But of course, when nature called (they stayed there twenty-four hours, remember), the other person just turned away, closed his/her eyes, and covered his/her ears, for that was the best they could do under the circumstances. When they finally were rescued, they just rushed in opposite directions. Jozek believes that it was bad manners, for after all they did spend a long time together. The circumstances not being auspicious for anything warmer, a cool 'Nice to have met you,' would have sufficed, according to Jozek."

During that long narrative each of the girls evidenced different emotions. Kinga attempted repeatedly to get mother to interrupt Nina's story, while Myszka and Krysia followed each of Nina's words with horrified fascination. Mrs. Ilski heard Nina to the end without any outward signs of displeasure. "It could well have happened," she commented, "and it must have been embarrassing, but I bet they were very happy to be alive. Much worse things have happened to our people and are still happening. There is no reason to be so shocked, Kinga; in situations of life and death normally embarrassing circumstances do not have great importance. One wonders however, how Jozek obtained all the details you related. I would not repeat his story, Nina, at any rate not in front of our neighbors." Grudgingly, Nina acquiesced.

Enemies – Near and Distant

Mother's hopes that the people moving to the next street (number 16) would just be common German soldiers proved futile, however. Nina had occasion to observe one of them buying cigarettes in a corner store, where she had placed their 'want to buy' add for another electric heater (the one from Mr. Lis was on its last legs). The owner of the store, a plump Mrs. Linkowski, appeared struck speechless when the German entered. She went white and pulling Nina behind the counter faced him with what appeared to be a desperate determination. But determination to do what? He moved his hand as if to put them at ease and asked in a soft voice for cigarettes. On getting the brand he wanted, he murmured the word "danke," put a bank note on the counter, which far exceeded the price of cigarettes, and slowly turned toward the door. Grabbing some money from the drawer, Mrs. Linkowski rushed to the door and blocked his exit. She handed him the change as if challenging him not to accept it. After he took the money, she let him leave.

Nina observed the German with interest. He certainly looked different from the soldiers she saw on the streets, with a brown shirt, grey uniform, and death-head badge on his cap. Mrs. Linkowski was now back behind the counter still breathing hard, making Nina her confidante. "As God is my witness, I would have shot him dead if it were not for my little children," she gasped. "For he and the like of him are not human beings, not even animals, they are devils incarnate!! That monster wanted to make me a present of his filthy money!!" Seeing Nina's incredulity, she embarked on a fuller explanation. "He is Secret State Police, girl, a Szuch Avenue person. Did you see his cap with skull? It is they who starve our people in the ghetto, they who conduct fiendish experiments in the camps, they that arrange public executions." With every sentence starting with 'they' Mrs. Linkowski became more upset. "You know what happened on Pius Street yesterday? Maybe your mom does not want you to know, but I will tell you and maybe ask her pardon when I see her. Fifty of our people from Pawiak prison were massacred on the street and their poor bodies left there for hours for us to see… . and there is hardly a week that such a thing does not happen! There is no doubt that they will try to kill us all! So when you see one of those black devils, run…" Here the woman's voice failed her and she fell sobbing into the arms of an elderly lady who had entered the store in the middle of the monologue and just stood there listening.

Frightened and depressed, Nina went slowly home trying to rub the traces of tears from her face. Her thoughts revolved around the terrible images of the prisoners killed yesterday and the advice given her by Mrs. Linkowski. She told me to run, but where? There is no free place in all of Poland, not even an inch. Everywhere there are either those horrible Nazis or the equally bad Soviets. God, what fate!

The two unfamiliar names that stuck in her memory were Szuch and Pawiak. Mrs. Linkowski mentioned them in connection with those horrors, but Nina did not know what the connection was. Rather than ask mother, whom she now seldom asked anything, she brought the matter to the attention of Jozek. She was not disappointed. Jozek informed her that the headquarters of the Secret State Police was on Szuch Avenue and that Pawiak was a huge prison. He did hear about the Secret State Police atrocities from his German contact and assured Nina that Hans was terrified of the Nazi police as were other soldiers. He also told her that the huge covered lorries whose sirens woke them at night were used by the Germans for transporting prisoners and not, as mother had told them, for moving furniture. But Jozek got very jittery talking about it and Nina did not breach with him the matter of executions. He is too young for it, she thought. It is different with me for I am practically an adult, thirteen next week. Jozek is barely ten plus, obviously much less mature and not up to such terrible revelations.

Although the Ilski girls did not pay particular attention to the German press, they could not avoid noticing during the Spring of 1941 that Nazi controlled newspapers intensified their efforts to influence public opinion. Pious assertions of the 'European' roots of German and Polish cultures, as opposed to some unidentified Euro/Asian despotic empire, were a radical departure from the past. Gone were avowals of the 'eternal' friendship of Russia and Germany so prevalent in late 1939 and 1940. Gone as well were photos displaying the smiling faces of Stalin, Ribbentrop (Foreign Minister of Nazi Germany), and Molotov, (Foreign Minister of the Soviet Union). Indeed, it almost appeared as if the treaty of August 1939, which precipitated the attack on Poland from both sides, had never been signed.

Kinga and Myszka received periodic reports on changed Nazi attitudes in their underground classes, but lengthy discussions on the subject were not pursued by the faculty. Neither mother nor Mr. Lis, who visited them frequently, appeared inclined to comment on this change, although it seemed obvious that a break in hitherto friendly Nazi/Soviet relations was imminent. Most Poles regarded this development with hopeful anticipation; what could be better for Poland than a quarrel between her two mortal enemies?

Still, there was a terribly depressing side to it. Even those Poles who had previously refused to admit that any nation on earth could be as bad as Germany, had to admit that the evidence of Soviet crimes, which the German authorities now allowed to surface, was overwhelming. Previously concealed and unavailable documents pertaining to mass arrests of Poles in the Soviet zone were now published, also describing deportations of families to Siberia and Kazakhstan, and confiscations of businesses, houses, farms, bank accounts. Letters from people living under Soviet occupation to their relatives in the West were sometimes permitted, and the Ilski family got one from mother's aunt Zofia in Lwow.

The appearance of those few pages gave testimony to the tragic news the letter contained. It was obviously sprinkled with tears. Mother read it to the girls after she came back from work late at night in April 1941. It described how aunt Zofia helplessly watched the deportation of her daughter Kasia, already in an advanced stage of pregnancy, and of her children by the Soviet military during the year before (i.e., in April 1940).

"I injured my back that winter (1940) and could not climb the stairs to Kasia's apartment," the letter went. "A kind neighbor, Dr. Maria Koresz, invited me to spend some months in her ground floor flat, in the building just opposite. In this way I could be nearby and see my two grandchildren after school. It was agreed that when the baby started to come, Maria would be in attendance. We anticipated that the event would occur very soon, for Kasia was already in some discomfort that evening."[19]

"Imagine my horror," the reading went on "when at three a.m. that night, I was alerted by the sound of a heavy military lorry stopping in front of our house. I was still not sure what was happening when I saw a group of Soviet soldiers with rifles pushing my pregnant daughter and the two children into that truck. They only had a few small bundles with them, my five-year-old grandson clutching a box of diapers! My first thought was to join them, but I could hardly move! Maria grabbed me as I attempted to get out and told me that I would be paralyzed if I tried to get on that truck, that I could in no way help my family in the state I was in, that the only thing to do was to gather the money and jewels in our possession and to catch them at the railway station. 'I had information from one of my patients that the trucks are heading toward Zamarstynow railway station' she gasped, frantically pulling on her clothes. 'I am going there and will try to find Kasia and give her some medical supplies, as well as money… but I must hurry.'"

"I immediately contributed my wedding ring, my watch, and the golden chain I had around my neck. I also gave her some money. She left in a taxi and I stayed at home wondering how on earth Kasia could survive, how the children could survive… . Well, my landlady came back after a few hours. She did find the wagon where my family was, but she had problems delivering the parcel, for the whole train was encircled by armed Soviet soldiers and the wagons (designed for transporting animals and goods) were already locked from the outside. Thousands of people surrounded the soldiers around the train (some forty wagons full of women and children) and

---

[19]   The following describes an experience similar to that of the author.

the people inside shouted their names to the relatives outside. Maria managed to get our parcel to Kasia's wagon through a small window, thanks to two teenagers who managed to distract the attention of the soldier in front of the wagon."

Mother stopped reading for a while, had a glass of water, and then continued, "Maria asked how Kasia was," the writer continued in her letter, "and she was told that Kasia's labor had already started, but the women in the wagon swore that they would take care of her, that she was now their sister... There was a nurse among the prisoners, and she was glad of the package, but there were fifty persons in the wagon, no conveniences, no water, no toilet or sanitation, and several babies.... 'You cannot imagine the atmosphere...' my friend told me. 'It took the people back over a hundred years, when after the 1830s Uprising 80,000 Poles in chains were marched to Siberia. All the Poles at the Zamarstynow station sang Konopnicka's anthem, those imprisoned and those still free... The train left soon after...'"

"The filthy fiends," exploded Kinga. "To treat pregnant women and children like this! No wonder aunt Zofia thinks that the Germans are better than the Soviets!"

"But they are not," retorted Nina. "The worth of each is as low as that of the other, the scum."

"They are not all like that," mother tried to interject, but that feeble comment remained unheeded. Myszka and Krysia were clutching one another, the latter whimpering. "Did the baby die, then?" she asked. "Did they both die?"

"Not at all," mother answered in a far more cheerful voice. "Aunt Kasia was very sick but she did not die, and her baby, Wiesia, survived too. Since her mom could not feed her, do you know what her nourishment was during the nineteen days of that journey? It was powdered milk which one of the ladies had with her, diluted in water that the prisoners were allowed to fetch once a day. When they arrived at their destination in Siberia, aunt Kasia could sell things that Doctor Maria managed to get to her and get some food."

That was not the end of the letter, but the older girls understood that mother did not want to read the last paragraph to Krysia. It was hardly more comforting.

"As soon as my back healed, I began trying to convince the Soviet authorities to let me join my family in Siberia," wrote aunt Zofia. "I already have the ticket, but no passport as yet.[20] Even if I get there, I shall not see all of them because little Edek died recently of appendicitis. There was nobody to operate in that Siberian kolhoz. Kasia, Alicja, and Wiesia are still there, but God knows for how long. There are famine conditions... We may just as well die together."

---

[20]   Soviet authorities introduced the system of internal passports. Without a seal on the passport, its owner could not leave the place of sojourn.

In June 1941, the news of the war between Nazi Germany and the Soviet Union, hitherto allied, exploded in the media. It now became clear – according to the Nazis – that "Bolshevik Judea" was threatening a world whose only hope of survival lay with the protective patron of Western civilization, that is, Germany. The names of Jewish VIP's in Stalin's government and the People's Commissariat for Internal Affairs were frequently mentioned. Even the tirades against the Polish resistance subsided for a while, and references to Poland's traditional problems with its eastern neighbor saw the light of day in print. Myszka and Kinga, who had studied the political situation in their underground classes, related the news to the younger girls. "It is exactly what happened in 1914 when Germany and Russia were at war," commented Myszka whose interest in history had earned her special recognition from Prof. Rojek. "The two partition powers promised Poles freedom, independence, and prosperity, if only Pilsudski and Dmowski (leaders of two movements for independence) joined their sides. But few Poles took it seriously. I do not think that our side should even listen to those overtures. Horrible though the USSR is, Hitler's Germany is no better."

"You are right Myszka!" exclaimed Mrs. Ilski, who appeared at the door with her inevitable basket (a box of matches and the official newspaper, Nina noted. Big deal!). "Our side has already refused!"[21] Having said it, mother looked as if she regretted her openness and immediately embarked on a convoluted saga of a girl with a broken leg she nursed in the hospital, but it was no use. The girls just waited, and when Mrs. Nowak took Krysia to have a bath at her house, all three of them began the siege.

"Please do not keep things from us, aunt Renata," Myszka implored. (The adoption of the word 'aunt' occurred after Myszka moved in with them.) "We are old enough to understand. Even Nina is basically an adult…"

"I sincerely hope so," Nina interjected with dignity. "Is there some secret Polish organization which is recognized by the Nazis?" Myszka continued. "The 'bandits,'" gasped Nina. "Have the bandits been approached?"

Mother waited with her answer for some time and when it came, it was only spoken with great reluctance. "There is an underground government in Poland responsible to our Government in Exile in London," she said. "The duty of the institution is to fight the Germans in every way, through the secret press, education,

---

21   German overtures toward Poles and their proposals of cooperation took a definite shape in January 1942. Polish refusal precipitated a massacre at Anin. See Alfred Tworkowski, *Polska Walczaca w Oczach CIA*, [Fighting Poland in CIA Records] Chicago, Wici, 1994), p. 62-63; also, Lukas, *The Forgotten Holocaust*, p. 115.

espionage and yes, force of arms. The responsibility for fighting belongs to a large underground army organization called AK (Armja Krajowa, Home Army).[22] Do not refer to them as 'bandits' Nina, even as a joke. They risk their lives every hour of the day and are under very strict military discipline. Absolute secrecy is mandatory. The resistance has been very effective.[23] The AK does not accept Soviet occupation of Eastern Poland and therefore considers the USSR a hostile power, similar to Germany. That is why German suggestions that Poles join them in the invasion of the Soviet Union, were rejected."

The girls listened enthralled. "I knew it, I knew it!" exclaimed Nina. "God, what news! To know that there has been effective fighting against the occupation forces, enough for the Nazis to consider Polish help in their attack on the Soviet Union! But of course, our people would not agree! 'Let criminals fight criminals,' they say.'" But mother did not look happy. "This is not good news," she said. "The whole existence of our secret government here is very precarious. There is a price on the head of anyone involved. When caught, they will be instantly executed. And now, after the refusal, things may get even worse."

It was hitherto silent Kinga who spoke slowly but with devastating effect. "How is it that you know about all this Mom? Aren't such things top secret?" Again mother did not reply for a long time. Nina told herself that she did not want to know the answer. She would much rather remain ignorant. Knowledge that their mother could be part of something so terribly dangerous… she didn't wish to hear any more.

"I overheard a conversation on a bus," Mrs. Ilski finally said, but the words lacked conviction.

---

[22] "On the military side, the A.K.… grew into a force of some 400,000 trained soldiers… ," Davies, *Heart of Europe*, p. 72.

[23] "Already in May 1940 the Germans were sufficiently alarmed by Polish resistance to carry out a special repressive movement, of arrests and executions, known as the 'A.B. Aktion.' The Poles decided to fight reprisals with counter-reprisals. When Polish patriots were executed, Polish resisters executed prominent German officials," Hugh Seton-Watson, *The East European Revolution*, (NY: Praeger, 1958), p. 113.

A Secret Agent in Their Midst

The next day, a Sunday, the family went to church, (since synagogues had been closed, Myszka sometimes attended a Catholic church, for she missed the spiritual atmosphere). Nina excused herself from accompanying them for a walk in the park after the mass. She was going to do some drawings, she said. The fact was, however, that after the revelations of the day before, her thoughts focused on the basket which mother always carried with her to work. Once an object of ridicule because of the invariably meager contents, it now assumed an intriguing significance. Could it be that it was not connected with the purchase of domestic items? Could mother's insistence on having it by her have some mysterious purpose? Once at home, Nina approached it with trepidation. It was empty, apart from the German-censored newspaper, and she heaved a sigh of relief. Yet, the lining of the basket seemed somewhat loose and creased, and the depth of the interior looked small, considering the size of the reticule.

"If I had not kept control over my emotions, I would have fainted away, like all the silly women in the novels that you are so fond of," she confided to Kinga later in the day. "The basket has a double bottom, a kind of a secret envelope under the lining, can you imagine? That is not the end of it. The lining has an opening and under it was an envelope. In that envelope there was a sheet of paper with 'In the Name of the Polish Republic' printed at the top! I tell you my knees buckled under me and stayed wobbly until evening, for I realized that this smacks of the 'bandits.' Of course I did not look any further and put it all back, but what on earth is mom up to?"

To Nina's surprise Kinga demonstrated an unusual calm. "In the first place, do not call our legal government 'bandits,' Nina. They are all great heroes. Secondly, yes, I have suspected for a long time now that mom has been in touch with some secret organization. Do you remember Dr. Stein's instruction to us not to ask mom questions? I bet he knew something. What about the sudden change of jobs? Wasn't it a good way to see various people and to have a pass that allows her to be outside after the curfew which is now stricter than ever? I do not think that we should talk to her about it, however. She obviously did not want to speak about it. Krysia must not be told."

"But do you know what it means, Kinga?" Nina was now close to nervous breakdown. "It means that any day they may find that secret part of the basket, and then..." This speculation was too much for Kinga also, and when Myszka arrived she found both sisters clutching each other and crying. She looked at them and then without a word started to prepare tea. "I got a jar of what looks like honey from Mrs. Rawicz, in the newspaper store," she announced "We shall have a nice podwieczorek (high tea)."

"Shall we tell her, Kinga?" Nina asked in a whisper. "She knows," was her sister's reply. "I told her this morning."

The deeply worrying but intensely exciting discovery of their mother's affiliation with the Underground opened up a new dimension in their lives, a hitherto little known subject for their thoughts and talks. Relatively uninformed though they were, they did know that there were different branches of the anti-Nazi conspiracy. After all, the older girls attended secret courses, whose faculty used assumed names. Students told only their first names to preserve anonymity. The classes were held in different locations every time, which were revealed at a very short notice. The children were also aware that Mrs. Nowak and Mr. Lis regularly read the underground press, which everybody knew was illegal. The tasks their mother performed for the Underground remained a mystery to them, however. She was not a teacher. Was she perhaps writing articles for prohibited publications? "I think not," declared Kinga. "Her job must deal with foreign affairs for why else would she be forever asking Mrs. Nowak to get her various dictionaries from the street market?"[24]

It was a fair assumption that their mother was employed to translate documents, leaflets, or broadcasts. But though the girls longed to know for sure, they considered it inappropriate to ask her. She was a member of that admired and eminently praiseworthy group of people who were entitled to keeping their activities secret, who deserved a high degree of respect and privacy. Nobody had a right to pry into that murky field of forbidden, dangerous work. Wasn't it also better this way? "If we do not know things," Kinga thought, "we could not inadvertently expose mother. God knows how very careful we are not to talk about her. But Krysia is still young and only the other day she was blabbing about mother's knowledge of languages to the children in the park."

The girls were also generally aware that the battle for Poland was still going on, for there were military units: the real AK or the Home Army. The soldiers of this army trained in secret under the noses of the occupying forces, took part in demolishing enemy transports, and occasionally engaged in battles in the open with regular German army troops. Such military units were mostly in the country while their chief command, their courts, and the intelligence headquarters were located in Warsaw. Mrs. Amelia told them that it was the duty of the latter to conduct espionage, and to monitor the courier service to and from the Polish Government

---

[24] Driven by the need to survive, many people would try to sell their book collections on the open market.

in London, usually once a week. Capturing such people and forcing them to reveal what they knew was of course the main goal of the Secret State Police.[25]

Late that year, after carefully deliberating as to the advisability of such an approach, Mrs. Ilski decided to explain to the older girls some of her duties as a member of the Underground, and to do so in a way that made these appear as innocuous as possible. She strenuously avoided the terms like "Gestapo" or "SS," which carried with them images of horror. "You may have guessed perhaps that I work for the Underground," she said lightly one Sunday trying not to look at them. "But it is not dangerous, not really. If the present authorities were to arrest me, which is very unlikely, they would not get much out of me. I mean, I could not tell them much. I simply do not know the people who send me materials for translation, and although I have an idea who out of our acquaintances is engaged in various illegal activities, no evidence of that kind had ever come into my hands. What they are really interested in is military intelligence; those brave men and women are their prime objects. Such people are constantly on the run, they do not even dare to sleep in one place more than twice. But I am different. You see me every night, don't you? So though you must remember that this is a deadly secret between you and me, which you may never, never reveal, you should not worry much about my safety, for I am a low priority." She looked at each of them with a smile, but they stayed there motionless and disinclined to say anything.

After she had left to collect Krysia and Ela's children from the park, her listeners broke the silence. Kinga was the first to express what she and the others felt. "Isn't it important to deal with foreign correspondence?" she asked her voice trembling. "Isn't it something close to espionage? She must know who sends her the materials and where the translations go! I do not believe that she is a 'low priority' at all! What she said about them trying to get things 'out of her!' Jesus Christ, it does not bear thinking of!"

"Do not dwell on such things, Kinga," Myszka urged her. "There are topics we must not even consider! This is why I keep anything relating to Father separate in my mind, not mingling any thoughts of him with my everyday problems."

"She is right," Nina acceded. "We must not ask such questions! If we do, we

---

[25]   "After the Polish Government moved... to Britain, courier lines were organized not only to send special messages but also to evacuate escaped Allied prisoners-of-war... right through Germany, France and Spain to Gibralter" Seton-Watson, *The East European Revolution*, p. 110. For a comprehensive description of the activities of the Polish couriers during World War II, see: Jan Karski, *Story of a Secret State*, (Boston: Houghton Mifflin Co., 1945), and Jan Nowak, *The Warsaw Courier*, (MI: Wayne State University Press, 1966). Both authors were couriers.

shall all go to pieces. We must be sensible. Still I wonder how the people who have the Secret State Police after them all the time manage. Imagine not being able to sleep in one place more than twice! But I am not going to speculate about what happens to them when they are caught. I won't!"

It was inevitable that the idea of torture would become familiar during the war, although they would have been hard put to say how they had heard about the Nazi's ways of obtaining confessions. Sometimes at night Nina imagined herself being hit, burnt, suffocated, struggling to keep from divulging the information demanded from her. Such nights were sheer torment, and the only relief for her lay in her companions' empathy and understanding. All three girls had experienced periods of severe pain, albeit brief ones, before the war. Kinga had had appendicitis, Nina a cracked tooth, and Myszka a leg injury. But they fully realized that their sufferings on these occasions could not be compared to what some Poles went through in the Szuch venue.[26] "I do not want to know if I could withstand torture, if I could keep secrets…" Nina told her sister one morning when, despite her best efforts to be 'sensible,' the horrific images surfaced again and again in her dreams. "I cannot even be certain of it, but I can say for sure that I would prefer to die rather than to divulge such secrets." Her face wet with tears, Kinga agreed that to die rather than to submit was preferable in such circumstances.

---

[26]   "They were taking prisoners, invisible behind grey steel sides… from Pawiak gaol to the Secret State Police centre in Szuch Alley and on the return journey they brought back what remained of them after their interrogation: bloody scraps of humanity with broken bones and beaten kidneys, their fingernails torn out." Szpilman, *The Pianist*, p. 69.

The AK Contact

It was Kinga's experience that certain questions discussed in the family often had a quaint way of getting answered, if only partially, from totally unexpected quarters. The unlikely source in this instance was a young nephew of Mrs. Amelia, who had descended on her for health reasons. He was apparently suffering from ulcers, and knowing that Mrs. Ilski worked in the hospital, Amelia introduced him to the family in the hopeful expectation of obtaining medications. "I would not conceal from you, dear Renata, the fact that I must beg you to let us have some drugs for my nephew. One need only look at him to see that he needs them desperately," she announced immediately after coming. Indeed, the young man's complexion looked very unhealthy and his eyes had acquired a yellowish tinge. "I understand perfectly that it is not easy for you," Amelia continued, "but you are the only person I know who is connected with the medical establishment, and I am certain you will do your best despite difficulties. Let us then proceed without delay." It was typical of the lady not to allow herself or anyone else to doubt other people's willingness to do what she desired, and indeed she was almost never disappointed.

The newly introduced nephew, called Janusz, stayed with them only a short time. For several days afterwards, he was the object of the affectionate ministrations of his aunt Amelia, mother, and Mrs. Nowak. The three ladies showered him with an attention which Nina considered excessive. "Do ulcers require rushing around with hot water bottles, or feeding the patient delicacies like toast with real butter and tea with sugar?" she inquired bitterly. "I do not know much about ulcers, but I do not believe that their healing requires sugar. I do not indeed!"

There was another reason for the girls' displeasure. After a few days of preferential treatment, Janusz was definitely on the mend and getting even better looking than before. However, he manifested a marked disinclination for company. It appeared that he was perpetually engrossed in the dictionaries which Mrs. Nowak had collected from mother, and had no time whatsoever for social life. His total disregard of feminine charms as represented by the older girls, could not go unnoticed. Not only did he always have an excuse not to visit them when invited, but the moment one of them crossed the threshold of Mrs. Nowak's house, he would leave the room, "as if it had become contaminated" according to Myszka. Such behavior could hardly incline the two older girls to look upon him with favor. As for Nina, his privileged status in Mrs. Nowak's household was to her far more irritating than his inattention.

But it happened one late afternoon that the three older girls were invited by Mrs. Amelia to drink tea with honey (immediately recognized by Nina as substitute) when mother was at work and Mrs. Nowak and Krysia had departed to keep a long sought-after dental appointment. On Mrs. Amelia's express orders, Janusz was present also. After some preliminary remarks, Amelia came right to the point. "Janusz," she exclaimed, "stop beating around the bush. These girls know a lot! There is no danger from their side! Tell them that you are not my nephew, that we saw each other only three weeks ago, that you are under a form of military discipline which forbids forming any meaningful friendships! Tell them that you will be leaving us soon. Do not be afraid! Tell them!" Janusz, after some hesitation, drew a deep breath and began to tell them.

It came out that throughout the last two years, he had slowly ascended to a high position in the AK. His prewar studies at the Lwow University enabled him to pass the rigorous exams constituting the qualification for such a position. "They observed me for two years before I got really important assignments," he explained. "At first, it was simply a matter of delivering or accepting various parcels. The note indicating the location and time would be left in my home with instructions to burn the note after reading it. I could not say who the organizers were, for I was not allowed to see them. The typical scenario was like this, for instance: go to the Nazi exhibition of their war power, stand before the display of a particular weapon at a specific time. Somebody behind you will give you instructions about where to find or deliver packages. DO NOT TURN. YOU ARE FORBIDDEN TO SEE THAT PERSON."

The girls listened to his narration spellbound. Here it was – the whole panorama of struggle for their country's independence, but so unequal a struggle! After lighting a cigarette, "Expensive brand – pampered, but forgivable," thought Nina, Janusz went on with his story. "In time, I became the leader of a formation in which I alone was known to all the members. They did not know each other. In its initial development, it was called 'the Five.' This is done in order to prevent the individual member from revealing the identity of his or her colleagues, in case he is caught and tortured. Of course the apprehended person would know the identity of the leader, but AK intelligence being what it is, the leader would have learned about the arrests and would have had time to disappear. It was a game we were playing with the Nazis, a fascinating game," he added with an air of longing.

"But of course, you were doing all this for Poland," Mrs. Amelia interceded, privately thinking that this kind of fascination would hold no appeal for people her age.

"What happened to me recently was due to sheer bad luck. Nothing to do with my job," Janusz continued conversationally. "I was in the Aleja Roz section of Warsaw, on the way to my destination in the country. I got right in the midst of a 'lapanka' (round up) with some other men and women. You know the scenario, don't you? The Germans close a street from both sides, taking all the people in between as hostages. That section of Aleja Roz presents no possibility of escape, for there are just walls on both sides." His listeners knew all that. They also knew that hostages were routinely interrogated and often shot.

"Well, I still hoped that perhaps they would not know who I was. My papers were the state of the art in forgery. But the officer who looked at them took quite a while and then told me that he would keep the documents and talk to me later. That certainly looked bad. Another blow came when I heard instructions given to the driver to take us to Secret State Police headquarters. I do not need to tell you how such interrogations proceed."

Amelia took advantage of the pause that ensued to fill the cups with some, by now, badly diluted tea. Soon Janusz continued his narration at a much faster rate, as he was obviously eager to come to the end of the story. "In recent months I had had many contacts in the country and had memorized literally hundreds of names. If I were to reveal them to the Secret State Police, there would be no way for these people to escape. I did not want to fool myself about my heroism, about my ability to withstand torture," he added with resignation, not lifting his eyes. "Perhaps some of my colleagues could. I knew that some young women in our unit were undaunted by blows... But I, well, I was afraid of my own weakness. Our bosses understood that. We were under orders to carry on us a poison capsule, in order to kill ourselves rather than cause death to others. It was not considered a suicide, in the strict sense of the word, but was rather seen as hastening what in the end would have been an execution, as well as the prevention of many other deaths. They told us to count to twenty before we decided to take the pill." Shifting in his seat Janusz lit another cigarette. "Well, I did count to twenty and I swallowed the capsule before we arrived at Szuch Avenue. I thought with satisfaction that I would be dead before they started hitting me."

"Isn't it exactly what we were talking about before?" Nina whispered to Kinga. "I am glad that Violetta is not here, she would have fainted a long time ago."

"There is not much more to tell," their speaker continued. "I knew that the poison would kill me within minutes if taken without liquid. I was watching with interest when the Secret State Police man started counting us. After he had ordered ten of us to be conducted into the building, he turned to the rest and shouted 'Raus! People behind me scattered in a great hurry but I stood disbelieving. My God, I was free to go, but I was about to die any minute! "Heraus," he repeated.

I turned and walked away, convinced that it was too late to do anything, but at the same time wanting to live so desperately! The incredible thing was that my perception of time was totally screwed up. It seemed to me that hours had passed since I took the pill. I was amazed that I was still alive!"

"A few steps from Secret State Police Headquarters is a hospital, and I remember rushing into it. In the reception hall there was a long line of people waiting for the attention of one nurse, a hefty middle age lady with pointy red fingernails. I became convinced that I was already hallucinating, for how could a woman with painted nails be a nurse in a hospital? Still I ran to her and told her that I was dying, that I had taken poison. She stopped bandaging the knee of some man sitting in front of her and whispered: 'AK?' and then: 'You must throw up, NOW!' But I was incapable of doing what she ordered. I next remember being physically assaulted by her. She pushed me into the nearby chair, pinched my nostrils and when I opened my mouth to breathe, she thrust her thick finger with this horrible crimson fingernail deep down my throat. It worked! I apologize for those details, but I confess that I did throw up partly on her, partly on the floor in front of perhaps thirty people who watched all this in stony silence. The only diversion after my dramatic performance was caused by the man with injured leg, who hobbled away as fast as he could with bandages trailing behind him. 'Just as well he had had a big breakfast,' the nurse noted after inspecting the mess. Then in a whisper, 'it will be O.K. It has only partially dissolved.' Turning to her patients she said, 'An unfortunate incident of alcohol poisoning. Common, quite common nowadays. And you, young man,' she continued addressing me in a hectoring tone, 'have hopefully learned a lesson not to booze. Go now and get yourself a glass of milk, if you can find it!' She calmly changed her coat and after waving away my offer to clean up, she ordered me out and told the patients to assemble in another part of the hall. I was terribly ashamed to leave all this behind me, but I really felt ill and desperately wanted to leave that part of Warsaw as far behind me as possible. Well... I owe her my life!"

"Being without papers, for the Secret State Police now has his I.D. with his photograph, Janusz has to leave Warsaw," Amelia explained. "Mrs. Nowak and I volunteered to have him for the length of his recuperation. You are now much better, aren't you dear?"

"Absolutely recovered, dear aunt," he answered laughing. Turning to the girls he said. "I owe you girls an apology for my uncouth behavior. I wanted to enjoy your company, in fact one would have to be blind not to, but I am above all a soldier and must follow orders to avoid unnecessary contacts. May I have your forgiveness?" It was readily granted.

"One of the terrible aspects of the war is that normal people cannot have normal relations," Myszka remarked gloomily that evening. "If it weren't for those Nazis we would have enjoyed knowing him better, wouldn't we Kinga?"

"Very much," was the eager reply. "But perhaps we could still meet him tomorrow? Surely he will not leave without saying good-bye?"

"He will," retorted Nina, the least romantically inclined of the three. "He only told us those things because he knew we would not see him again. Mark my words, he will be gone by tomorrow morning." He was.

Reminiscences and Reality

Meanwhile Warsaw had been changing its appearance in a progressively more apparent way. It was not only the bombed buildings. Actually, they became far more acceptable to the Varsovians than the ever increasing number of uniformed strangers, lording their way over the streets, shouting for service in restaurants and cafés. Those of whom they were in control now looked so bedraggled, so poorly clothed. The Ilski girls commented on this phenomenon and found it difficult to remember how their city had appeared before that fateful September, when the women of Warsaw had a reputation for chic second only to the Parisians. Krysia especially had few memories of elegant ladies and kept asking her sisters detailed questions about them. Did they wear long gowns when they attended one of the operas the city was famous for? Were they escorted by gentlemen in evening clothes? What about their own parents?

Kinga assured her that yes, mother had owned a long dress, but she had acquired it only some years before the war on account of financial problems (grandma lost her husband early as she did the family fortune) and on account of the long mourning for mom's brother Stefan, who was killed in the Polish/Soviet war in 1920. Krysia remembered that there was a picture of Stefan in the house, and that the girls were not supposed to talk about him, for the slightest mention made grandma cry. In fact for years after World War I,[27] many people were in mourning for their loved ones and women wore dark dresses. But in the 1930s things improved and when mom received a prize from the university, a distant but wealthy relative from Lithuania came to Warsaw in order to congratulate her and offered to buy her an evening gown.

"You do not remember her Krysia, but I do," Nina interjected, "and I must say, dress or no dress, I did not like her. You remember, Kinga, when she wanted us to walk around with books on our heads and to 'sit gracefully'?"

"Well it was a beautiful dress mom got, a bluish velvet, but it had quite a decollete, too low for mom's taste," Kinga noted.

"Quite right too," interposed Nina again. "I, for one, hate those decolletes! The idea of exposing your bust and derriere to public view!"

"Not your derriere, surely," gasped Myszka. "You do not mean…"

"Top or bottom, it makes little difference," Nina asserted virtuously. "Private parts are private and should be covered, I say."

"So when the wealthy relative left for her estate in Lithuania," Kinga continued, "mom bought a piece of lace and grandma sewed it to the opening of the dress to

---

27 For Poland, World War I ended only in 1921 with the Treaty of Riga.

make it more modest. But the lady did not know it, and when she asked for our parents' picture from the university ball, mom had used her fan to cover the new front so as not to hurt her feelings."

Myszka had lost her mother when she was a baby, but was able to tell stories about her aunt's gown which had fifty-five little buttons at the back. "She did not allow for the time needed to button her up, and when the carriage arrived she was not ready, and was afraid that it would be very impolite to come late to the ball opened by Count Potocki in honor of Pilsudski's Legion. There was my uncle Zachariasz in a gala uniform with a saber at his side being very fidgety and asking every five minutes whether she knew what time it was, and her two cousins trying to hurry and fix all those little buttons while she stood without movement for over thirty minutes. There were no zippers at the time, you know." The girls wanted to know what happened then, but Kinga believed it necessary to give them the social circumstances as well. "How very like her," thought Nina. "Here we want to know what happened, whether perhaps the auntie dashed to the ball unbuttoned, and she is talking sociology." But those comments she kept to herself.

"Professor Rojek gave us statistics which showed that Polish Jews were very visible in law, medicine, and trade professions in independent Poland,"[28] Myszka went on, "but my uncle was an officer in the legionnaire regiment and he would never let us forget it."

"So?" asked Nina impatiently, "just tell us what happened with the dress."

"Well, the two cousins acquitted themselves well, although they pinched auntie in the process of doing it, and she got to the ball on time. She was introduced to Count Potocki and he kissed her hand, which displeased uncle... He believed that you should kiss only older ladies' hands, and auntie was twenty-five at the time, so a simple handshake and a bow would have been enough. So uncle took a dislike to the Count and (behind his back) called him 'a civilian'."

The girls pondered on the significance of this allegation with great seriousness. A civilian. Was it so very bad? "But uncle Zachariasz did not mean anything really very horrid," Myszka hastened to add, sensing uneasiness among her friends, "and when my mom decided to marry my father, he only commented on the unfortunate circumstance of papa's not being a military physician. But he did not try to prevent the marriage," she concluded triumphantly. There was no comment from the older girls, although they knew that their parents had believed that the military had too much power in pre-war Poland; it was very probable that Dr. Stein shared those sentiments.

---

[28] Jews "constituted nearly 50% and of the free professions, virtually dominating medicine and law," see Peter Wandycz, *Price of Freedom* (London and New York: Routledge, 1992), p. 211.

Apart from ruined buildings, hateful uniformed strangers, and shabbily dressed people, Warsaw had undergone other alterations. Some city parks began slowly to assume the appearance of agricultural plots. Driven by shortages of food, many Varsovians turned to growing vegetables in the parks, turning a deaf ears to those who bemoaned the disappearance of luscious and exotic plants and flowers.

"My dear, when I saw how those beautiful rose beds were turned into cabbages, as if by the wand of an evil fairy, my heart nearly broke," Mrs. Sawicki was confiding to mother. "It is just one of the ominous signs of our deterioration! For we are deteriorating, make no mistake about it." In vain did Mrs. Ilski try to talk about shortages and fear of famine. Mrs. Sawicki was disconsolate. "Why must we sink to the material level, dear Renata?" she cried. "Why must we think about our stomachs when we could think about our souls? When I remember the sweet little arbors and the dear cacti, I cannot hold back my tears, I cannot indeed…"

While mother did not appear unduly sympathetic, Jozek – on hearing the conversation from Nina – was downright contemptuous. "Cacti indeed! What are they good for?" he demanded. In his estimation any vegetable was superior to the plant one could not eat, but he was especially partial to cucumbers. "A superior veg in more senses than one," he declared. "A pleasing torpedo shape, with aesthetically acceptable coloration. Many uses including cosmetics, although Sister Hermencia did not approve of it and I am inclined to see her point. Excellent in salads (you slice them thin and add pepper and sour cream) fit for a king. But the best of all are pickled cucumbers. Give me a big juicy one, a chunk of brown bread (with a thick crust), a spot of butter, if available, and you can keep your pheasants and partridges, Nina. I do not want them!"

Nina who had never tasted any of those exotic birds, kept silent. Now, more often than she cared to admit, she was thinking about food, and even dreaming of it. But in her dreams she did not see cucumbers. She saw her grandma's 'lane kluski,' plump noodles served with melted, slightly browned butter. Jozek, however, had continued his rhetoric, showing off his acquaintance with culinary matters, when it slowly dawned on Nina that he looked as if he had not had a square meal for days. It was a fact that things such as white flour, butter, fresh vegetables, and milk were no longer obtainable and the various substitutes on the market varied from tasteless to downright nasty. No wonder mother was now worried about their nourishment, and was especially concerned about Krysia, who has been losing weight. But looking at Jozek, Nina became aware that he too had grown thinner and more pale and that the dry cough that he'd had for a long time had turned into a frequent wheezing.

The realization of Jozek's health problem awakened feelings of guilt in Nina's breast. How could she, two years older, not have noticed such changes before?

Surely her concern for her family did not excuse her from seeing that a friend, a mere kid in comparison to herself, was obviously in need of help. She did not even know where he lived, what nourishment, apart from the Thursday soup, he had. And he was very shabby. Nina told herself that the rough side of their lives had affected him more than it affected her.

Sitting companionably on the steps of an empty building, their favorite place of rest after the long standing in line for soup, Nina gently drew from Jozek various details of his life. It came out that, during the bombing that laid the orphanage flat in the early days of the war, a group of orphanage boys and a nun had been in the park. When the news came that there were no survivors, Sister Margerita, after consulting with some clergy, put before the boys two choices. Either they agreed to join her in trying to reach a sister convent in Krakow, (a trip fraught with dangers in the war-torn country), or they stayed in Warsaw with relatives and friends. Jozek was the only one who decided to stay. "She was not happy to leave me," he reminisced, "neither were the other kids. But at that time I thought that I had friends in Warsaw. I liked the lady who brought cheese to the orphanage from the country each week and gave Sister Hermencia a black puppy. There was Mrs. Linden, the librarian in the school library, who knew I liked books and let me read them in my free time. She even invited me to a podwieczorek (high tea) in her house and I met her family. How could I have known they would all be swept away?" Here Jozek started sniffling but tried to cover it up with a cough. After taking a few spoonfuls of soup (he always carried a spoon in his back pocket) he went on. "So I had no friends and my group left for Krakow, and the orphanage was just a huge heap of rubble. But a priest from St. Andrew's parish let me sleep on a mattress in the pews and he shared his meals with me for a while. He acquainted me with a cleaning lady called Marta who was working in a German canteen in the Praga suburb. She did not like working for them but beggars cannot be choosers, can they? She took me to help her and there I met a manageress. Though German (Marta believed she was from Austria), she was nice, she did not yell at Marta and she complimented me on my speedy acquisition of the German language. After a while I could even translate the instructions she gave Marta. So this German lady told me that if I managed to obtain shoe shine equipment, she would let me stay in the canteen in the afternoon and clean the shoes of the soldiers. The priest from St. Andrew's gave me some money for brushes and shoe polish and cloths and I set up a shoe shine establishment. At night I slept in Marta's kitchen. Things went on very well financially and I even managed to set some money aside for winter clothing. But I missed books, so I went to the public library and asked the lady there if I could come just to read books in the youth section. She was not too accommodating at first, ordered me to wash my hands before getting to the books (and when you have a shoe shine establishment your hands often appear dirty although you wash them) but later relented and let me sit there in the warm library and read the books. So, it was all right till a few moths ago."

What happened was the disastrous removal of the manageress and her replacement by a German man, who ordered Jozek to clean the shoes outside the building in the open. In bad weather it was very difficult for him to keep warm and the outcome of his work was sometimes unsatisfactory due to frozen fingers. On several occasions, the police told him that he could not stay there without a licence. The sleeping arrangements also deteriorated due to the presence of Marta's son, who appeared out of the blue and wanted to cook his breakfast at five o'clock in the morning. Even the librarian was becoming difficult, and when he asked her what had happened to the pictures of Maria Curie Sklodowska which used to be in a prominent place on the wall, she told him sharply that if he did not like the new decor he should stay out. "The priest from St. Andrew's was arrested and Marta says was sent to Dachau," Jozek concluded mournfully.[29] Nina did not even attempt to ask why. Being arrested and then sent to the concentration camp or shut up in the Ghetto were now normal events in their existence. But while Jozek's narrative went on, she reached a decision to consult Kinga and Myszka on ways to help him. Three heads are better than one, she told herself, and perhaps we could come up with something constructive. It did not occur to her to involve mother in it. Ever since the discovery of the false bottom in the basket, she saw her parent as inhabiting a different world from theirs – a dangerous, but immensely fascinating fourth dimension, separate from the one where her children lived.

---

[29]   "With the consent of Archbishop Adam Sapieha the Catholic clergy and several monasteries participated in the secret aid program [for the Jews]," Bartoszewski, *The Warsaw Ghetto*, p. 61. Also "For the carrying out of special tasks, commissions of clergy... were appointed as executive branches of Civil Resistance... . The Polish clergy... conducted themselves splendidly from the point of Civil Resistance," *Fighting Warsaw*, p. 171. Also "Almost 2,800 out of approximately 18,000 Polish priests and monks were killed,... some 400 of them and 400 clerics were interned in concentration camps. Of the almost 17,000 Polish nuns, more than 1,100 were imprisoned and 289 were killed," Piotrowski, *Poland's Holocaust*, p. 28; "In Poland the Church's stand against the Nazis led to mass persecutions of the clergy. Many bishops and priests had been sent to German concentration camps and Father Kolbe, later canonized, died for a fellow prisoner." Piotr S. Wandycz, *The Price of Freedom*, p. 244.

The Baudienst[30]

But the consultation did not take place. Later Nina asked herself how she, a reasonably intelligent adult who had lived under the occupation for almost two years, did not foresee such an eventuality, why her fears and her anxieties had always focused on her parent only, instead of involving every member of her family.

It was on a warm September day when Nina was cooking a vegetable soup (part potato, part a variety of vegetables bought from the people working the new vegetable plots in the parks), when looking through the window, she saw Sister Cecilia coming. Nina's thoughts centered immediately on the inadequacy of their dinner service, for they possessed only four bowls. It had worked out all right so far, since mother's soup was served late at night in one of them, after the girls had eaten. (Usually it was eventually consumed by one of the girls, since Mrs. Ilski always claimed that she had eaten.) "Kinga and Myszka will be here any moment, ravenous as usual," she thought. "Perhaps Sister Cecilia will not stay, but if she does, I will give her my bowl and eat the soup from the mug; it is not very chunky today." Having thus satisfied her idea of hospitality, she called on Krysia to open the door to the visitor. But when she looked at the nun's face, her everyday concerns vanished in a split second. It was obvious that the visitor had some tragic news to impart. All Nina could say was, "Mom?..."

"No, no, your mother is safe, Nina," the nun cried at the same time enveloping Krysia in her embrace. "She is safe and God willing the girls are safe, too. They have just been picked up by the Arbeit Kommando from the Jasna Street, but they are not held as hostages, neither are they to be sent to concentration camps. You must believe me, girls, when I say it. They are not hostages!"

Nina carefully turned off the primus and sat heavily on the bed. "Baudienst? – Work force? But Kinga is only fifteen!" she muttered. Sister Cecilia came closer and holding Krysia to her left side she hugged Nina to her right. "It simply means that they will be sent to a factory, and not to a munitions factory. No. No. They are being taken to a radio factory near Hamburg. This is good, believe me I know. It means that they will be given food, for the Germans want a labor force to be able to work effectively. They will be entitled to receive parcels occasionally and even write short notes several times a year. Nina, you will now be head of the household, seeing that the girls are gone and your mom... you know. Your mom has other concerns."

---

[30] "In the General Government [i.e. Central Poland]... a form of compulsory labor service, under miliary discipline, called Baudienst was introduced for all non Jewish inhabitants between eighteen and sixty years of age who were not German subjects." Seton-Watson, *East European Revolution*, p. 76.

Nina's attention now turned to Krysia who stood there pale and trembling. "It is all right Krysia," she managed to say, although she would have much rather cried aloud. "It is all right, we will manage and they will manage too. Listen to your teacher."

The visitor meanwhile retrieved some notebooks and pencils from her capacious pockets and proceeded to ask Krysia questions about the progress the little girl had made in her reading and about the *Flying Carpet* book. "I will stay with you all tonight if your mom will have me," she announced, "and I may be able to remember some stories that Krysia would be interested in. In fact, one of them is about a girl elephant who could have been a friend of Mizio."

"How lucky it is for Krysia to be a child, entitled to be diverted from tragic events by a kind stranger," Nina thought wearily, "while I must bear the full weight of such news." At that moment she longed to go back to childhood, where responsibility is minimal, where all the worry, calculations, and fears are borne by adults. Childhood was not that far behind her and now looked doubly enchanting, although unreal. But soon she scolded herself for such selfish thoughts. She was thirteen, practically an adult, and as such must play an adult role in this world. She welcomed with relief the idea of their visitor's stay for the night. At least the duty of telling mother the terrible news was removed from her, for Sister Cecilia was there and would do it much better.

The important thing now was to think about the parcels, if it were true that the Germans would allow them to send packages to the forced labor people. What things would be needed by the girls and how soon could she assemble them? Kinga and Myszka had only summer clothes on, and sandals. Therefore it was absolutely necessary to start thinking about fall and winter. Hopeful though Sister Cecilia was, her behavior indicated that this work assignment would not be short term. "We may not see them for a long time, for years perhaps, if ever," Nina thought, struggling against a new wave of desperation. Above all those worries, one thought stood out in stark relief against the gloomy background. How would mother react to the news?

It happened, however, that no information was to be given to Mrs. Ilski when she entered the cellar earlier than usually. She knew. She put away the (by now detested by Nina) basket, and without a word sat down covering her face with her hands. For a long time nobody said anything. Then she whispered in a strange voice, "First it was my husband, then my mother, then my daughter and Myszka. What kind of a mother am I that I could not protect my child and the child of a dear friend?"

"Who can do it, nowadays?" Sister Cecilia calmly interceded. "The power of protecting anyone has been taken from us by that anti-Christ. But I tell you, my dear, that what happened to your girls is more fortunate than what could have happened.

They, together with other Poles who have been kidnaped, are now members of a work force necessary for the Reich. As for Myszka, she is without doubt better off now than if she were with her father. Race is not stressed much in factory work."

"If I were still more or less normal and retained some capacity for surprise," Nina commented to herself, putting the final touches on the soup, "I would be wondering how come Sister Cecilia has all the information about the Baudienst, mother, and Myszka. Here we are fooling everybody including dear Mrs. Nowak in claiming Myszka as our cousin, while a virtual stranger, Sister Cecilia, appears to know all about her and her father. But I am dead tired and my curiosity is gone. If the devil himself appeared in front of me and said 'hello' I would refuse to be surprised. I would simply tell him to go and join his own in Berlin."

It appeared that Sister Cecilia's information was accurate. In the next few days a scribbled note came to them from Kinga saying that both girls were all right, that together with other young Poles they were being taken to Germany by railway, that "Mom, Nina, Krysia and friends should not worry." Soon, a message from Dr. Stein was received by Mrs. Ilski in the hospital and it fully supported Sister Cecilia's assertions. Dr. Stein, now in the Ghetto, was aware of what had happened to the two girls, but was not unhappy. In fact, he thought it a positive development. "When I think that she could have become an innocent victim of those insane ideas and at the same time, when discovered, had brought death to you and your family, dear friend, I am glad that they are both now in an environment where labor counts and race is – hopefully – no longer emphasized..." ran the note. All three Ilski females shed tears over it. Later mother explained to Nina that according to the official announcement, anyone helping a Jewish person would face death together with his/her family. "But, is it now certain that we would have been killed if Myszka were known to the Secret State Police?" Nina asked just to confirm what was already known to her. "Probably," mother replied. "We live in unbelievably crazy times. Still, we must take risks sometimes. Talk about it to Sister Cecilia if you can get her away from Krysia, who is much too young to understand these things, and she will explain better than I can."

"I do not need Sister Cecilia to tell me," Nina replied proudly. "I know."

A New Family Member

All these happenings put Jozek's problems right out of Nina's head and it was only when she saw his small ragged figure at the soup kitchen that her previous ideas of trying to help him resurfaced. This time mother had to be involved, whether she had other matters on her mind or not. That same day Nina explained to her parent Jozek's predicament; the increasingly difficult work as a shoe shine boy in bad weather, lack of sleeping space, and lack of food. "He knows a German soldier called Hans who occasionally supplied him with some canned food in exchange either for shoe shining or for scarves, which Jozek acquired a great number of, I forget how. But even this source is no longer available, for there are no more scarves, the shoe shine business is dwindling and Hans said that the Secret State Police is now protecting the army food supply from so-called 'saboteurs,' and poor Jozek, who has a terrible cough…"

"Bring him right in," mother interrupted, evidencing neither hesitation nor surprise. "He can have Myszka's bed. From what you say he is an enterprising youngster and when he is better may even help you in getting provisions."

"He will, he will," cried Nina. "Thanks mom!"

The delight on Jozek's face when he heard about his new lodgings was wonderful to see. He only asked Nina to come with him to get 'his business box" from Marta's kitchen, a bundle containing his meager possessions and a mattress. Marta was also glad for him, although she cried, hugging both children in parting. Her son was now thinking of getting his pregnant wife to live with them and Jozek's departure was opportune for them.

Jozek approached his new milieu with gratitude and readiness to improve conditions for everybody. His greeting of Mrs. Ilski and Krysia was all Mother Superior might have required. Next, he shyly asked if he could have a bath in the improvised 'bathroom' behind the partition, and proudly displayed some clean underwear and a huge cake of a soap. Afterwards, clean, happy and smiling, he retrieved from his bundle a bag of noodles (a good-bye present from Marta) and a bar of chocolate which he had kept for 'a special occasion.' This was presented to Krysia who, however, insisted on dividing it into four equal parts. For the first time since the departure of the girls, the Ilski family spent an evening meal in relative contentment and hope.

"When I agreed to welcome Jozek to our cellar, I never dreamed that we would be so lucky in having him with us," mother was telling Mrs. Nowak some few weeks afterwards. "The boy is very good and conscientious, a great help to Nina who, poor girl, is now my great comfort. But he is also a great companion to Krysia who has been sadly missing the older girls. The truly amazing thing about him is his sophisticated language. That orphanage must have had an excellent school which gave him an extensive vocabulary. He loves books and has a talent for reading aloud."

Jozek, who was then employed in cleaning the family shoes with one of his 'superior' brushes, heard some of that conversation and became pink with pride. Later on he told his new family that he had been chosen by Sister Margarita to read to the younger children of the orphanage. "Actually, I was at first uneasy about it, for the books dealt with animals," he announced with the air of an artist who has been asked to perform a difficult role. "For example there was a tiger in a story but he, after a life of eating meat, became sick of it and started to prepare salads for himself and his family. So, there was a question as to what kind of a voice should be used for him. A tiger is a fierce animal, but a vegetarian tiger? I compromised and used a mild voice for his words, but not too mild. The really soft sentences were spoken by a mouse called Szarusia on account of her grey hair. Her speech had a sweet ring to it. But the trouble I had with a lady lion, you would not believe! Sister Margarita expressed full confidence in my judgement, however."

So did Sister Cecilia when she came to visit them again. Jozek greeted her with the gallantry which a member of one religious institution extends to another. He also took care that she saw the medal of St. Jude that he wore. After that they had a cosy chat over mugs of cherry tea with Krysia assisting in respectful silence. Sister Cecilia made some unobtrusive observations of Jozek's wardrobe and the next time she came, she brought him an almost new pair of slacks and a sweater. The latter did not possess buttons but Jozek undaunted by this difficulty, transferred the missing fixtures from his old torn shirt to the newly acquired garment, and proceeded to use the discarded one for a thorough washing of the cellar floor. Both actions were heartily approved by the nun.

After inspecting himself with every sign of satisfaction in the window glass of the cellar, the boy announced his intention of approaching Hans, with a view to going back to the shoe shine business. "Looking as I do now in my new jacket, I would not be afraid to face Himmler himself," he confided to Krysia. "'Jak cie widza tak cie pisza' (You are judged by your appearance) Sister Hermencia told us, and she was always right. I will try to meet him outside of the canteen and inquire about the possibility of finding a warm spot for my business. Should he be able to help me in this, I would be happy to reciprocate by giving him a super shine whenever he likes for free. Kein Geld, Frei!" (No money, free!)

The main reason why Jozek desperately wanted to earn some money was his gratitude to his new friends. They had taken him in when he was unwell and practically homeless. Mrs. Ilski brought him syrup from the hospital and Nina ordered him to stay in bed for at least three days, during which he slept undisturbed under warm blankets and ate food served by Krysia. Now, when he was well again, the desire to help the family became overwhelming. He knew that Mrs. Ilski earned very little, that his ration card was grossly insufficient for keeping him fed, and with every spoonful of soup and piece of bread he was aware of their generous hospitality. So, he made his plans. But the urgent business now was, as he understood it, the problem of getting warm clothing to the two girls doing slave work in the German factory.

The trouble was that after almost three years of war, the family had already gone through the inadequate clothing left them by the bomb and that given them by kind friends. The pieces of jewelry that Nina, her percipience, had hidden in the cellar before the air raid had already been exchanged for what the family needed during those years. Now Kinga and her part-time job were gone, Dr. Stein could not help his daughter from the Ghetto, and awareness that the girls had been kidnapped in summer clothes totally inadequate for fall and winter preyed on everybody's mind. "I have to get some clothing to them and soon," Nina told Jozek. "We still have their winter coats (Myszka gave her extra coat to Kinga) and mom can send her good shoes, for the hospital provided her with a pair. But what about the rest – underwear, socks, sweaters, skirts? Mom wants to sell her wedding ring but I would rather sell the golden chain I got for my first communion. I can still wear the medal on a string. We must find how much I could get for it, for you know that there are people who would like to rip one off. Mrs. Nowak knows of some used clothing stores and I will try them after I get the money."

Jozek listened to all this with sympathetic understanding. Both of them completed a list of things the girls would need and calculated the price. After a while, however, Jozek's attention drifted away and suddenly he surprised Nina with, "When the bomb fell, what happened to the things you had in your apartment?"

"Well, they were crushed when the walls caved in and the ceiling dropped. We were lucky to have the cellar which could carry the weight of the house," Nina answered. "There are no doors, no windows, and the entrance to our basement is blocked by a ton of cement. The whole structure, apart from this, is condemned and fit only for removal. But of course nobody bothers about it now."

"But there is a balcony hanging crooked on one side," Jozek persisted, "and the balcony has a door to the interior, doesn't it?"

"Yes, but the door is pushed out by the rubble from the inside, you can see it," Nina said wearily. "Nobody can do anything about it." Then she suddenly sat up with a start. "You are not seriously thinking..." It appeared, however, that he was doing exactly that. Sitting comfortably on one of the chairs supplied by Mrs. Nowak, Jozek slowly divulged what he believed could be done.

One evening, after curfew, both of them would get a ladder, and he, being skinny and small, would climb up to the balcony. In the dark, nobody would see them. After testing the balcony floor, he would try to squeeze through the rubble into the interior and see if some things could be retrieved. This is how far he got before Nina registered her violent opposition to the project. "In the first place, if anyone should attempt it, it is myself," she insisted. "But I am not going to do it because it would be suicide. The whole balcony could easily collapse, and there is rubble inside which would prevent anyone from entering even if the balcony held. This is what we were told by experts." But Jozek pooh-poohed the danger. If there was anything to fall down it would have done so some time ago, he argued. The house had been standing like this for more than two years in storms and windy weather. "It is out of the question that you should go Nina, for you are much too big. I am not saying width wise, but your length! I do not know how it is that you are becoming such a giant, your mom being quite normal. You probably weigh twice what I do with all those long bones. So it is only logical that I should venture, actually," he finished in the tone he reserved for creating impressions.

But Nina was not convinced. "If something happens to you, what could I do? Go to the police and give myself up as a murderer? Of course, when I think about them freezing in those blasted factories... but how on earth could we get a ladder?" she concluded in an uncertain voice. Yet she remembered very well that there was a light metal ladder in the vicinity. Mr. Lis bought it when he was painting their windows before the war. It was in his garage. Both of them realized, however, that asking him for it would precipitate many unwelcome questions. But they also knew that, due to the so called 'pacification' of Polish villages near Zamosc,[31] Mr. Lis wanted to leave for the country in a few days in order to get his daughter, her husband, and their three children from that region to the basement apartment in his house. He told mother that then at least he would know what was happening; the suspense of being separated from his beloved grandchildren was simply killing him. "Thus it would not be necessary to tell him," Nina thought, although they certainly would do it on his return. "This is simply borrowing, and borrowing in an emergency situation is acceptable," Nina declared, and Jozek supported this contention with the assurance of a person whose opinions could be fully trusted. Didn't he have a religious upbringing?

Neither was Mrs. Ilski to be involved. "She would object to it. She would say she was responsible for you, and may even bring up your mom talking about it from beyond the grave or some such thing," Nina noted. "Better not to risk it." But the whole idea of a conversation between the two ladies, one alive and another long dead, had

---

[31] The farmers were shot, wounded, and deported, and their farms burnt. See Lukas, *The Forgotten Holocaust*, pp. 21-26, 161.

a strong appeal to Jozek and he pondered on it in a spirit of pleasurable excitement. It appeared that Sister Hermencia had also suggested that his parent might have been looking after him from afar, and it was all very reassuring. However, he did see Nina's point and reluctantly agreed with her that such a communication, should it take place, could complicate matters. He could not but foresee that Nina's mother would prove the stronger party, with formidable powers of persuasion. His own parent, on the other hand, would not be equally resistant to their plans, unless so instructed. "Better not provoke your mom to contact mine," he advised. "It is not that mom would be indifferent to what happens to me," he insisted. "She simply was not inclined to worry. There is no denying, however, that she did understand about clothing and such, better than anybody. When we had to move from our apartment before the orphanage claimed me, there were no less than three suitcases all filled with what she called her stage outfits. Many of the dresses had feathers, ribbons, and sequins. Some were just black mesh; simply beautiful," he added proudly.

"But Krysia will have to be told, if only in case somebody saw us carrying the ladder and came to ask why," mused Nina. "But what on earth would she tell that person? Perhaps she should say that we have gone to gather apples. She would not be obliged to know where the apple trees are…"

Thus a heavy-hearted Nina finally agreed to Jozek's plan, after extracting a solemn promise from him that he would immediately come back should the floor of the balcony be in the least wobbly.

The day arrived when Mr. Lis departed and the clouds made the daylight short. A light rain contributed to poor visibility. At about seven o'clock, after the curfew, there was nobody in the streets.

Mr. Lis' garage was just opposite their home, and Nina knew that the garage door did not have a lock. "The door is unlocked but it may be rusty," she whispered to Jozek. "When I say go, we both pull the handle." But the door flew open with such a terrific noise that Jozek lost his nerve and, abandoning the venture, hid in the Ilski's outhouse leaving Nina to deal with developments. "For heaven's sake Jozek, must you do it NOW?" she hissed. "If you are going to behave like this, we may as well give up the whole thing!" A chastised and humbled Jozek emerged from the outhouse and attempted to cover up this act of cowardice. "It was such a terrible creaking that I was afraid that the Secret State Police would hear it," he whispered guiltily. "Please do not be angry Nina. Now let me take the other end of this ladder. It is quite close."

Both of them arrived under the balcony in total darkness. "We have to raise the end of this ladder and rest it against not the balcony but the wall close to it, but we must not push it," Nina was saying softly. "God, why did you let people make bombs? This balcony looks as if it were hanging by a thread."

"It doesn't," responded Jozek firmly, trying to reassure both of them. "If it did, it would have fallen a long time ago." But the fact remained that the balcony, from what they seemed to see in the darkness, appeared to sway dangerously as if moved by some evil force. Tormented by guilt about exposing her junior to injury or worse, Nina was now considering going back to her original view that it was she who should attempt the climbing. But here Jozek would not agree. "I climb or I go home and you stay here with the ladder. Don't be silly Nina. You know that a skinny guy like me will have no problems."

"I do not know it," Nina whispered miserably, holding the ladder tight while Jozek began to climb it gingerly. "Come back if the floor of the balcony gives the slightest wobble, do you hear?"

This time there was no reply. Straining her eyes, she could not distinguish Jozek's form on the balcony. With a beating heart she kept her ears open for any sound which signaled danger. Minutes went by and she felt sick, weak, and desperate. "If I had to choose," she told herself, "I would prefer the Secret State Police to grab me rather than have Jozek there, perhaps in mortal danger. Why doesn't he say anything?" There was no sound of rubble collapsing, but what if a damaged pipe were emitting some gas which suffocated him? Was he gasping for breath at that very moment? "The tragedy is that I cannot climb the ladder without somebody holding it for me," she thought. "But maybe I should climb anyhow and trust in St. Jude to hold the ladder. If I do not hear from him in another minute or so..."

What she heard, however, were mysterious thuds close to her, which indicated some soft objects raining from the balcony. Her palms, moist with sweat, held the ladder tightly while a timid hope suggested that perhaps, just perhaps, everything was all right "Jozek, are you all right?" she managed to whisper.

"Actually, I am not all right for I tore my sleeve on a nail somewhere," was the reply that made her want to sing with joy. "Not my best outfit, by any means, but still possessing a degree of usefulness. As for the rest of my clothes..."

"Jozek, you come down right now, do you hear?" urged the girl. "If you don't..."

"Okay, okay, no need to get hysterical," was the dignified reply, and in no time Jozek was on the ground collecting the items of clothing that he had thrown from the balcony. Only then did Nina consent to look at them. Although the darkness prevented her from seeing each item clearly, she knew that their venture had met with astounding success. "We have to take the ladder back and come back for these," she breathed, "but Jozek, you are great, you really are." Satisfied that his lapse a short time ago was now fully forgotten, Jozek proceeded to make a bundle from the things on the grass and to deposit them in a dry place under the balcony. "No need for them to get drenched. An ounce of prevention is worth a pound of cure," he declared sententiously, helping Nina carry ladder back to the garage.

They were in the garage and back in a couple of minutes. In a triumphant march with the huge bundle they arrived at their door, where an anxious Krysia met them as heroes and inspected each item brought with an air of delighted bewilderment. "Let's spread those lovely things on bed, so that mom can see them all the moment she enters," she pleaded. "I never knew that they were so clean and so lovely."

Indeed it was a true treasure trove, the clothing was that which had been contained in one undamaged cupboard, by luck in the room giving out onto the balcony. That room was the only one in which some of the walls remained upright, Jozek reported.

They looked and looked at those new/old things, and loudly proclaimed what they were. "Three sweaters. One of them grandma's I think... two woolen skirts, one jacket of mum's, and best of all, two pairs of mum's ski trousers!!! What splendid parcels for the girls!"

"Four, no five pairs of woolen socks, three caps, and three scarves corresponding in color," added Jozek, commenting on the importance of keeping one's head warm in winter. "Warm pink underwear, a pair of mom's shoes, a navy blouse and... A teddy bear! A teddy bear!" cried Krysia. Nobody knew how the tiny toy got into the pocket of grandma's sweater, but they all agreed that it must have been destined for Krysia. She gratefully accepted that it was hers, and immediately made a bed for it close to her own pillow. "I will think about the name tomorrow," she remarked.

When Mrs. Ilski entered the cellar, she stood at the door looking at the display of the pre-war clothes. Then, as if awakening from a dream, she turned to Nina: "You didn't, you didn't go there... they warned us that the whole structure was extremely unsafe." After listening to a detailed report of the expedition, she demanded that Jozek give her his solemn word of honor that he would not do anything like this without telling her ever again. "Never again," she insisted sternly. Surprised but flattered by the solemnity of it, the boy readily obliged. The same oath was extracted from Nina. "The most important thing is our lives and the lives of others," mother said. "They are truly irreplaceable. To risk one's life even in an emergency like ours, is the height of folly..." But even while she was talking, her hand crept toward the pair of warm ski slacks, patting and folding them lovingly.

Parcels were prepared and a small portion of the retrieved things benefitted all of them as well. Mother got one of the sweaters, Krysia some warm underwear, Nina a jacket and Jozek stockings and a cap with a long scarf which he wound around his neck in the way he saw in American films before the war.

Chapter Three
Other Acquaintances

Another note from Kinga arrived through mysterious channels. It was obviously not processed by the post office and to everybody's amazement was delivered by Mrs. Nowak's elderly friend, who was moving around on crutches. Her name was Amelia. After giving the note to Nina she effectively put an end to any possible enquiries by announcing her need to hurry, and after some words of polite adieu, moved slowly toward the end of the street. There, some months before, a garish café had opened its doors. It was mostly frequented by the German military, and seemed an unlikely place to visit for a lady of Mrs. Amelia's vintage and frailty. Yet go into that café she did, at least twice a week to have a cup of ersatz coffee. People in the neighborhood commented on this strange behavior. The prevailing sentiment was that she was lonely (surely Mrs. Nowak was no substitute for family) and broke, and that she hoped to fulfill her need for companionship. But to choose a basically German establishment? Well ladies of that age tended to be eccentric and the proximity of the café was convenient, at least geographically.

The mystery of Amelia's possible link with the girls' slave labor camp receded in the joy of reading Kinga's note. They were well, no need to worry about them, she scribbled on a piece of a discarded German newspaper. Would it be possible to send a sweater or two? Hugs and kisses from Kinga and Myszka 'who wears a kerchief to work.'

This was of course the issue that Nina, for one, had had at the back of her mind for some time without actually realizing what it was that troubled her. Myszka's last hair tinting occurred just before their kidnaping. By now, the dark roots of her hair must have been showing. Nina knew how extremely sensitive she was about her allegedly 'Jewish' appearance, and how anxious she was to be blonde. Could the dye be dispatched to her with winter things?

A family conference that evening revealed a difference of opinion among them. Jozek was adamant against sending the girls hair dye, even if the hairdresser lady obliged them with a new supply. "Each parcel sent from Warsaw is closely examined at the post office," he told them. "Even Hans had his opened. If they find the dye they may become curious and interested in the addressee. Why should not Myszka have two-toned head of hair?" he asked. The listeners were told that at a certain time of his life with mom, she possessed a coiffure in which several different colors could be clearly distinguished, though the prevailing hue was green. "I see nothing wrong with it," he declared defiantly.

But the three females were not so sure. "It may be not so safe for Myszka," Nina remarked and mother was even more assertive, pointing out that Myszka was very worried about her dark curls because she believed they would make her more vulnerable. Having her natural hair showing beneath blond was certain to make her even more unhappy. That alone was a good reason for sending the dye. Jozek was right. It cannot be sent in its original packet. Apart from anything else, the Germans may suspect that there is somebody in the labor camp who is trying to conceal his/her true appearance.

"Why not send it as pudding?" Krysia, hitherto silent, suggested. "Remove the bag it comes in, and put it in one of the German erzatz pudding boxes! We could write on it 'for Myszka only' so that they would guess." The idea was accepted, although a diversion was created by Nina's suggesting that some German inspector might appropriate the 'pudding' and proceed to eat it. "Would we like to see him doing it!" was the comment among the shrieks of laughter.

Next Thursday, Nina went to the soup kitchen prepared to ask the lady beautician for more dye. She was not there, however. Rather than waiting another week – since the matter was urgent –Nina and Jozek made enquiries. The latter's energy paid off, and they were given an address in a suburb of Warsaw, where Nina went right away.

The young woman who owned the house appeared to welcome her with open arms. "Am I glad to see you girl," she exclaimed. "Yes, yes Violetta (if that is her real name) is here, living in my attic room. I befriended her, the poor soul, after she was evicted from the premises close by. The German office is there now, and they gave the inhabitants of the building just three hours to move out. How can you do it, if you have a business? She stored some of the equipment in my basement, but some furniture and things those fiends just threw away. To her it was as if she had lost a baby!" Nina's enquiries about the health of Violetta were followed by another flood of words. "She is not too bad, but mad! Here we are at war, losing some 3,000 people every day,[32] with

---

[32] "Each day of the German occupation cost the country an average of nearly 3,000 dead. Besides enormous material losses, more than 6 million Polish citizens, half of them of Jewish extraction, perished during the German invasion and occupation," M.K. Dziewanowski, *Poland in the Twentieth Century* (NY: Columbia University Press, 1977), p. 143.

the economy dead, schools closed, and she is raving about hairdos, mirrors, and wigs! Depressed about the loss of panache, whatever it is! Go to her, dear, and cheer her up. While you do, take this sandwich and a cup of soup to the weirdo. Crazy she may be, but I do not want her to starve."

Close to starvation Violetta appeared. When Nina knocked on the attic door, there was no answer. After waiting for a while, she entered and found the beautician lying on a bed in a state of collapse, with curlers in her hair, surrounded by the numerous accessories of the hairdressing establishment. Hairbrushes, nail polish bottles, and face creams were piled everywhere – on the bed, the chair, and the floor. At first, she did not even want to look at Nina, but the latter's timid request for a dye revitalized her. "My dear, of course, I am happy to learn that there are still persons in this cultural desert that pay some attention to aesthetics! Your aunt, I believe she had used my product before, is obviously one of them. Give my love to her, dear. Yes, yes I still have it," she continued, opening a cabinet overflowing with boxes and packages. "There is no problem with the supply, for I manufacture it myself. You do not think that I would expose my sophisticated clientele to chemicals, do you? No, no it is a herbal preparation, a secret recipe that has been in my family for ages. Do not mention reimbursement, dear. I am delighted to present it as a little gift to your aunt, who I know is a WOMAN!"

Nina did not have the heart to correct her misconceptions and patiently listened to an account of all the glories of Violetta's professional work before the war. She also saw to it that the lady took the nourishment she had brought, and extended an invitation to visit her family (although something would have to be done about the fictitious aunt, she thought uneasily.) On the way out, she talked some more with the young woman she had met an hour or so before. She learned that Violetta had some friends in the country, who brought her produce from time to time. All this Nina stored in her mind. Having the packet of dye securely in her pocket, she meditated about different human types she had met since the war. "We are all of us in it together, but each of us is different," she mused. "What would Violetta have in common with mother, for instance? Hardly anything," she answered herself. "Perhaps a little more with Mrs. Nowak. Mrs. Amelia was an unknown quantity as yet, and Mr. Lis's family would have to be counted out. But Mrs. Sawicki?" Here Nina laughed aloud, remembering the lady's moans about the 'dear little cacti.' "Would she and the beautician not be likely to hit it off?" It would help them both, Nina decided, for they were very depressed, though for different reasons than Nina and her family.

At home she displayed the package of blond rinse, and acquainted the other children with her experiences that day. "Actually, I am not such a dilettante in the hairdressing culture as you may think, Nina," Jozek remarked. "I am sure that we, lady Violetta and I, will be able to find common ground, so to speak. My experience with mom's coiffures did not leave me entirely ignorant of the subject..."

A gasp from Nina interrupted his exposé. He looked at her in surprise, but the girl was silent. She now remembered what it was that she thought significant about Violetta's monologue. It wasn't the fact that the beautician could make some products herself, interesting though this was. It was her assertion that "I could make a person look different from the way he/she looked before entering my establishment." That was what was worth remembering! Would not such skill prove useful nowadays?

Subterfuge
The Nuns' Initiative

Life went on with only small changes this third winter of the war. Sister Cecilia, who from the time of the girls' kidnapping became a frequent visitor in the cellar, now seriously undertook Krysia's and Jozek's education. "This is the least I can do for you in the circumstances," she told Mother. "Both children are bright and it is a joy to do it. Of course their levels are totally different but it would not hurt Krysia to participate in Jozek's lessons. However, I must admit that Nina is beyond me. I am not qualified to teach young people fourteen and older, although of course I am there to supply books."

"This is exactly what I wanted to talk to you about," Mrs. Ilski admitted. "She is fourteen now, and could get admitted to the Flying College (illegally held classes for high school and college) at least on a part-time basis. But you know how terrified I am to have her going to different parts of the city, since they do not teach in one building more than twice, when there is such danger lurking everywhere. Nina is tall for her age and may be taken for older. What if what happened to her sister and friend…"

"Therefore we must take precautions," exclaimed the good sister. "We must have her look as if she had injured herself. Dear Renata, with your access to hospital supplies, getting a small supply of plaster for your child to cover her right forearm would not be displeasing to the Almighty, I assure you. The Arbeitsdienst is looking for young persons able to work. Unfortunately, such subterfuge has been our practice for some time now. Only yesterday, our Sister Teofila simulated a fainting fit on the stairs, to allow the persons in that building to get out over the roof. It was necessary to delay pursuit, you know. So she dropped right down across a very narrow staircase and became wedged between the wall and the railing. They had quite a job dislodging her, due to her plumpness (over three years of the war and she is still big, I don't know how she does it) and by the time they did, the others were gone. As I said, God sees our hearts and understands what we are doing. While I am on the subject, I would strongly suggest that the birth date on Jozek's i.d. card be changed. I am sure the authorities do not have his papers in this part of the city, in fact they were probably buried when the orphanage was hit, and it is far better for him to be ten than twelve. I know that Mr. Lis keeps a record of the tenants on this street. Let me have a word with him…"

So it happened that Nina wore a thick plaster on her right arm and Jozek's i.d. (which Poles were obliged to carry on them) reflected a later date of birth than previously. Both of them considered it a submission to the exaggerated sensitivity of the adults, but seeing the anxious face of Mrs. Ilski, they agreed without much protest. At home, Nina discarded the offensive plaster but wore it outside.

While Jozek began job hunting by placing himself outside the German canteen in hopes of catching sight of Hans, Nina's thoughts focused on school. A three-year 'vacation' made her uneasy about going back to the world of letters. She knew that she would have to work hard to adjust to learning again, and both longed for it and feared it. Jozek, whose lessons with Sister Cecilia never caused him much worry, attempted to boost her confidence. "Never mind the flying college classes," he would tell her. "They are like any other. School is school, whether you like it or not. There is nothing to worry about but to sit straight, pay attention, and answer 'yes sister,' or its equivalent whenever appropriate. You have a good head, Nina. You will manage." Neither of them seriously contemplated the danger of exposure and its consequences.

A Wheelchair Lady

Lack of food became more and more commonplace with ever increasing German restrictions on the farmers willing to bring it to the capital. Nina's trips to the villages surrounding Warsaw had decreased after a harrowing experience during which she was deprived of her hard earned milk and potatoes and was warned that "next time you will catch it." She informed Jozek and Krysia of this but none of them thought of telling such upsetting stories to their elders. On hearing such tales, Mrs. Nowak would invariably burst into tears, bemoaning their fate, while Mr. Lis would embark on fantastic and totally impracticable plans of his own. As for Mrs. Ilski, they all agreed that she had too much on her plate already and should be spared worry as long as possible.

It was Jozek's role, during times of depression, to dramatically describe new cases of the German failure to combat Polish ingenuity. As always, he delivered his tale with facial expressions and vocal modulations that never failed to enchant his audience. He was at his best when the audience included the neighbors. Taking advantage of a get-together in Mrs. Nowak's house which included Violetta, he started to tell them a story about a lady in a wheelchair.

"It was a nice winter day. At the Warsaw station, there were preparations being made for the coming of a train from south Mazovia. Mazovia, as sister Lydia taught us, has been blessed with agricultural products and cattle, and at present it is also full of farmers who entertain Christian feelings toward their countrymen in the cities." Here, Violetta, after an unsuccessful and rather noisy search for her handkerchief in several pockets, finally located it in her sleeve, and begged Jozek not to mind her and to proceed.

"The bandit Germans," Jozek continued after a long pause, to let the listeners know that although he did not mind small interruptions, his elocutionary skills might suffer a decline if such obstructions were to be repeated, "know it, and make it a point to inspect all the bundles, bags, and suitcases brought by Poles on that train. To help them in the search, they have the huge beautiful dogs known as German Shepherds, which I – well I do not believe in insulting innocent animals – call just shepherds."

"Well, the train arrived. As usual, the Bahnpolizei proceeded to stop the passengers and inspect their belongings when a bundled up person in a wheelchair was carried down the steps of the wagon by three people in white coats. One of them approached the German officer, explaining that as a medical team, they felt it their duty to take the lady suffering from cholera, a bad case, to the hospital for infectious diseases as quickly as possible. Necessary papers would be produced if needed. The official, cautiously staying at a distance, waved them on, shouting instructions to the station people to keep away from the afflicted. And they did." Jozek ended triumphantly. Another pause followed during which Jozek appeared to forget that the story had no end, and gave his attention to the contemplation of the cracks in the cellar's ceiling.

"So?" Nina asked impatiently, and Krysia demanded to know if the dogs did not hurt the sick lady. "They barked like crazy but it is probable that it was the white uniforms which excited them," was the reply.

"There must be something about the bundled up lady that Jozek is going to reveal," suggested Mrs. Ilski with a smile. "Did she perhaps conceal food?"

"Warm but not hot!" exclaimed Jozek. "There was no lady at all. It was the carcass of a huge pig that was sitting in a wheel chair and the people involved worked for the homeless of Warsaw. Imagine what they did with all the meat they got! A simple roast perhaps, and may be some pork chops, sausages, ham..."

"Jozek stop, you are making me very hungry," Nina cried and Krysia remarked that she had not seen a pork chop for ages and was not even sure what one looked like. As always when conversation focused on food, their elders tried to distract them, talking about things unrelated to nourishment. But even so both Nina and Krysia dreamt about unobtainable pork-related delicacies that night.

Nina's Outfit

The story provided Nina with some new ideas. "They took milk and potatoes from me because I carried them in my rucksack," she mused. "What if I brought something that I could hide on my person? Suppose I were to encircle myself with a string of sausages beneath my coat, should such a treasure come my way? I am skinny enough to conceal them, am I not?"

The other children listened attentively. In order to make sure that such a project had a chance of success, Jozek rolled a small blanket and put it around her waist. With this around her, Nina fetched Mrs. Ilski's raincoat and walked slowly to and fro in front of them. "Does it show?" she asked anxiously. "Not bad, although your stomach sticks out," was Krysia's comment. "But maybe they will think that you are going to have a baby," she added helpfully. Jozek believed it too obvious, however. "You should have it wrapped around your whole body, not just the waist, distributed evenly like so," and having unrolled the blanket he proceeded to wrap it around his skinny frame. "If you get a piece of meat, you should slice it thin and place it in various pockets which we can attach to the insides of your clothes or hang from the inside of your skirt. Or we can hang pockets over your shoulders with straps of some kind. I may try it myself."

"Well the fact remains that I am the only person who can smuggle anything! You are both skinny and shrimpy, and shrimps are not able to conceal anything on their bodies. Now I, although thin, am at least tall. Give me the blanket Jozek!"

This time the result was more acceptable. "You look like some ladies did before the war, sort of round all over on thin legs," Krysia noted encouragingly, while Jozek embarked on a comparison of Nina's present contours with those of Sister Hermencia, who was known to eat thirty pierogies at a sitting.

Next day, Nina was engaged in doing strange things to grandmother's skirt, which she rescued from the box of so called 'szmaty' or cloths destined for floor washing. She also found a half torn shirt of father's and worked on it. Then, after extracting from her companions a solemn promise not to tell anybody, she left them one morning carrying mother's raincoat on her arm.

Hours passed. Krysia, and even more so Jozek, became progressively more anxious. What on earth kept her so long? Wasn't she supposed to take a tram both ways? Jozek was especially disturbed by the recently perused excerpts from Sienkiewicz's Trilogy (a classic in Polish literature) and the prevailing belief of its heroes that causing harm to a woman was irreconcilable with a man's honor. "Not that Nina is a woman, exactly," he tried to defend himself. "But she is still a female. Maybe I should have gone with her. Maybe I should have taken the risk, even though I am a shrimp. What shall I say to Mrs. Ilski if Nina is not here when she gets home?" At the height of his anxiety, he promised himself that in such a case he would simply run out and never come back.

Fortunately Nina came safely back with some produce concealed in the concealed pockets, and Jozek got a chance to assert himself again.

The Bath Tub Mystery

Meanwhile there was new excitement across the street. Mr. Lis's relatives moved into the basement flat and since there were three children, one of them Krysia's age, the new arrivals were doubly welcome – as Mr. Lis's family and as Krysia's companions.

Mr. Lis's daughter was called Ela Rawicz and her husband, seldom seen, was known as Artur. The happiness of the grandfather when he carried around the children was delightful to see. Their apartment, although a basement, was far superior to the Ilski's cellar. It was almost like an ordinary apartment, and it had its own primitive cellar, the entrance to it being in the kitchen floor. When they were helping Mr. Lis to prepare the rooms for his family, Nina, Jozek, and Krysia managed to lift the flat cover exposing a ladder which led down to a dark hole, one part of which extended beyond their vision. Krysia was quite scared to look down into it, and Nina swiftly put the cover back on. But after Mrs. Rawicz and the children arrived, the cover was concealed under a piece of linoleum, atop which was a low table with a child's bath on it. Why Mrs. Rawicz should have such a makeshift bath arrangement in a small kitchen when there was a bathroom in the flat the children did not know. It was only later that they were told that the shower in the bathroom did not work, and indeed parts of the pipes which had been there before seemed to be missing now.

Mr. Rawicz must have had a peculiar job, for he came home only at night and for very short periods. Mother told them not to talk about it, and by now they understood that there were things not to be discussed. It was, however, obvious that Mr. Lis, although happy to have his daughter and kids in his house, became very agitated from time to time, and during Mr. Rawicz's brief visits kept vigil at the door of their own cellar. The Ilski family got used to it, and were happy to have him there. When the mysterious Mr. Rawicz was gone, Mr. Lis invariably would sigh with relief and depart for home.

"Mr. Lis does not like his son-in-law, does he?" Krysia asked mother one day. "He never greets him, for he is always inside our home looking disturbed, when Mr. Rawicz visits his family."

"I had no alternative but to tell her straight out that our dear neighbor is at our door on such occasions because, from that point of vantage, he sees both ends of the street. He likes his son-in-law very much and worries about his safety," mother told Sister Cecilia. "I had to explain that Mr. Lis was hoping to warn him before the Germans arrested him. Krysia is almost eight now, she must know those things. The other two guessed the truth from the start, I believe. They needed no explanation."

Two events shook the neighborhood soon after. On a wintry fall evening in 1943, the German police did visit the basement apartment. Mr. Lis, at his post of observation saw them and reached his daughter's door in a second, while around a small cellar window looking out, his friends watched breathlessly. Holding all three of them in her arms, Mrs. Ilski stood motionless, while four hearts pounded in a united rhythm. For a while there was silence and then the high voice of Mrs. Ela reverberated in the dark. "You looking for my husband? He is my husband no more!" she shouted. "Ask that sluttish barmaid where he is, and when you get him you can put him in prison for life!" Her furious voice intensified and made Krysia tremble. "Here I am his legal wife, with his three children and the fourth on the way, and I have not seen him for months, MONTHS! Because of that jerk, I cannot even have a quiet time to bathe my children, poor orphans that they really are, for you barge in looking for him! Good luck to you, get him as soon as you can, the filthy womanizer! Bring that blonde she-devil to me, I will deal with her!"

After some time the police emerged empty handed, their interpreter apologizing to the Germans for not being able to translate all the abuse heaped on the vagrant husband by the outraged wife.

A mood of tremendous relief and happiness became general. The police departed and Mr. Artur was safe. Mother announced that they should celebrate, and opened a bottle of orange juice kept for special occasions. Mr. Lis, beaming with pride, partook of it and talked about his daughter. "She is a first rate actress and would be quite a sensation on any stage," he mused fondly. "But her performance tonight took even me by surprise! The language! To call dear Artur such names! I did not realize she knew them! But it worked out. She has warm water ready for any emergency you know, and when they came she put the youngest into the bath! They looked all over, they went up to my apartment and even sounded the walls, but they did not remove that tub with the child in it..."

The episode had a sequel. This time it was in broad daylight on Sunday and Ela's children were all in the park with Nina and Jozek. Mr. Lis was at his observation post, talking to mother. "Since they did not find him last time, we may have a time of peace and quiet for a while," he noted hopefully. "But Ela is still very anxious and today there are two of them." It was at this very moment that a group of strangers in civilian clothes became visible at the end of the street. "My God, they are looking at the house numbers," Mr. Lis stammered, "my God, the children are in the park... Krysia!" Without waiting for him to finish his sentence, Krysia threw the door open and flew across the street into the arms of Ela who had appeared at the entrance to the basement. What happened later, was related by the little girl in the family circle.

"I understood what Mr. Lis meant when he called my name. I understood perfectly that there were no children in the apartment, no one to put in that the tub over that hole. When I got to Mrs. Ela, she stripped me of clothing and put me into the tub – rather small – with very cool water. She had no time to heat it up, see? But I didn't mind. She threw a rubber duck at me, it belongs to little Lila, and of course I don't play with such things. Anyhow, I put a towel over the part of me that was sticking out of this basin, and she started to furiously wash my hair with some terrible stinking soap, hissing into my ear that it did not matter if I cried. When they came I had soap in my eyes and could hardly see. Well, they looked around, tapped the wall, did the same in Mr. Lis' apartment and left."

"Did Mrs. Rawicz abuse her husband for their benefit?" asked Jozek. "And how! She has sore throat now, so her voice did not carry. But she called Mr. Artur terrible names, something about being a two-penny Casanova, and the bar lady even worse," was Krysia's recollection. "But the two gentlemen who were underneath me never stirred. When did they get out?" she wondered. Mrs. Ilski explained that the dark cellar under the Rawicz's kitchen extended into a tunnel, the opening of which emerged some distance away.

The word 'tunnel,' hitherto having an ordinary connotation relating to railway or street passages, acquired a totally different meaning. For a while the children considered it as a way out for the pursued. "Wouldn't it be possible," mused Nina, "to dig a tunnel that would allow the inhabitants of the Ghetto to get out?" This time she did not hesitate to ask mother about it, neither did she try to exclude Krysia from the conversation. In the last months Mrs. Ilski realized that her initial efforts to conceal her activities from the children, and Jozek was now included, had proved futile. Even Krysia, although much less knowledgeable about them than the other two, understood that there were things going on in which her parent participated, about which they were not supposed to talk to anyone. The little girl did not remember when she became aware of this. The knowledge seemed to be acquired gradually, and only became a source of a terrible anxiety when her parent was not home at nine p.m. as scheduled. Thus, the possibility of having a tunnel which would lead from a place of concealment in Warsaw under the streets and buildings into the Ghetto was a topic of a free, passionate discussion in the presence of all the inhabitants of the cellar.

"I could get to where little Icek's family was and lead them all to safety," Jozek fantasized, "or at least to a place which would be less dangerous. Perhaps we could have them here? He would love your teddy bear, Krysia! But it would have to be a very long tunnel, for the whole Ghetto is surrounded by the military." Nina added that the noise of digging and the necessity of getting the earth out of there would present grave difficulties. "Even in Mr. Lis's hole, the air was terrible. There would have to be fans installed and wall supports, and all this done in secrecy," she noted, discouraged. Mother said that all those points were very valid, and that the Ghetto itself had its own police which would not hesitate to put an end to such a project, if detected, and to severely punish the people involved. Even if by a miracle that tunnel were dug, how many people could escape that way? Obviously the unfortunate

Ghetto inhabitants were already very frightened and might feel mistrustful and unwilling to support such a risky scheme. But she admitted that this project was being discussed by the Committee for the Aid to the Jews, called ZEGOTA,[33] and that a lady whose books Kinga and Myszka had to read in school was one of the members of this wonderful but very dangerous organization.[34]

"So what can be done about all of us?" Krysia asked helplessly. "There will come time of liberation," mother replied with confidence. "A liberation by our own forces and later perhaps by our allies. As you know there is a Polish Government in Exile residing in London. It commands the Polish forces in the West as well as in the underground here. The British and the French are fighting the Germans also and so are the Americans. They are on our side. Even the Russians..."

"Don't mention them to me, Mom," Nina exclaimed, "Considering how they treated our people, I am sure they prefer Germans to us. God forbid that they should come here." But mother expressed a pious hope that perhaps the western allies, who were now helping the Soviet Union to fight Germans, would prevent Stalin from misbehaving this time.

---

[33] "In December 1942 the new organization formally constituted itself as the Council for Aid to Jews... [and] adopted the cover name 'Zegota,'" Bartoszewski, *The Warsaw Ghetto*, p. 46.

[34] Piotrowski, *Poland's Holocaust*, pp. 106-8, 112, 117-18, 131-32, 311; Lukas, *The Forgotten Holocaust*, pp. 119, 120, 147-51, 175, 180, 259; Davies, *The Heart of Europe*, p. 73.

The Secret Arsenal

Nina had thought often that a topic which came up in casual conversation could somehow become a harbinger of events to follow. The talk about the liberation of Warsaw "by our own forces" made them think about the military equipment for such forces. How else would they prevail? The weapons used by Poles at the beginning of the war were either destroyed or had fallen into German hands. Poles were not allowed to have any firearms, not even those used for hunting. Everybody in Warsaw knew that possession of a weapon was considered a capital offence according to German law. So those Polish units which were to fight the Germans would have to either get the arms from the Germans (and how would they do it?) or perhaps be helped by the allies. This thought bothered Jozek very much, and he told Nina about his visions of unarmed members of the resistance attacking the superbly equipped German units surrounding the Ghetto and being shot at by machine guns. The inhabitants of the Ghetto would not be able to help because they were also defenseless, as was Icek's mom.

In February of 1943, their friend Mrs. Nowak became quite ill. Soon after the execution of her brother and nephew over three years before, Mrs. Nowak's sister-in-law and a niece left Warsaw and there was no news about them. Mrs. Nowak's old friend Amelia had moved in with her, but this lady was also frail, moving with the help of a crutch. During the winter of 1942/43, the Ilskis tried to help them as much as they could, Nina doing shopping for them, Jozek and Krysia cleaning and – when the nearby laundromat was working – doing the laundry. Luckily their house was small but warm. It had huge tiled stoves and a heap of coal in the cellar, consisting of the remains of prewar supply. One of Jozek's tasks was to light a fire, every day, in a big stove in the living room using very inadequate kindling. The two ladies became very attached to the three children and liked to spend time with them, telling them about the times of their youth or playing cards with them.

On that day, after his lesson with Sister Cecilia, Jozek told Nina that he would have to attend to the fires. Nina, having got some aspirin from mother for Mrs. Nowak and seeing that Krysia was still writing a dictation with Sister Cecilia, decided to accompany him. The aspirins being thankfully accepted, the two ladies proposed a game of cards, when Jozek descended into the cellar. He reappeared with a pail of coals, looking very strange indeed. Mrs. Nowak immediately suggested that he was coming down with a flu and insisted on Jozek's taking two valuable aspirins right there. But Nina did not think that he was sick.

After lighting the fire, he, usually such an extrovert, departed with some perfunctory words of adieu, without even looking at the cards, which had always held a great attraction for him. On the way home Nina found him sitting on the stairs with his face in his hands. "So what is it that you saw in Mrs. Nowak's basement?" she asked sarcastically. "Were there ghosts perhaps? Why, you hardly said thank you to the ladies for inviting you to play cards!" This had the effect of leading Jozek to pull himself together. He got up, and looking straight into Nina's face said very distinctly, "I did not see ghosts in Mrs. Nowak's cellar. What I saw were guns, sticks of dynamite, and ammunition." Nina was stunned. "Whaaaaat? Who... are you sure?" she gasped. "You may not be able to distinguish between guns and coal Nina," he replied, becoming more himself, "but I spent a long time in the military canteen with guns all around me. I can tell you that not all of them were handguns; some were small machines guns, which when fired kill many people all at once."

"God Almighty, who put them there and when? I was in that place only three days ago and everything was all right then." Nina was dumbfounded. But Jozek calculated that this arsenal had to have been brought through the basement windows very recently, without anyone knowing about it. Obviously Mrs. Nowak and her friend were now in grave danger.

"The cheek!" Nina was enraged. "How dare they, whoever they were! They must know what will happen to the ladies if the guns are found. It was only a few weeks ago that the Secret State Police visited Mrs. Nowak after they searched Mr. Lis' house! But Jozek, we must not tell her about it. She is too sick for such news!"

"Well, we cannot keep it from her indefinitely," her friend pointed out reasonably. "It is her cellar and sooner or later she will go down there."

"But those things cannot be left just lying there," Nina cried. "Think about the consequences! It is virtually impossible to hide them, from what you have said. Oh, I would like to lay my hands on the people who put Mrs. Nowak in this situation!"

Jozek remained silent for a long time. Finally, he said with an uneasy look, "What if they are, you know, friends of your mom... the underground people..."

"What? Jozek you are mad, you are completely crazy, mom's friends would never..."

Nina's outrage prevented her from articulating her indignation. "Perhaps they had nowhere else to store these things," Jozek continued in a conciliatory way, "and they have to prepare for what your mom called 'liberation.' Perhaps they thought that two old ladies would not look suspicious to the Nazis, and that Mrs. Nowak would not mind, not terribly anyhow..."

"But they did not ask her, did they?" Nina retorted angrily. "They had no right to enter her house without permission, let alone store those things there. The question is, what on earth should we do now? I am against telling her that there is an arsenal in her house, but you are right. We cannot keep it from her for long. Is there any way to either throw these things away or hide them somewhere?" But she herself knew that those suggestions were totally futile. With capital punishment hanging over Varsovians for far lesser misdemeanors, they could not hope to find anyone in their circle of acquaintances willing to keep the weapons. And to throw them away? Where?

"They must stay there, at least for a while, I think," Jozek proceeded reasonably. "We can keep it from the ladies for a while, also. What if we wrote a note to the people who left the guns there and begged them to take them away? I think that they would check on the place from time to time... We could leave it on the dynamite."

"There is another way which neither I, nor mom, nor Krysia nor you would contemplate, for we know how desperately short of weapons our people are," Nina said slowly. "That is notifying the Secret State Police that some 'criminals' have deposited guns in a private house whose inhabitants only want to live in peace. That could spare Mrs. Nowak, you know." While Jozek, red in the face, was thinking of a crushing reply, Nina added hurriedly. "Hold your horses Jozek, I said we were not going to do it. This was simply an objective way of looking at the problem. The question now before us is the note. How about giving them, whoever comes (if anyone comes at all), our names to contact? We are not afraid to give our names and the address, are we?"

"If you are not, I am not either," Jozek said loyally. "We are in what Sister Hermencia – whenever pierogi disintegrated during boiling – described as a 'situation without a solution.'"

So Nina wrote the note and Jozek deposited it on the most fierce looking gun. After a couple of days it disappeared together with some weapons. However, others were still there. So then came a period of waiting, which seemed to stretch out indefinitely. Mrs. Nowak was slightly better, but not well enough to brave the steep steps to the basement. Nina and Jozek kept an uneasy vigil over the house, while Krysia received instructions to tell any stranger coming to the door that "My big sister will be home at five o'clock; please talk to her then." In her flights of fancy, Nina often visualized the 'contact person' coming to talk to her about the weapons. She saw herself delivering a very articulate speech on the total irresponsibility of the people involved, reducing the 'contact person' (a young and presentable male) to abject apologies and promises of the immediate withdrawal of the offensive materials. What she was not prepared for was the sight – quite familiar in Warsaw during the war – of a girl of twenty or so, selling combs, soap, and other items from door to door.

To Nina's polite "we do not need anything right now, thank you," the vendor prevented her from closing the door by the simple stratagem of inserting her foot in the opening. Then, in a peremptory tone totally unsuited for dealing with customers, she inquired if Nina were Nina. Hearing the affirmative, she adopted the manner of a patient teacher explaining self evident phenomena to a not-so-bright pupil. "There is a problem, you write. So what? Every Pole has a problem. The whole country has problems. Do you think that we are going to take those things out, all of them? Save your breath. We had enough trouble getting them in. Windows are small," she added in an accusatory tone looking gloomily across the street toward Mrs. Nowak's house.

Seeing Nina incapable of answering, the girl put her knapsack on the floor and asked if she could have a 'breather' inside, and a cup of tea if there was any. "Substitutes are welcome," she asserted, pushing past undecided Nina into the interior where, after depositing her baggage on Jozek's bed, she sank into one of the chairs with a sigh of relief. Nina eyed her with a mixture of hostility and disbelief. The visitor appeared to be disinclined to offer any explanation whatsoever. In fact, it seemed to Nina that the strange girl was waiting for Nina to give it. She did not appear in a hurry. After removing her wet shoes, the vendor inspected the Ilski's living quarters without any sign of surprise, and focused her hopeful attention on the kettle which was sitting on the family primus. "Wouldn't mind having a cup," she commented after a while, "have some sugar cubes on me. What about sharing?"

It was then that the door opened, issuing Jozek and Krysia carrying with them a dilapidated but still workable baby's carriage. "We will not have to carry things now," Krysia announced triumphantly. "We just put them into this, apply a slight push and wheee!" Having noticed the visitor she stopped embarrassed. But the visitor appeared completely at her ease. "My name is Janka," she announced, "I am here to talk with Nina. The carriage is a fine idea – excellent for transporting perishables since it still has a hood. Good thinking!" Nina then remembered her manners and introduced Jozek and Krysia, the latter already looking with interest at the knapsack bulging with colored combs, hair brushes and other accessories, all with German names on them. Since Nina did not show any tendency to move, Krysia decided to do the honors of the house; she filled the kettle with water and lit the primus, upon which Janka, looking approvingly on such preparations, repeated her offer of sharing sugar cubes with them.

It was only then that Nina managed to get Jozek aside. "She is them, they, those…" she hissed and seeing his incomprehension she added "guns!" Jozek was nonplussed. "But she sells combs," he whispered. "Combs, ha!" Nina had a hard time controlling her emotions. "She deals with weapons, and what do you call it, that blows up... Would not be surprised if she had a bomb in her knapsack," she concluded, looking at the visitor with apprehensive wonder.

The kettle hissed and cherry tea was infused by the youngest member of the household and then served to all, the visitor receiving hers in a blue mug reserved for dignitaries. True to her promise, Janka dipped into her bag and retrieved five sugar cubes which she deposited on a plate Krysia handed to her. The atmosphere became more relaxed after that, the visitor entertaining them with a detailed description of the ski trip she took last year, which contained many strange episodes. Krysia and Jozek considered them very amusing indeed and loudly expressed their appreciation. Nina, wary and suspicious, stayed on the side observing all this with disapproval. "They are infants," she thought angrily, "just silly infants. It may be more acceptable for Krysia to behave this way with a complete stranger. After all, she is young. But for Jozek to be so chummy with her after the danger her people put Mrs. Nowak in! A teenaged infant!"

After refreshments, Janka suggested to Nina that the two of them should take a walk. During the walk she discussed the matter of the weapons. "It is out of the question to remove them, although we may probably need some quite soon," she told Nina, who still kept her unrelenting attitude. "But your complaint has been looked into and I have been authorized to submit a proposal for your consideration. Briefly it is this: We keep those very necessary things in that basement, and hope they will stay there undetected. But just in order to put your mind at ease, we will supply the lady with a letter from the AK (Home Army) telling her that if she dares to notify the authorities about those materials, she will be shot by us."

"I am not hearing this," Nina was thinking during this elaborate speech. "Surely this cannot be happening."

"You are not satisfied?" Janka remarked with surprise. "Yet it offers a perfect solution to the problem. Nobody could object to it."

"You don't mean that you would shoot Mrs. Nowak if she tells the Germans that somebody has stored guns in her basement?" Nina finally regained her voice. "Surely you cannot mean it."

"What we will or will not do is not an issue here," Janka replied impatiently. "The important thing is that the Huns may believe it and spare your friend's life, should the worst happen and the materials be found. All she would need to do is to show them the letter and claim that she did not notify the authorities for fear of losing her life. A very legitimate reason, when you consider it."

"Would they believe the letter? What if they don't?" Nina stammered the vital question. Janka looked unconcerned. "They very well may, although nobody can guarantee it," was the cheerful reply. "They know we are in business and there is a special department in their government to deal with the AK – and they know our stationary. All you have to do now is to talk to the lady. Simplicity itself," she added confidently, handing Nina a sealed envelope.

She actually proved to be right, unbelievable though it had seemed to Nina. Both she and Jozek supposed that the ladies' reaction to the 'arsenal case' would probably be difficult to deal with. After prolonged consultation, it was decided that she would approach the ladies alone, while Jozek would stay behind the door ready to act in an emergency. "If they faint, pour water over them but not too much," Jozek advised knowledgeably. "Talk to them soothingly, the way your mom talks to Krysia before she falls asleep. But better close all the windows before you start, in case they both start screaming."

To their surprise and enormous relief, those gloomy predictions did not bear fruit. Both ladies listened to the story of the guns in their basement not only with commendable calm, but with something that Nina later described to Jozek as a spark of interest and defiance. "Now we are in it, whether we want to be or not," they told each other with something resembling glee. "We must do our duty. There is no other way." The reading of the letter produced a similar positive outcome. "It was nice of those brave people to write this letter," Mrs. Nowak confided to Nina. "I would like to convey to them our thanks for their thoughtfulness."

"You never know how people will behave, do you?" Nina mused on their way home. "You never know. People are unpredictable."

The Ghetto Uprising

Meanwhile, the news from the city was grim. More and more people were arrested, caught in 'lapanka,' and executed. Transports from the Ghetto increased, and by now people called the camps described by the Nazi as places where "Arbeit Macht Frei," by their true name, i.e., DEATH CAMPS. Jozek was now what Nina described as 'in a state' worrying about little Icek, bombarding Mrs. Nowak with questions about children's welfare in Nazi camps, (to which she could only give very depressing answers) even losing interest in his shoe shine business which had been going reasonably well during the winter. By a strange assimilation of ideas he now turned against their new acquisition, the baby carriage, which had recently proven very useful in carrying their purchases. He passionately criticized the whole idea of using a baby carriage for produce. "Abnormal, decadent and hardly decent," he would announce after bringing goods in it. "This carriage has been made for human habitation, and only what Sister Hermencia called a 'crisis situation' inclines me to reluctantly to compromise. There is no doubt that there should be a baby in it, not onions. But we are not going to have a baby, are we? Your mom is too old and you are too young, Nina," he concluded scathingly.

"A baby! Are you out of your mind?" Nina exclaimed. "I have no patience with such nonsense. Anyhow there are no husbands around, haven't you noticed?" Jozek appeared to give serious attention to this complication. "That too," he admitted after a pause.

It was in April, when the sound of sporadic shooting in the area of the Ghetto woke them up at night. "Has it started? Is it the beginning?" Nina asked her parent. "If it has, it has no hope of success," Mrs. Ilski replied hastily dressing herself. "Dear God it is too early, much too early."

"But cannot your people help them?" pleaded Jozek. "Can't something be done?"

"Do you know what equipment we have?" Mrs. Ilski replied with bitterness. "One weapon for ten! How successful can they be?"[35]

That night Mr. Lis, accompanied by a strange gentleman, Sister Cecilia and Mother assembled in Mrs. Nowak's house. In deference to her age, Nina was allowed to remain. Although overwhelmed by the importance of this meeting, she could not but notice the welcome change in Mrs. Nowak's demeanor. Gone was her previous lethargy. Both she and her friend appeared animated, laying out genuine tea and sandwiches and listening attentively to what was said.

---

[35] Lack of arms was the endemic problem of the A.K.

"A tragic end to this infamous experiment of the Nazis," the stranger was saying. "Some of them, a mere handful of young people, could not tolerate this systematic deportation to the camps any longer. But there is every chance that they will die doing it."

"What about our underground?" Mr. Lis echoed Jozek's question.

"It is the AK that supplied the weapons that the Ghetto youth is using now," replied the stranger. "There will be some efforts from the outside, equally hopeless I am afraid. The conflict will last some time, for I believe that the Germans will not put an end to it all at once. They will play a cat and mouse game. But the outcome has already been determined. Almost all of Europe is still under Nazi control. We are too weak to start a major offensive now. The allies could not help us."[36]

"They did not even do what our Government in Exile asked them to do, namely to bomb railways leading to those horrible camps," Mrs. Ilski noted bitterly. "The answer London Poles got was their assertion that in war, military objects and only military objects count."[37]

Thus for over three weeks the inhabitants of Warsaw living outside the Ghetto walls saw fires blazing, smelled the dust of destroyed buildings, and heard shootings interspersed with renditions of the Polish national hymn. To the very end, on one of the buildings, a Polish flag was waving together with a Jewish banner. After the Germans entered the Ghetto and executed the freedom fighters, they transported the rest of the population to concentration camps and razed the whole quarter of Warsaw where it had been. Profound gloom descended on the city.[38]

---

[36]   For Polish help in the Ghetto Uprising, see Bartoszewski, *The Warsaw Ghetto* pp. 76-77; 79. "We are witnesses to the greatest crime in human history." These are the words of the Polish Prime Minister in London, p. 79.

[37]   For the Polish Government in Exile's continuing efforts to inform the western governments of the plight of the Jews and its demand for action, see Lukas, *The Forgotten Holocaust*, pp. 152-168. Also Piotrowski, *Poland's Holocaust*, pp. 112-113.

[38]   The exact number of victims is not known. SS General Juergen Stroop suggested that 56,065 Jews in the Ghetto had been apprehended; of that number 19,929 had died in the struggle. He claimed very few German losses. Lukas, *Forgotten Holocaust*, p. 181; Seton-Watson, *The East European Revolution*, p. 113.

More Bad News

But this was not the only tragedy suffered by Poles at that time. News about the discovery by the Germans of a mass grave of Polish POW's in the Soviet Union[39] was well publicized by the German authorities. "Poles, look what your ancient enemy, Russia, did to your boys who surrendered, many of them wounded, to the Red Army in the fall of 1939," the notices ran. "They were all brutally massacred in violation of the Geneva Convention, which is observed by every civilized nation, including the Reich. Don't think that the Soviet Union, the present ally of Britain and the U.S., has only killed those whose graves we found. Prepare yourself for the fact that there are other mass graves of Poles on the territory of Russia, many more of them, including those of your mothers, wives, and children deported by criminal Stalin to Soviet Asia." Such announcements were invariably followed by comments on the prominence of Jews among communist leaders.[40]

This announcement was first read to Nina's class by professor Rojek, but later she saw a version posted on the walls of the city. It brought to her mind the letter mother received from her relative in Lwow. Professor Rojek told them that the facts mentioned in the proclamation were undoubtedly true – that the Germans had offered a guarantee of safe passage to Polish underground authorities to go and check them, and that it had been done.[41] He then asked the students what possible consequences, real or intended, this information pertaining to Polish POW's would have, short of causing more heartache and more tears among Poles. Nina was sure that other students, older than she, would be eager to reply. Wasn't it clear that the Nazis were trying to impress Poles with their alleged sympathy for victims of Soviet crimes? As if they themselves were not equally guilty? Hidden behind this 'sympathy' there was the suggestion of common action against the Russians, probably under Nazi command. Weren't similar hints made in the summer of 1941, when the Nazi invasion of the Soviet Union started?

Since nobody seemed eager to say anything, she timidly raised her hand. "Aha, the new student," the teacher noted good humoredly. "Let's hear what the

---

[39] Stalin did not recognize the Geneva Convention rules covering the POWs. His murderous plans also involved civilians. Russian sources indicate that some 26,000 Polish prisoners, military and civilian, were murdered in the spring of 1940. Lavrenty Pavlovich Beria's letter to Stalin {top secret}, dated March 5, 1940 in Z. Brzezinski *Out of Control* (NY: Charles Scribner's Sons, 1993), p. 13.

[40] Seton-Watson, *The East European Revolution*, p. 346.

[41] The crime of Katyn became internationally known. Among other writers, see Janusz Zawodny, *Death in the Forest*, (IN: University of Notre Dame Press, 1962).

young lady has in mind." Blushing and stammering, Nina expressed her thoughts, adding that in this case neither the Russians nor the Germans should be trusted. Professor Rojek asked the class if they agreed, and Nina had the satisfaction of having them all behind her. Emboldened by it, she mentioned another, possible consequence of the Katyn revelations. "Our allies depend on the Soviet Union in this war," she explained, remembering mother's words. "They would not like to see Russia embarrassed by proof that it has acted against international law. But our government in London," she added, trying to control her emotions, "will naturally demand an explanation and apology from the Russian government for this and other Soviet crimes. This will not be appreciated, either by the Soviets or by our allies."

Professor Rojek's demeanor had visibly changed from patronizing to respectful. "Well said," he commented. "This is exactly what Bismarck called REALPOLITIK. Thank you. We may rely on your political astuteness in the future." Later Nina told mother that was one of the best moments in her life and firmly decided from then on to study history and become an expert in the subject.

Violetta's Establishment

After the preliminary introductions took place, and much to Nina's surprise, Violetta hit it off not only with Mrs. Sawicki. She was readily accepted as a new acquaintance by all the friends of the Ilskis. Part of the reason had to be traced to her truly stellar hairdressing skills. Even mother, so apparently immune to seduction, agreed to have her hair 'fashionably cut' (the proposition of 'discreet frosting' being politely rejected), and there was no denying that the treatment did make a difference. "Dear Renata, you look twenty years younger. What happened?" inquired Mrs. Nowak entering the cellar. Similar treatments conferred on other persons ended in an avalanche of profuse thanks which the beautician accepted with modesty. "It is not that I do not accept my limitations," she confessed. "Apart from the problem of blunt scissors, there is a dearth of important oils and, above all, the loss of my salon, whose decor and ambience were so necessary to my creativity as an artiste."

These sentiments were expressed in the presence of the two elderly ladies from across the street. The next day, the two visited the Ilskis again and proceeded to reveal their plans for Violetta. "Our house is small, but it is too large for us," Mrs. Nowak elucidated while sitting on the sole remaining chair (the other one has been broken during an unsuccessful display of gymnastics by Jozek), while Amelia occupied an inverted wooden crate. "Indeed we do not need more than two rooms and a kitchen. The largest room in the front is actually being wasted. It has a nice entrance from the street, and a door connecting it with the corridor and bathroom. Why not turn it into a salon? Violetta says that some of her equipment has been salvaged. Why not establish her with us? The kitchen is big enough for a dining table and the front room has an alcove for her bed."

"Also, simply from the humane point of view, we should not abandon her," added Mrs. Amelia. "The loss of her business fractured her, and she has had no proper nourishment for weeks, according to that young woman. She should get a new interest in life and be fattened up! Who would not do it better than my dear friend here, who is the best cook in the country?" Flattered and pleased, Mrs. Nowak readily agreed. "It has been said that my casseroles are exceptional," she modestly acknowledged. "Of course, the products we now get are inferior; still, they are usable. I hope she will like my cooking. So what remains? If she agrees – and I think she will – we must arrange the transport of her things from the house where she is staying now."

"We can bring her hair dryers and whatnot in our baby carriage," Jozek offered enthusiastically. "Can't we, Nina?" But the girl did not respond. "What about the arsenal in Mrs. Nowak's basement?" she thought uneasily, "can we keep it a secret from Violetta? No wonder mother is so happy about this project," she added seeing Mrs. Ilski applauding the idea. "She knows nothing about it."

While she delivered to the ladies the purchases she had made on their behalf, Nina mentioned the difficulty to Mrs. Nowak. "Nobody knows about the guns, except you two, Jozek and I, and of course those people… and the fewer of us the better. Violetta does not strike me as a person who would be happy sleeping over dynamite!"

"But she need not know it, dear child," was Mrs. Nowak's response. Her friend seconded by adding that the basement would be locked with a padlock on the door. If coals were to be fetched, the two brave and clever young people would do it discreetly. "This is you and Jozek, dear," Amelia added fondly to make sure there was no mistaken identity.

The baby carriage not being sufficient, Nina and Jozek borrowed a wheelbarrow from Mr. Lis to collect Violetta's remaining possessions. He volunteered to help, after they had told him about the project. The hairdresser's participation was firmly rejected, on account of her 'skeletal frame' (Jozek's comment) and her tendency to shed copious tears over the equipment that had been lost whenever she looked at the items still there. Thus, Krysia was delegated to keep the lady occupied in the cellar, and Nina, Jozek, and Mr. Lis got the bulk of the remnants from the salon in three long hauls. On the way many people helped them, so the task was not as difficult as it had initially seemed, but Violetta's gratitude was nonetheless boundless. "Unbelievably noble deed!" she exclaimed tearfully upon the completion of the project. "Chivalry personified! Aristocracy of spirit!"

Soon there was no time for painful memories; the new establishment needed all her time and energy. Mr. Lis, who proved to be very handy at wiring additional electrical outlets and sharpening various cosmetic implements, created a large sign bearing the inscription: LA PARISIENNE *Superior Hair Fashions; M-F 1-6 p.m.* Whether it was the French tone of the establishment, Violetta's undeniable skill, or the very moderate fees, there was an indication from the very beginning that the venture would be successful. Mrs. Amelia, after consulting with the manageress of the German café, posted an advertisement there in German, and before long the clientele of the new hairdressing business became at least partly foreign. Violetta kept up her French ambience. Both Mr. Lis and Krysia, who delighted in visiting the new establishment, acquired French names when addressed in public. Monsieur Henrique was an appellation close to his name Henryk, but Krysia's name left Violetta dissatisfied. "It is a royal name, suitable for rulers, without so much as an ounce of sophisticated femininity in it," she claimed. "It is too serious for our establishment." On learning that the little girl's second name was Monika (in honor of a wealthy relative from Lithuania, according to skeptical Nina), 'Monique' became

Krysia's name in front of customers. 'Monique, regardez s'il vous plait,' followed by 'merci, mon enfant' was heard frequently during working hours. Krysia, now attired in a pink coat (a more capacious model adorned Violetta) and sporting a large pink bow in her hair, was delighted to perform the little tasks required of her, and on coming home would regale her audience with her experience in "La Parisienne."

"But why does Mrs. Violetta use French with the German clients? The French are fighting the Germans also, aren't they?" she asked mother. "Some do, and some don't," was her parent's reply. "But France has for centuries been known for high fashion and elegance. When I was a little girl, there was a choice to be made as to what language I would learn, French or German. Your grandmama was for the French, your grandpapa for the German. Finally I was taught German, because it was considered more important for Poles."

Nina listened to this exchange with deep concern. Her initiative in finding Violetta was now having consequences of which she strongly disapproved. She waited to be alone with Mrs. Ilski and then she made her feelings known. "I want to talk to you about the corruption of Krysia, mom," she began. "Corruption?" exclaimed her parent in amazement. "Yes, corruption. It is not enough that she spends hours in the company of an unbelievably silly woman," she continued, ignoring Mrs. Ilski's remark that Violetta did no harm, "but now she has actually started to associate with Germans. My sister is dancing attendance on our enemies, the fat manageress of that vulgar café and her spotty daughter! They call her 'Liebchen,' (darling)! I heard it with my own ears! Mom, you must put an end to this!"

"But the manageress and her daughter are not our enemies, Nina," Mrs. Ilski commented reasonably. "Neither is Jozek's Hans. Not all of them are evil, you know. It is the government and the police that are."

"Why do they allow THEIR GOVERNMENT AND THEIR POLICE to torment us so?" Nina was now beside herself. "Why don't they do something about it?"

"Perhaps they cannot, perhaps they are afraid," her mother replied, but seeing Nina's expression of disdain chose to say no more.

The same evening, Mrs. Ilski talked about her daughter to Sister Cecilia. "Nina has many excellent qualities, and I am very proud of her. But she is so headstrong and is becoming radicalized, as are so many of our youth. I often think that if I were to be arrested, (it may happen, you know), I would much rather be taken from the hospital, or the street. I never have a weapon in the house for fear that I would not be able to control Nina, were the Secret State Police to come here for me..." Both of them were silent for a long time. Sister Cecilia's eyes wandered across the street and stayed for a while on the shaded basement windows of Mrs. Nowak's house. "We will pray that such an event does not occur," she said.

Epidemics

Thoughts about what might happen had to recede before the stark present. Epidemics of different kinds swept the city and many people succumbed to them. The Ilski family did not escape them but Mrs. Ilski, Nina, and Jozek managed to survive flu and pneumonia viruses with no discernible ill consequences. Things were different with Krysia.

At first, she seemed to be less ill than other members of the family but then her cough got worse and her temperature would not go down. Never very robust, the little girl was becoming wan and lethargic. Everyone of the Ilski's acquaintance visited her, bearing modest gifts (sometimes a piece of cake, sometimes a glass of milk) and suggesting various cures. Mother, after exhausting various remedies, brought a lady physician to see Krysia. This person, at first cheerful and smiling, became rather serious after examining her. "The little patient is not very strong, and the bout of flu has exhausted her. I am afraid that it is pneumonia now," she declared. "She needs good nourishment and fresh air. The air in this cellar is not very good."

"Is there anything we could do besides?" mother asked in desperation. "I believe that the new 'wonder drug' could help her," replied the doctor. "It is called penicillin, and is an extremely potent antibiotic. But I must tell you that I could never get it for Poles. The Germans keep it only for their own use. It is quite scarce."

"But if the Germans have it, perhaps we could get it also," exclaimed Nina. "I am opposed to dealings with them in general, but in a case like this…"

"You should not maintain contacts with people only if you need them," Mrs. Ilski pointed out. "Perhaps Jozek's Hans could help? I still have my wedding ring to offer. Of the three Germans with whom we have had any contact, i.e., he, the manageress of the café and her daughter Berta, Hans being in the military may have easier access to medication than the two women. As for the better air, Mrs. Nowak has already prepared a bed for Krysia in her bedroom. (She will share a room with Mrs. Amelia.) The windows there open on a park and the air is much fresher."

"If it comes to that, my communion chain goes first in exchange for that new drug," Nina asserted. She was a little ashamed of her previous unconditional condemnation of all Germans. "Let Jozek try Hans. Perhaps he is halfway decent?" Violetta, whose liking for 'Monique' had grown into deep affection, pounced on the suggestion. "Jozek!" she exclaimed, "naturellement! Please enquire of Mr. Hans if he perhaps has a girlfriend. I could make her beautiful, you know, at no cost to him!"

Impressed and duly aware of the importance of the task assigned to him, Jozek, who was sitting on the top of the ladder, (Nina borrowed it from Mr. Lis to hammer some nails into the more accessible portions of the wall) surveyed the females beneath in a thoughtful manner. To the best of his knowledge, he indicated, the only ladies that Hans had contact with were his mom and sisters who resided in Germany. "Hans is not a ladies' man, although he would like to be," he continued knowingly. Then came the boy's analysis of Hans' alleged problems and complexes. It was revealed that the German lad had a very disfiguring case of acne, which made him shy and introverted. "He told me that other soldiers laughed at him because of it," Jozek continued sympathetically, "and that all the treatment he had received from the medical officer in his battalion was to no avail. He even gave up chocolate which the German troops receive sometimes, in the hopes that this would alleviate the problem. This tells you how important it is to him. To give up chocolate, wow! It shows real desperation!"

"Bring him to me, mon ami, bring him to me," Violetta cried in a shrill voice. "I will try my method on him! First the mask (my family's recipe,) than the herbal bath! I have already tried it on the German girl from the café, and the improvement was there for everybody to see. The manageress told me that Berta received a marriage proposal the very same month from a corporal! Tell him that I will take care of his hair and nails as well. Tell him that ladies like well groomed men." Mrs. Ilski said nothing but hugged each of them in turn before leaving.

Closely observing her mother, Nina came to believe that for some time now her parent had been expecting some monumental upheavals, something that she longed for but at the same time feared. "She seems more anxious than ever," the girl thought uneasily. "It is not only Krysia, it is something to do with the Germans. Maybe she thinks that all of us will perish before long…"

It was a relief for them when Sister Cecilia barged in carrying two jars of substitute honey. "Krysia is ill?" she asked giving the jars to Nina, "well we shall soon make her well! How is Mr. Teddy Bear? Not ill too, I hope?" The little girl's pale face brightened in a smile as she drew from under her cover the little toy. It now sported blue trousers, a goatee, and a rakish hat, the whole outfit made by Violetta. "He is well," came the little hoarse voice.

Violetta now proceeded to give the nun details of her plan to beautify Hans and obtain penicillin. "Excellent thinking, combined with a noble heart," Sister Cecilia declared approvingly. "Krysia would recover even without the drug, won't you dear? But this will make it much faster. Of course we all know Jozek's powers of persuasion. There is no doubt that he will rise to the occasion far better than any of us could in the circumstances. Still, I believe that there should be a discussion on the strategy to be adopted," she continued, placing herself on the upturned crate (she would not allow Violetta to vacate the only chair). "It is always better to examine all possible approaches before the venture. Let us give ourselves a five minute break to think about it."

Jozek who had got down from the ladder to receive Mrs. Ilski's kiss, climbed slowly back to the top, vainly struggling to appear immune to compliments of any kind, even when they came from a person of religious importance. He tried to assume a pose of indifference but was not altogether successful as his bright eyes and high color showed. Nina looked at him with amusement. "How he loves to be praised," she thought and promised herself to tease him later about his alleged 'powers of persuasion.'

Nobody was surprised when after a while it was Jozek who started to suggest a plan for action. "Actually, my knowledge of Hans leads me to believe that he would not be adverse to a little relaxation," he began. "I thought that if I were to invite him for a glass of beer, for instance, ONE glass of beer," he added looking uneasily at Sister Cecilia, "it would be conducive to a talk about acne, man to man." To the surprise of all, Sister Cecilia appeared to be all for it. "One glass of beer never killed anybody, and might have helped some," she announced with a truly cavalier tolerance. "But Jozek, will you be allowed into a bar?"

"No problem," was the eager reply. "I was there once already with Mr. Lis when we were bringing Mrs. Violetta's hair dryers. Mr. Lis had beer, and I refreshed myself with lemonade. I intend to limit myself to this beverage in the foreseeable future," he added virtuously.

Thus Jozek was dispatched on his errand. He was told that in case Hans seemed amenable, not only Nina's gold chain but Mrs. Amelia's brooch would be available to him.

However, unforseen complications threatened the project from the very start. Although he had accepted an invitation to have beer, Hans appeared very reluctant to go to a non-German beauty establishment. Jozek's assurances that it was practically French assuaged his anxiety somewhat, but he still insisted that he would contemplate such a visit only if accompanied by a German person, and only at night. Due to Amelia's good services, Jozek was able to assure him that the fat manageress from the German café could be persuaded to accompany him to Violetta's salon. That seemed to remove one obstacle. The second problem was more difficult. Penicillin was scarce and Hans was afraid to approach his medical officer about it. When Jozek suggested that he could prevail on the German medical officer to give him the drug for his acne, Hans turned chicken and refused to do so. He was scared of being accused of giving the medication to... Here Jozek unconsciously used the standard abusive German term for Poles. Seeing Nina grow pale, he hastened to add that his German contact did not mean it, that he said the bad words absentmindedly and that he, Jozek, chose to ignore them this time, in pursuit of the greater good. "I used my powers of persuasion to make him see that his face not only repelled the ladies, but that it also served to discredit the Third Reich," Jozek resumed his narration. "A member of the superior race with acne? Phew! What would the Führer say? So I indicated that, on patriotic grounds alone, the medical officer was obliged to try to improve his appearance!" He paused dramatically reliving this scenario. "I must acknowledge that this was a real brain wave! A 'touché,' the French would call it," he continued in a self congratulatory tone. "So I told myself . . ." But he was interrupted by Nina. "Tell us how he reacted to your suggestion Jozek, and don't show off," she ordered.

"Actually, my arguments might have done the trick, but the mention of the chain and the brooch aroused his patriotism even more," her friend continued without taking offense. "He wants to see them."

There was nothing for it but to show Hans the two items in the presence of a witness he could trust. The only such person was the manageress of the German café, by now known rather well to Mrs. Amelia and Violetta. The occasion for sounding the lady's willingness to cooperate in obtaining the drug came when, on hearing about Krysia's illness, she expressed her wish to visit the 'Liebchen' and actually arrived in the girl's bedroom with a cake. Even Nina was touched by this, and voiced no objection to Amelia's telling the visitor their secret. This was done with spirited assistance from Violetta, who did not speak much German but made up for it by exclamations along the lines of "Pauvre petite!" and "Penicillin magnifique!" Hans had access to it, the manageress was told, but he and the medical officer needed 'gentle persuasion' in which a golden chain, a brooch, and free sessions with La Parisienne could be instrumental. Would the German lady help?

To their great relief, the manageress agreed without hesitation. She had no problem with the manner in which the penicillin was to be obtained 'fur die Kleine.' Not only did she promise to convince Hans that she personally was behind the plan, she even offered him a free ticket 'fur Zwei' to partake of breakfast in the café on Wednesday.

Jozek now took on the role of messenger and, occasionally, of interpreter among the parties, doing it with gusto, and introducing into his German speech many phrases he had learned from Violetta. "Bien entendu!" he would exclaim. "Madame tres bon!" and for that, and for calling the manageress' daughter "jolie mademoiselle Berta," he got himself a free ticket for the café lunch. "One does what one can, under the circumstances," he explained somewhat guiltily to a skeptical Nina.

News of Father

Two happy events occurred almost simultaneously in the lives of the family. The first was the successful acquisition of penicillin and a dramatic improvement in Krysia's health. She was soon pronounced out of danger and moved back to her old quarters where her family eagerly awaited her. This development had its sad side, however, for they all knew that their little girl had received medication unobtainable by other Poles, who at that time could seldom hope for even basic medical treatment. The second event verged on what Sister Cecilia later called 'the miraculous'; it left an indelible mark on them all.

It happened in the Spring of 1944. One evening, soon after Mrs. Ilski had arrived, the door burst open and in barged Mrs. Amelia in the highest state of excitement. That a lady so frail, mild, and restrained should crash in wielding her crutch and then proceed to embrace Mr. Lis (who was there repairing their window) amazed all present. After the emotional greeting of Mr. Lis, who stood there looking thoroughly flabbergasted, the visitor looked triumphantly around and, taking in the insufficient seating arrangements, attempted to climb the overturned barrel which Nina had just scrubbed and emptied in preparation for their weekly ablutions. Discouraged from treating the barrel as a stool by its height, Amelia then headed for Jozek's bed and, having collapsed on it, exclaimed in a voice choked with emotion, "what do you think I have in my pocket?"

"A delicacy for Krysia?" crossed Nina's mind. "But would that account for this extraordinary behavior?"

After arranging herself and her crutch in a more dignified position, Amelia assumed a commanding tone of voice. "Renata, sit down please. Mr. Lis leave the windows alone now. Nina, Krysia, Jozek, listen! I have wonderful news!" Then in a slow and ringing voice that Nina remembered for years to come the words came: "Roman Ilski, yes, your husband, father, and friend, IS ALIVE IN THE ALLIED FORCES IN SICILY. He has been ill for a long time, and is still in a hospital, but he is recovering. He will be all right, do you hear? I have got THIS from him for you!"

"This" was a small handwritten note dusted with flour. "Smuggled in a bag of flour," Nina said as if in a dream. "Could it really be? When we thought he was dead... are you sure?" stammered Mrs. Ilski. Then she grabbed the note and read it aloud. "I am sending this through special channels. I am recovering. Courage! God be with you. Love to you and my musketeers!' Signed Roman Kalinski."

"Kalinski is Grandma's maiden name," Nina interjected. "Why should father use it?"

"There is no doubt that it is his handwriting," her mother remarked through tears. "He was obviously afraid that the note might be intercepted and therefore avoids mentioning our names. He is using the surname my brother adopted when he was in Pilsudski's Legions fighting the Russians in 1920. Stefan did it in order to prevent the Russian border guards from stopping your grandmother and me when we were coming from Siberia. The Russians might have heard his real name, connected him with us, and punished us for being his family."

Mr. Lis, after supplying mother with a handkerchief for which she was vainly searching her pockets, whispered a few words to Jozek, and the latter went out with alacrity. Then the only male in the room took control of the situation. "In the first place, it is now necessary to acknowledge that our friend Amelia is a member of the underground Special Forces," he announced. "I had my suspicions for a long time, and so – no doubt – had Renata. Did you visit the café for a purpose unconnected with coffee?" he enquired of the lady, and seeing her nodding he went on. "It is not necessary to acquaint others with the fact, or to discuss it. I have sent Jozek out, not because I distrust him…"

"He is absolutely trustworthy and knows things some of you don't," Nina interrupted defensively.

"Not because I distrust him," Mr. Lis repeated patiently, "but because my daughter made a special cake for Krysia (carrots mainly), and I asked Jozek to fetch it, together with Mrs. Nowak and Violetta, if available. We must celebrate!"

During this speech, Nina got an atlas from the pile of books in the wooden crate and was studying the map of Europe. She felt as if she were alone in the room, alone with a father, long presumed dead, and now calling to them from Allied Forces in Sicily! "He is going to be all right, and the Allied Forces will help us!" she mused. "Now I can face anything, anything!" While Krysia, happy but overwhelmed by the news of a father she hardly remembered, busied herself with the teapot in preparation for the cake and Mrs. Amelia related some things to Mr. Lis in a whisper, Nina traced with a pencil on the map various roads her father might travel to join them. Only Mrs. Ilski sat motionless, her face bathed in happy tears which continued to flow.

Allies Approach

Later it seemed to Nina that from that time on, their personal everyday problems receded and the all important political issues were their main preoccupation. They thought, talked, and read about the war, about the advance of the Soviet troops, and above all the victories of the Western armies in Italy. The victory of the 2nd Polish corps at Monte Cassino, although given a specific interpretation by the Germans,[42] galvanized all Poles and the church bells in Warsaw rang in thanksgiving.

Nina was sixteen now, and relived all the news in her discussions at home and in the classrooms of the underground college. Occasionally, the realization of her age came upon her with sudden force. Then, she let her fancy linger over the future she might have had if the war had not occurred, over her passion for light music and dancing. Such musing included an unidentified male, and later perhaps marriage and a family. But these thoughts were infrequent; there was no time for a personal life in a country so terrorized, in a political situation which, although increasingly more hopeful as far as the final outcome of the war with the Germans was concerned, did nothing to decrease the savagery of their behavior in Poland. Now, when she knew that her father was hoping to see them, her worry about her second parent became greater than ever. Could mother continue to do whatever she was doing without falling into the hands of the Secret State Police? What if father came and she was not here? What if father came and found only two daughters instead of three daughters and a wife? Despite all their efforts to keep in touch with Kinga and Myszka, contact with them became almost non-existent and terrible rumors about the treatment of the forced laborers in Germany circulated among Poles.

In the secret classes, the teachers told them more about the happenings in prisons and camps, and more and more about the underground Polish administration. The students knew that there were fighting units (Mr. Lis's son-in-law?), espionage (Mrs. Amelia?), an underground press (mother?), and even courts. Half forgotten comments by Janusz, Mrs. Amelia's alleged nephew, resurfaced with a vengeance. It now became clear that all the VIP's of the Underground, military and non-military, had to carry poison on them, with orders to swallow it when apprehended. "You should not believe those stories in which a person heroically withstands torture. Such people are very rare," professor Rojek told them. "The government believes

---

[42]   "They [the Western Powers] want you the Polish soldiers to risk your necks as a foreign legion.... You have been treated worse than their colored colonial units" Tworkowski, *Polska... CIA*, pp. 249-250. Such repeated appeals invariably ended with promises of security and good jobs. All of them proved to be totally unsuccessful.

that it is better to have one person die than to endanger the lives of many. It should not be considered a suicide but a defense of others."

Such comments made a very deep impression on all the students. Nina in particular could not stop thinking about this now, when she fully realized how dangerous her mother's work was. Could it apply to her, a civilian? To be actually told by the people you are allied with to take poison! Didn't it imply lack of trust among Poles? But she also knew that the Nazis had fiendish ways of inducing people to talk and that poison alone could prevent some people from breaking down under torture. She asked herself again and again how she would behave in such circumstances, but in no way would she admit thoughts of her mother's torture. That she could not contemplate, not even for a moment. All this was so upsetting and so horrible that when Mrs. Nowak suggested one day that Nina was becoming a very good looking young lady, the girl answered sadly, "It has no meaning at present, has it? It has no meaning when there is this constant threat hanging over us like the sword of Damocles!"

This politicized existence grew even more so in the summer of 1944. Despite strict censorship, news came of the landing of the Allied Forces in Normandy. It was also known, despite German propaganda efforts, that the Soviet front was advancing, and that the once victorious German army was now withdrawing rather rapidly from the USSR. Mother was now more preoccupied than before, frantically translating into Russian the proclamations which the AK was planning to present to the Red Army on their entering Poland. "God only knows how they will behave," she confided to her children. "Formally, the Soviets were our allies since the moment they themselves fell victim to German aggression. But we know that only two years ago they actively helped in the Nazi war effort, swore eternal friendship with Hitler, and committed horrible atrocities on Poles. Our Government in Exile (London) instructs us to meet them as friends but judging by their behavior toward us only two years ago, it is very difficult to imagine that they have changed. Remember aunt Zofia?"

"What will happen if they meet our AK?" Jozek wanted to know, "Hans was telling me that they murdered more Poles than the Germans did."

"It may be true, for all we know," mother replied unhappily. "We can only guess at the number of victims, on both sides. The Soviet Russians are allied with Britain and the U.S. and so are we. But in this alliance, the Soviet Union is much more important than we are. That fiend Stalin is still their leader. I would not be surprised if they frowned upon our AK, and I am afraid that the West would not scold them for it."

"But this is just horrible," Nina exclaimed. "It is horrible to think that our anti-Nazi units may be turned on the Russians, who after all are also fighting the Germans."

"Horrible but possible," was the dispirited reply.

Their First Secret Mission

The first serious introduction into the mysteries of underground activity came to Nina and Jozek in June of 1944, when the news of the Allied invasion of Normandy revived among Poles the never suppressed but diminished hope for liberation. At that time, mother announced an impending temporary absence from Warsaw, in order – as was explained to the hospital authorities and anyone who wanted to believe it – to visit a sick relative. For the two girls and Jozek, the separation, even a short one, was difficult to bear. They had gotten used to Mrs. Ilski's evening arrival and to feeling that at least for one night they were there, together and intact, for rumor had it that the Secret State Police seldom 'visited' people at night. Mrs. Nowak volunteered to stay with the children during the time when their mother was with the 'sick relative,' but she was no substitute for mother, short of producing truly excellent meals (almost equal to those of Sister Hermencia, considering the availability of ingredients, according to Jozek), and could hardly be relied on for information, advice, or simply for understanding each of them. Nina especially was becoming eager to discuss with her parent the fact that the college classes were now mostly crash courses in military service and first aid assistance. Besides, the old teachers were all gone, among them Prof. Rojek whom Nina sorely missed, while the new ones cared more about their acquisition of a variety of survival skills (how to safely traverse the city canals, how to distinguish between different kinds of enemy aircraft, how to safely violate the curfew, and recently, how to load and reload guns) than the academic courses she was used to. Although she submitted to all this without a murmur, Nina missed her previous classes and developed a special revulsion toward the militaristic discipline introduced by the new instructors. It was obvious that all the training was in preparation for… she did not know exactly what, and wanted to talk about it with her mother.

But mother was not there when Mrs. Ela came to them in tears one afternoon and, having embraced Nina, begged her to do for the 'cause' and for the Lis family one thing, one very important thing. This 'thing' consisted of a procedure, which Nina considered childishly simple, at first. She was asked to transport Lila, Ela's youngest daughter, to a church on the other side of the city in the Ilski's by now very dilapidated baby carriage. There, she was to leave the carriage outside the church door, and to take the child and a parcel, which was earlier to be placed under the mattress, into the church, at a time when there were no services. She was to stay for a short while before the statue of St. Anthony, leave the parcel under the third bench facing the statue, and go home after retrieving the carriage.

"Of course I would go myself," Ela sobbed, "but I am afraid to leave the other two kids unattended. Besides I do not speak German and you have to cross the bridge where there are German guards. Suppose they were to ask questions? The idea is that you are visiting friends on the other side of the city. My father is away for a few days, as is your mom, and this matter is extremely urgent." It didn't even occur to Nina to ask where Ela's husband was; they all knew that he was in hiding.

"I do not think that Nina should accept this task while her mother is absent," Mrs. Nowak was adamant. "It is not entirely safe, for I presume that the parcel you mention contains illegal material. But, if it is so important, maybe I could do it," she ended weakly, seeing the strong disagreement on the faces of her audience. "You, dear Mrs. Nowak, are not suitable for this, if you'll excuse me for saying so," said Ela. "You are too nervous, too inclined to look guilty. While Mrs. Amelia has also offered, she could not manage with her crutch. Besides, you two ladies are not the people Lila knows and trusts. I suggested this task to Nina because she and Jozek played with my baby many times and could keep her quiet. Besides, teenagers with a small child are less likely to fall under suspicion than are adults."

"No problem. I will go and so will Jozek, I am convinced," Nina announced. "All I want to know is what is in that parcel. Not dynamite, I hope?"

"Not at all," Ela responded with a sigh of relief. "It is a very humanitarian parcel. It contains penicillin, the same drug that worked wonders on Krysia. We got it from England (a plane dropped the supply last night), and it is very important that it gets to its destination. We will wrap the medications in diapers, put them under the mattress, and Lila will sit on them. After the parcel is placed in a designated spot in the church, the mission is accomplished."

"But if it should be discovered, the penalty would be horrific," interjected Mrs. Nowak who suddenly started crying. "Don't you know those vicious Nazis? My God, are you willing to risk these kids' lives?"

"I have risked my children's lives many times already," was the somber reply. "I am willing to do it again. Nina and Jozek are perfectly capable of refusing. But please remember that this parcel would save lives. Last week there was quite a serious skirmish between our units and the Germans, in the woods not far from Warsaw. There are many wounded, and infections set in easily in their conditions. This drug is of tremendous value."

Nina now had time to consider the whole project. It looked far more serious than it had at first. The guards on the bridge were especially malicious, often stopping people and harassing them. She was told in her classes that churches were not immune from being frequented by Nazi spies. She quickly revised in her mind the procedure in which she had been drilled by her instructor. "Always have with you some things you have bought, and put the compromising items at the bottom. If you are stopped and the items found, remember to register surprise. Try to convince them that the material (leaflets, letters, even a gun), was given to you without your knowledge. You asked a stranger to keep your shopping safe for you when you visited the public lavatory, and this is how it happened. Train yourself to act. Not that this will necessarily work, but it is worth trying," was his less than encouraging conclusion.

It occurred to Nina that, if it came to acting, Jozek might be a great help, and she waited anxiously for his return. She was not disappointed. He immediately agreed to participate in the project. Indeed, he used the occasion to acquaint the people present with his talents in dealing with children. "I do not remember if I related to you my success in keeping little Icek happy," he began, but hearing Nina say that he had, more than once, Jozek simply noted that Lila was no problem. "She is a cute kid, even Hans said so. He compared her to his little niece in Berlin, Lotti. He misses her very much."

"Tough luck," Nina retorted unsympathetically.

It was decided to make the trip the next morning. Meanwhile, Ela supplied the additional instructions. They should leave early. Lila would be sleepy after breakfast, and that was the time when she felt at peace with the world. After putting the parcel under the third bench in front of the statue (St. Anthony, not St. Jozef whose statue was also there), they should stay for a short while in the church, sitting on the bench in front. If after some five minutes there was no movement behind them, they should leave. If there was movement, THEY SHOULD STAY QUIETLY WITHOUT TURNING AROUND. THIS WAS AN ORDER OF THE AK AND MUST BE OBEYED.

Nina did not sleep well that night and she suspected that the same was true of Jozek. Their first secret mission! Mrs. Nowak, who stayed with them, spent part of the night with a rosary, murmuring from time to time that she had no idea how she would face Renata if, God forbid… However, she collected herself enough to produce an extraordinarily good breakfast, an omelet made with artificial eggs plus ersatz coffee with honey. Nina and Jozek perked up noticeably after this feast and departed with the baby carriage to Lila's apartment in high good humor. But there the first obstacles became apparent. Lila was irritable this morning. She did not want to eat breakfast and was not in the mood for 'a nice walk.' She objected to sitting on a thin mattress under which there were some hard things she wanted to inspect. She would not be pacified by her toys and having rejected each of them in turn, announced (in terms which only Ela could understand) that she wanted to sleep in her own bed. Her harassed mother was at her wit's end and so were the two teenagers. Since carrying the valuable parcel without camouflage was deemed very risky, the obvious course of action seemed to be abandonment of the mission, at least for now.

The predicament of giving up on it was avoided thanks to Krysia, who arrived with her teddy bear. "His name is Rysio and he wants to go for a trip," she declared. It was a lucky thought. Lila settled down with the toy in her arms, and the two conspirators moved slowly toward the feared encounter with the German military units on the bridge.

"When we come to the bridge with those fiends on it, we have to pretend that we are totally free of any anxiety," Nina instructed Jozek. "In other words, we have no problem in the world. Let's keep our conversation flowing free and easy in what grandma called 'a light tone exchange,' but not too loud," she added looking uneasily at the baby who had finally fallen asleep. "I would even introduce some totally natural and unassuming laughter. How does it strike you?" Here she emitted what she considered to be peals of sophisticated mirth.

Jozek was no stranger to affectation himself but had no patience with similar attempts in others. "Nina, you sound like a sick hyena," he remarked brutally. "For heaven's sake stop this awful noise. There are enough crazy people around us because of the war, without our pretending to join them."

"Well, if it is not going to be a light conversation, what then?" asked Nina accepting the rebuff with diffidence unusual for her. "How should we behave? Tell me!"

It was not often that Nina asked Jozek for advice, and, despite the precariousness of their situation, he could not but derive satisfaction from it. "You might have noticed that decorum and dislike of the artificial were strong points in my upbringing," he replied loftily. "Good natural manners are a must in any circumstances. Just observe the way I act."

"All right, fine," Nina retorted, "but if they start asking questions you talk to them. Just imagine that he is Hans. You gabble with Hans readily enough, don't you?"

They proceeded in silence, trying to rehearse in their minds possible answers to questions. But perhaps there would be no questions. Perhaps Ela was right that the baby in a carriage would allay suspicion? But that happy thought was soon shattered. From afar they saw the bridge with a ramp constructed across it. At the ramp stood a German policeman with a dog. He seemed to talk to every person crossing the bridge, condescending to lift the ramp only after a lengthy interrogation and a search of belongings. "Holy Mary help us," Jozek exclaimed after both of them looked at this scene. "What should we do? Do you think we should go on?"

"I do not know," groaned Nina. "It looks pretty bad, doesn't it? But that drug is absolutely vital for the wounded. Yet, even though the parcel pretends to contain diapers, one poke would convince that German that it was something totally different. What do you suggest we do?"

"You are older," was the evasive answer. "You remind me of it all the time. You decide!"

"All right, on we go," Nina decided, although she was not sure whether she did it out of pique or out of conviction.

"If you insist," he said now in his more normal tone. "I am not the one to object. I only hope that St. Leokadia can be helpful here, for it is to her that Sister Hermencia prayed when she was making paczki (Polish doughnuts). Now, paczki are tricky to make, you understand, what with the yeast issue, the filling made of rose petals, the physical appearance of the product..."

"Jozek, shut up," his companion was again in control. "They will see us any moment now and I do not know about St. Leokadia. I put my money on St. Jude."

"Money on St. Jude? Where do you get these low expressions?" Jozek's shocked whisper showed how scandalized he was. "You do not put money on saints. You put money on horses!"

"They have seen us. Look natural," was all he heard from her. The die was cast. Slowly they proceeded toward the bridge to join the line of people waiting for the soldier to let them pass.

Many of them were women, some elderly. Each was asked questions in a raised rude voice. Most of the bundles they carried were inspected. Many were turned away. The line moved slowly on and Nina felt her knees tremble. She was afraid to look at Jozek, who pushed the carriage looking unconcerned, humming some tune. Suddenly Lila woke up and sat up still holding Krysia's toy. She nodded to Nina and Jozek, and started examining the people close by, one after another. Suddenly her little face brightened and a stream of delighted gibberish escaped from her little mouth. She stretched her arms toward the soldier and proceeded to send him kisses, an art she had recently mastered. Her happiness was so vocal that the attention of everybody centered on her, including the surprised German.

"This kid is impossible! Why is she so pleased to see that monster?" Nina hissed into Jozek's ear. "She is laughing at the dog," her more perceptive companion answered in the same manner. "It is not a bad thing, either."

"Your little sister is a nice baby! Why is she so happy?" asked the soldier in a manner totally different from his previous commanding accents. "She is laughing because she likes the dog and . . . you," the boy answered readily, at the same time praying to his patron St. Joseph that Nina's face would not betray her. "She is a very friendly child."

"All right, you can pass, please," the soldier muttered and waved good-bye to Lila who responded in the same way cordially using both her hands. The ramp lifted and stayed up.

"Incredible though it seems, he is passing all the people that were behind us," Nina breathlessly informed Jozek after looking back. "The ramp is up and he is not stopping them!" Still not believing in their good fortune, she hurried on, until a voice behind her caused her to slow down. "Do you know that German?" inquired a middle-aged man with a suitcase. "How come he allowed us to pass without harassment? Thank you so very much for your help in this matter. I dreaded that encounter more than you can imagine."

"Oh, we can imagine it," Nina answered but had no time for more because Jozek reappeared next to her and pushed the carriage forward with increased energy. "The soldier is in trouble now," he whispered regretfully. "His boss saw what was happening and shouted at him. The ramp is down again and there is a group of people waiting for admission."

"But at least some of them passed freely with us!" Nina responded joyfully. "We have done it, haven't we?"

"True enough," Jozek responded with dignity. "Much as I dislike that soldier, I believe it is my duty as a Christian to say a short prayer for him. A very short prayer."

"Very proper, I am sure," muttered his companion trying to suppress her merriment.

Unfortunately, their difficulties were by no means over. The baby kept looking back and demanded to be returned to the 'doggie.' Realizing that the parting was probably permanent, she first manifested her displeasure by throwing her hat and shoes out of the carriage; then seeing the futility of such actions, she started crying, determined to stay deaf to any arguments, pleas, and promises her companions advanced.

"Unnatural kid, with the lung power of her mother," Nina remarked irritably, pushing the carriage with vigor. "People are already looking at us. What if they think that we have kidnapped her? I have never seen such a fractious child! How are we going to go to the church with her screaming her head off?"

Later Nina acknowledged freely that Jozek's help was invaluable. Not only did he start to sing to Lila a story of a yellow puppy, he also found in his pocket a piece of beetroot 'cake' (dirty and full of germs, just as well her mother was not there, Nina noted) which, after blowing on it to remove foreign substances, he offered to the little girl. It was graciously accepted.

When the church loomed before them, Jozek lifted the child, and Nina, after putting the carriage under the church porch, followed him with the 'diapers.' As Ela predicted, the church was empty, although some voices were heard from the sacristy. "One, two, three, this is the third bench. I put the parcel under the seat. So that is that. But is it really St. Anthony's statue? Jozek, perhaps this is not he! He looks slightly feminine to me! It is so dark that I cannot see properly!"

"Of course it is St. Anthony," Jozek reassured her. "Feminine indeed! Don't you recognize St. Anthony when you see him? What nonsense you talk despite your age!

But I think we should leave. Lila is becoming restless. She has finished her cake!"

This time Nina grabbed the baby, who on top of wanting more cake, impatiently demanded to be rid of her wet diaper. She was doomed to disappointment, Nina told her. They left the church in haste, but when they reached the carriage, they saw it held another occupant. A large black cat was peacefully sleeping in it. "Doggie," Lila exclaimed joyfully, her knowledge of the animal world being still undeveloped. When Jozek picked the cat up and tried to shoo it away, a piercing scream from their charge warned him that losing two animals in one hour was not to be tolerated. Besides, the cat, rather thin and with a matted fur, was not to be scared away. He doggedly followed them across the street and along the avenue, keeping some steps behind, but refusing to go home as instructed. Lila, who had switched her sitting arrangement to be able to look back, attempted to keep communicating with him all the way.

The German on the bridge was not the one they had encountered before. He ordered them to remove the child and searched the carriage while they congratulated themselves on the luck that had attended the outward journey. When he finished pounding on the sides of the carriage, he threw the mattress back and told them to go. "Take the cat with you or it will go into the river," he shouted. Without a word Nina ran back and picked up the animal. After they passed the inspection booth, they put the cat into the carriage, where Lila showered it with kisses. "If your filthy piece of so-called cake did not harm her, I think kissing a dirty cat will not either," Nina commented to Jozek. "If I had to chose between this child and the cat, I would take the latter anytime! He seems to be looking for a home, and when we feed him and brush him he will be presentable."

"I will make him a nice bed in a soap box, and he will get a meal of porridge and powdered milk," Jozek proposed. But in their plans, they did not consider the little girl. When they arrived at Lila's apartment, she absolutely refused to part with the cat, and her mother suggested that, if they had no objection, he could belong to both families. The animal itself, after inspecting both establishments, found Lila's home superior to the Ilski's cellar. Nevertheless, he visited their humble quarters occasionally, each time looking fatter and more dignified.

Chapter Four
Preparations for Struggle

Mother returned from the country in a mood of elation. Gone was her previous worried look; no longer did she sound pessimistic. "It won't be long now," she announced the same evening. "The Allies are in Normandy, the Soviet armies already in Poland. We will simply be another force fighting the Germans – and it is high time too!"

"But will the Soviets help?" inquired ever cautious Nina. "Only a few weeks ago you doubted their intentions."

"They themselves are broadcasting appeals to us to rise," mother replied with conviction.[43] "Surely they understand that in this part of Europe we are their best friends as far as fighting the Germans is concerned! Besides there is evidence that the governments of Britain and the U.S. are in touch with Stalin, and will get involved in our struggle. They are urging the Red Army to help us and they will try to drop the necessary supplies to us.[44]

Even Krysia listened attentively to every word. "'The necessary supplies,' means weapons," remarked Jozek. "Hans has been telling me that our side has no weapons. He told me that they are aware how angry and willing to fight we are, but that their side is much, much stronger. He said that any attempt by our people to rise would be suicidal."

---

[43]   Seton-Watson, *The East European Revolution*, p. 116. Also Davies, *The Heart of Europe*, p. 77.

[44]   "Roosevelt and Churchill expected Stalin to lend all possible aid to the Polish fighters. Stalin would do nothing of the kind, and when Roosevelt and Churchill sought permission for their planes to land at Russian-controlled airfields after dropping supplies to the Warsaw patriots, Stalin said no to that request as well," *Roosevelt and Churchill Their Secret Wartime Correspondence*, Francis L. Loewenheim et al., ed., (NY: Dutton & Co. Inc., 1975), p. 67. Also pp. 511-512, 560, 563-566.

"We will get help from the allied air force," mother responded optimistically. "The Russians must realize that the more we fight the Nazis, the better for Russia. But it is also true that our people cannot stand this oppression any longer, help or no help. Five years is too long."

Krysia, whose imagination was fired by the vision of planes dropping supplies on parachutes, became quite enamored with the idea. "Perhaps not guns alone will be dropped," she mused. "Perhaps some candy? Nina, can you draw a plane and the parachutes please, can you do it?" But though Nina got a pencil and paper and prepared to grant her sister's wish, it was evident that her heart was not in it. "I'll believe it when I see it," she murmured to herself.

Then significant events began to occur in swift succession, although the individual days seemed inordinately long. Mrs. Nowak came to them all excited one rainy afternoon, bearing in her bag a piece of thick, folded cloth. In it, in separate little compartments, were sewn golden coins, some precious rings, diamond earrings, brooches. Cutting the thread with trembling hands and revealing these riches one by one, she kept them dazzled and speechless. She told them that she had been on the point of entering a particular building on a visit to her sick friend when an incredible incident had occurred. The staircase in the house was circular, so that you could see from the bottom of the stairs what was happening on the stairs above. Mrs. Nowak heard some commotion on one of the upper floors, but since there was no police car in front of the house, she did not think that anything tragic was going on. However, when she looked up, she saw the familiar sight of German uniformed men walking down in front and behind a young man whose face was smeared with blood. Descending close to the railings, he extended his hand between two bars and dropped – from the height of the second storey – the cloth parcel that they now had in front of them. It happened that it landed in their friend's half opened umbrella, which she had been about to close before ascending the stairs. Clutching the umbrella so as not to reveal its contents, Mrs. Nowak stood pressed against the wall as the police and the prisoner passed by her. "I don't even know if he saw me. Perhaps he did. All I could think about was not to look conspicuous. But who was the poor boy? Amelia has already gone to the building to make inquiries," she noted.

But Amelia came back no wiser. The young man had lived in the building for only three days. The owner of the house let him have the attic room without asking his name (a widely practiced custom at the time). As far as Amelia could discover, AK sources did not know of such a person. "So what to do with this treasure?" asked Mrs. Nowak. "It does not belong to us, but we do not know to whom it belongs! I do not even know where to keep such valuables! Suppose there is a search of my house?"

"If there is a search, they will find more interesting things than the jewels," replied Amelia. "We should assume that the valuables belong to the Resistance and should be given to them. Let's keep them temporarily at the bottom of the sack of rice Jozek managed to get. I will be glad to undertake the deposit of the valuables with the AK when I find out the location of their present headquarters." But she was too late. The Uprising, legitimized by the Polish Government in Exile (London), erupted two days later, on August 1, 1944, and turned Warsaw into a battle zone.[45]

---

[45] On circumstances surrounding the Uprising see, among others, Dziewanowski, *Poland in the Twentieth Century*, pp. 129-139; also, Arthur Bliss Lane, *I Saw Poland Betrayed: An Ambassador Reports to the American People*, (Indianapolis: Bobbs-Merrill, 1948), pp. 177, 203; Seton-Watson, *The East European Revolution*, pp. 115-118.

The Uprising

The first shots were heard in the late afternoon of August 1, 1944, when Nina, Jozek, and Krysia were busy preparing the evening meal. On the menu that day was so-called 'Tuhaj Bey kasha,' (a concoction of flour and water) plus potatoes and beet-roots. Though deceptively modest, the dinner required quite a lot of attention. The flour available was polluted and had to be sifted. While natural ingredients like chaff and unmilled grain were acceptable, stones, pieces of wood and rodents' droppings were not. Potatoes and beets had to be carefully examined and the rotten or badly frozen parts discarded. Nobody dreamed of peeling the vegetables. It simply diminished the weight of the produce and also was deemed a sinful waste. Wasn't it known that skins had the highest concentration of vitamins?

As usual, Jozek produced a surprise with the air of a conjurer. It was a large onion, in moderately good condition, which he pulled from his pocket and, after blowing on it, presented to Krysia. But that is as far as they got with the preparation. The sudden blast of artillery made them stop what they were doing and rush out of doors. There, the first thing which met their sight was a huge white and red flag, held out by Ela toward her father, who was preparing a place for it over their doorway. Within seconds, the flag was proudly waving in the wind. All three children stood motionless before the beautiful sight in silent admiration. Violetta and her customers joined them and then, one by one, other people from the street. Even Lila's black cat left his sleeping place on the window sill and sauntered slowly to join the crowd.

From the top of the ladder Mr. Lis made a short, emotional speech. "Friends! We are now in a state of war with our occupiers! The Uprising was declared an hour or so ago! Our street is now free of Germans. They fled this morning and the corner café is now declared temporary AK headquarters for this district. But please remember that it is temporary. While the Germans have fortified their positions along Jasna Street, our forces have taken over some sections in the north of the city in Zoliboz i Wola. Here is Mrs. Amelia to tell you what she has heard at headquarters. Long live Poland!" A shout as if from a million throats reverberated in the street. Nina and Jozek helped Amelia to climb the three steps of Mrs. Nowak's house.

"Darlings, beloved people," she cried. "Please remember that there will be temporary setbacks before our final victory. Our street does not belong to the 'priority districts' for AK action. Our forces are now concentrated in the center and in the northern part of the city, trying to force the Germans out of there and to liberate the 'Gesiowka' camp, named for the street on which it is located, where there are apparently some 400 Jews. The AK command is confident that if we manage to keep the Germans engaged for a week, or at most two, assistance will come. The Allies promised to dispatch planes with supplies and the Russians are in the suburb of Praga (Warsaw's suburb)."

Each of those sentences was interrupted by applause. Nobody slept that warm August night. In anticipation of the AK units, people placed tables in the street, putting on them what food they had. Mother arrived in a state of absolute bliss. "Remember this momentous day," she told them, "remember this day."

Toward the morning, the first AK units appeared. Deprived of uniforms, they nonetheless looked amazingly military in their formation and behavior. There was an effort to present them as non-civilians even in their attire. They wore high boots, short jackets with belts, and red and white arm bands. And beyond the men, women! Oh, how Nina longed to be with them! They too looked like a fighting unit! Walking four abreast in military formation, they exuded discipline, confidence, and seriousness of purpose and appeared perhaps even more impressive than their male counterparts. The crowd, already in a high state of emotion, went absolutely crazy at the sight of them. "Angels, Joans of Arc, our saviors!" shouted tearful voices among which Nina distinguished the shrill accents of Violetta who, accompanied by Mrs. Sawicki, was holding a huge poster on which a female figure with long golden locks, dressed in a cape, was resting a foot adorned in an evening shoe with a pompom upon a German military helmet. The caption announced: 'Civilization will win!'

Seeing Nina's face, Jozek hastened to inform her that the two ladies had worked on the poster in secrecy for a long time. "They even asked me for advice regarding Nazi helmets. I strongly urged less ornate footwear for the female, considering the militaristic ambience of the picture (there seemed to be cannons in the background), but they were enamored of the high heeled model. Of course the lady seems to have two left hands," he continued anticipating Nina's remarks, "but that could not be helped. They may not be Matejkos,[46] but they mean well."

Nina no longer paid attention to him. The units passed and she was sure by now, that out of four men, only one carried a weapon. In the female formation, the ratio was one to six, and they were going to face hostile professionals who were armed to the teeth! She knew now the sensation described in literature as "a sinking of one's heart."[47]

---

[46]   Polish painter of the nineteenth century.

[47]   Desperate lack of arms is described in Karbonski, *Fighting Warsaw*, pp. 355, 390. For a full account of the Uprising and the allied attitude to it, see Norman Davies, *Rising '44 The Battle for Warsaw* (NY: Macmillan, 2003) and T. Bor-Komorowski, *The Secret Army* (Nashville: The Battery Press, 1984).

When the young lieutenant gave the command to disperse and accept the hospitality of the local population, Nina and Jozek started mingling with the AK members, driven by an unspoken but almost identical wish to join their ranks. She waited as a girl appearing to be of senior rank finished the sandwich Mrs. Sawicki had provided, and shyly brought herself to the girl's attention. Then in a single breath she blurted out, "I am Nina Ilski. I know how to reload a gun; I want to belong to your unit. Please accept me." The older girl looked at her with sympathy. "We have rules which forbid us to accept anybody below the age of eighteen," she said. "Also, to belong to the AK, you must undergo a lengthy period of training. Still, we have other forms of employment. We have need of couriers and medical staff. But there are stringent requirements. Above all, family status and reliability."

"Oh, then it is all right," Nina interjected. "My family is very reliable. Dad is in Sicily and mom has worked for the Resistance for years."

"This is far from all, although it is a good start," the female soldier answered. "You will have to undergo various physical and psychological tests. If you know your mother's pseudonym in the Resistence, you could begin your inquires at headquarters. But my advice is to wait."

Nina suddenly felt deeply embarrassed. To think that she did not even suspect that her parent had been known under a different name! Hurt and let down she parted from the young woman and went in search of Mrs. Ilski. At the first opportunity, she addressed the latter in an accusatory tone. "Here I am, knowing for ages that you are a member of the Underground," she began in a voice trembling with emotion. "Here I am guarding Mrs. Nowak's cellar, in which the amount of dynamite would blow up ten houses. Here I am smuggling forbidden substances under the noses of the Secret State Police, but despite all this I am not considered worthy of knowing my own mother's pseudonym! Father would never have done it to me!"

Mrs. Ilski responded in a conciliatory and affectionate tone. "It was not that I did not trust you, darling. It was simply a precaution should you fall into their hands and be interrogated. Don't hold it against me, Nina," she continued. "You know how highly I think of you!" But Nina brushed aside such pleasantries and demanded to know what the name was. "It is Lesmian," responded Mrs. Ilski with a sigh. "They wanted me to have a name that would do for both genders." Nina accepted the explanation with a cool thank you, although she was rather disappointed. Really, mother tended to be sadly uninventive! Whoever heard of a Lesmian doing anything worthwhile? What was the sense of picking the name, insipid at best, when you could have had Plater, (Emilia Plater was a military commander of Polish forces during the 1830 Uprising), Kossak (Zofia Kossak was a writer and a member of Underground Committee for Rescuing Jews), or Curie (Maria Sklodowska-Curie was a scientist and Nobel Prize winner) which would also do for both sexes!

During that night and for the next day there was no news of Jozek. On the third day, Mrs. Amelia, who had the best contacts with the Polish administration, received notification of his whereabouts from the female contingent of couriers used for carrying messages via the city sewers. "God Almighty," moaned Mrs. Nowak on hearing this piece of news. "How on earth did he get there and what is it about the sewers?" Mother seemed equally upset. "He is just fourteen, much too young for any dangerous mission, and the sewer girls have an exceptionally taxing duty. Here we are into the second week of the Uprising, and there are already terrific losses among those girls. Some of them have drowned, and some were shot by the Germans!" She stopped to regain self control and continued in a more restrained manner. "If you stay with the girls, Mrs. Nowak, I will try to get some information about Jozek from my contacts in the hospital. I may be out all night, please don't worry about me."

"So this is what it has come to," Nina thought that night, turning upon her bed in agitation, insensible to Krysia's pleas to lay still. "Here I am, peacefully resting in perfect safety, while all the members of my family above the age of ten are exposed to grave danger this very moment! Nobody can tell me that father is out of danger, for didn't we hear that Sicily and southern Italy are being bombed? Mother, Kinga, and Myszka are in peril, and if I am to remain sane, I cannot even let myself think about them. Now Jozek! More than two years my junior, he has managed to become part of a fascinating although extremely dangerous mission, and in the company of women, while I was put off by that girl's nonsense about having to be eighteen! What I wouldn't give to be in his place! Of course, on top of the Nazis, they have to deal with rats and I imagine they are not very clean there swimming in all that muck.[48] But give me sewers, give me rodents, just let me do something!"

In the morning, mother reappeared, giving them the news. 'Gesiowka,' the concentration camp holding the Jews, was being assaulted by Polish forces and there was some indication that the Germans might not be able to withstand the attack. The courier service was now operating both on the ground and in the sewers, but she had no information about Jozek's unit. There was some anxiety about the total

---

[48]   "Frequently you had to crawl, sometimes ankle deep in sewage, in total darkness encountering rats. It was very easy to lose one's way, or die from the suffocating gas pumped into sewers by Germans," Leslaw W. Bartelski, *Powstanie Warszawskie* (Warsaw Uprising) (Warszawa Iskry, 1988), pp. 108, 240.

lack of response from the Soviet army, located now just fifteen miles from the city. Although the Soviets were being urged to help the Warsaw insurgents by the Allies, including such personalities as Roosevelt and Churchill, and although they knew how desperately short of weapons the Poles were, they simply had not responded. All was quiet on their side, no artillery, no air force. Yet they had urged Poles to rise against the Germans for many weeks![49] But it was still early, she concluded hopefully. "They will probably start the offensive before long."

"And supplies," Nina asked breathlessly, "are we getting supplies by air?"

"Again, we are only in the initial phase of fighting," was the response. "The allied planes would have to refuel in order to reach us and get back to their bases. The Russians will have to let them land in their airfields in order to do so."[50] Nina raised her eyes and looked at each of the people assembled. Krysia and Mrs. Nowak looked full of confidence. So did, although to a lesser degree, mother and Mr. Lis. But when Nina met Mrs. Amelia's eyes she trembled. The elderly lady looked positively gloomy. "She does not believe that anyone will help us, not the Russians, not the Allies, although the latter probably want to," Nina thought in desperation. "She is probably right."

---

[49]   "It gradually became clear to us that the Soviets wished the Germans to destroy the Capital and its population," Korbonski, *Fighting Warsaw*, p. 394.

[50]   Mid-air refueling was not known at the time.

The Sewers

Jozek appeared on the following day, totally exhausted, disheveled, and subdued. After a number of hugs, a wash, and a dinner prepared by Mrs. Nowak, he stretched luxuriously on his bed and commenced his narrative.

"The young soldier that I struck up an acquaintance with was named Staszek and he told me about the plan to liberate Gasiowka (the Jewish camp) and other parts of the city. Then I decided to be part of it, although he warned me that they do not accept boys below eighteen. I got information from him about where the front lines were, although I had to swear not to divulge it to anyone, but even without it I would have known where to go. My friend from the orphanage once lived on Gesia Street." He stopped in order to greet Violetta, who arrived together with the black cat, carrying a mysterious savory dish covered with a white cloth. The cat settled himself in Jozek's lap and appeared regard him with affection. "Even an animal recognizes moral achievements," muttered Violetta to herself, depositing the dish on the makeshift kitchen table, and sitting next to Krysia.

"Well, I was stopped by the Polish sentry who told me that the AK would not accept me," Jozek resumed after the contents of the dish revealed four plump pancakes and were duly acknowledged. "'A skinny kid like you could be useful in our sewer units,' the soldier told me, half joking. 'They have trouble finding guys and even girls thin enough to push through the sewer entrance from Jasna Street. That opening was always narrow, but during the bombing the pavement shifted and it is now so small that only human skeletons can get through it.' Well, that was enough for me. I went to the officer in charge in the place designated and told him straight out: 'I am skinny, I am willing, send me down!'"

What became clear from Jozek's narrative was that the sewer tunnels were vital for the Polish administration's maintenance of communication with diverse military units in the city. The sewer opening on Jasna was in a strategic position and they were just trying to see if three slim girls could get through it. Jozek's arrival created quite a diversion. The young officer in command was obviously torn between conflicting emotions. In the first place, he believed that no decent man should expect a woman to travel through narrow, dark and slippery sewer passages to carry out dangerous missions. Any half decent man would much rather go himself. "He was so upset by it that we thought he would break down and cry," was Jozek's comment. Secondly, the messages, orders, etc. were always given to a group of three, in case some of them were unable to complete the journey. "I did not ask why the carriers might not complete the journey," Jozek commented, "but I figured that the reason for it might be either Germans or gas. We were told that there is foul air there." Another difficulty was the lack of a third girl. The volunteers who wanted to join were all too big, although very earnest. "One of them actually appealed to me as an objective bystander. Delicacy prevented me from commenting on her generous proportions, though. Not that she was plump, who can be nowadays, but the breadth of her bone structure in a certain area…" The rest was left to his audience's imagination.

Jozek's eagerness to be the third 'girl' met at first with stern refusal but when new efforts to find another suitable candidate proved unsuccessful, and one of the girls vouched for the past existence of the Orphanage described by the boy, and thus for his truthfulness, the officer reluctantly consented. "He looked at me for a long time and then asked me if I respected ladies," Jozek said in a tone that indicated displeasure. "'Not only do I respect them, but I feel very comfortable in their company, unlike some,' I answered, and though I had meant Hans, I hoped that he would take it personally. Well, that helped to shut him up on the subject. He told me that I had to obey orders from Basia, one of the skinny two, no matter what, and of course I said yes. Then he asked me if I were Jewish. When I said no, I was Christian, he ordered me to swear on the cross that I would do my very best, even if it meant death, to carry out the mission. I presume that if I were Jewish they would have found something else to swear on."

Mother kissed him in passing to the primus and Violetta drew a pink handkerchief from her pocket. "Look at our hero," she instructed the cat, who obligingly increased his purring. "Look at him and learn from him." The rest of them sat motionless.

It was evident that Jozek was now fighting to keep his voice level, the more so since Violetta's crying was now joined by that of Mrs. Nowak and Krysia. He briefly described the journey over slippery stones in almost total darkness, ankle deep in sewage, following the map held by their leader, Basia. They had been warned that the torch should be used only in an emergency, that the valuable packet with dispatches carried by their leader was the responsibility of all of them, that it was absolutely vital that it should never, never fall into German hands and… that there was a strong possibility that the Germans were posted at other openings with machine guns.

"Mala, the skinny girl shorter than Basia, got sick right away and Basia advised her to keep her kerchief close to her nose. I bet she was no more than fifteen and lied about her age to be accepted. I felt queasy also, and tried to think about things unconnected with food. We passed the first opening without incident, Basia ordering us to tiptoe silently close to the brink of the sewer where the stinking mass was many feet deep, for she thought that they would concentrate on the passage close to the wall. Then Mala slipped and almost fell into that horrible muck, but Basia grabbed her in time. There were only two openings indicated on the map, and we passed both successfully. How were we to know that the Germans opened an extra one and were waiting there?"

These words augured some terrible mishap. Even before the boy actually described it, they sensed it. Mother attended to the two ladies whose sobs became audible. Krysia was lying on the bed with her face in the pillow and Nina was telling herself that she owed it to Jozek to behave normally. "If he can relate those horrifying moments without breaking down, so can I by merely listening."

"Jozek, please finish it," Krysia pleaded from behind the pillow. "They saw us and they shot at us," Jozek continued hesitatingly, "and they hit Basia. She was badly wounded, blood rushing from her mouth and stomach. Mala wanted to bind her wounds but Basia ordered us to leave her there and run, run with the dispatches. We did and I do not know if we should have," he added miserably. "When we arrived at the Polish station they sent us to a medical station for a check up and they told us that they would try to rescue Basia. But I don't think it was true."

"They would tell the couriers anything, all they cared about were the blasted messages," thought Nina. "I wonder if he knows what has happened to Basia. Did she die there or was she killed? Perhaps I will ask him about it, but not now."

Mrs. Ilski was distributing tea, when the door opened and the jubilant Mr. Lis appeared. 'Gesiowka has been liberated!" he exclaimed.[51] "Over three hundred Jews of all nations! Some ours, Polish. Those able to do so have joined our forces." In an instant Jozek's eyes brightened with hope. "Any children among them?" he asked breathlessly. "Just adult men," Mr. Lis answered and looked with incomprehension at Jozek's sorrowful face.

---

51   Bartelski, *Powstanie Warszawskie* (Warsaw Uprising), p. 93.

Disillusionment

Their lives during the following weeks were a see-saw existence, according to the apt description of the once plump (but no longer) Mrs. Linkowski. They were continually suspended between euphoria and disappointment. Although the Uprising went well in the first two weeks, or rather, amazingly well considering the imbalance of power, the long awaited help arrived neither from the Soviet army sitting on the shore of Vistula only several miles from Warsaw, nor from the Allies. By now, it was well-known that there were difficulties between the Allied Command in the West and the Soviets, and that the request by the former for permission to land and refuel in Soviet-held airports in order to help the Warsaw insurgents met with Stalin's categorical refusal.[52] Several planes belonging to the Western air force did appear on the horizon during the fighting but unaided by their Soviets allies and not sure if they could make it back safely, they dropped supplies beyond the reach of Polish units and hurried back. It gradually dawned on all the Poles that the Soviet side reserved for itself the role of observer only, and not a strictly neutral observer at that.

At the beginning of September 1944, there was still hope, despite the general conviction that the Russians, although formally allies in the war against Hitler, were quite willing to see their Polish ally destroyed. "What I do not understand," Jozek was saying, looking with melancholy at the four small potatoes which were to be their dinner, "is why the British and Americans pay attention to what Stalin wants. If I were in their place, I would tell him that if he didn't like it he could lump it. Everybody now knows that without American help the Red Army could not manage the war. What are Roosevelt and Churchill afraid of?" Mrs. Amelia, whose radio was a source of information to all of them, only nodded her head in sorrow. "That was exactly what Mr. Churchill heard in the British parliament a few days ago, and I am sure that Mr. Roosevelt also had members in the American Congress who cried 'help Warsaw.' But the Western governments are afraid to start a quarrel with Stalin, and Stalin hates us. They are afraid of complicating the war alliance. But they are still trying to convince him. Maybe..."

"Bah," exclaimed Nina, "trying to convince that criminal to help us, who are fighting on the same side! I have no patience with all of this! My God, I would not

---

[52]   "Stalin denounced the leaders of the Home Army (A.K.) as 'a handful of power seeking criminals' and withheld Soviet assistance. For sixty-three days, the fighting raged with unprecedented savagery while the Soviet army, miles away across the river, looked on in virtual passivity. A quarter of a million civilians died.' Davies, *Heart of Europe*, p. 78. Also, *Roosevelt and Churchill*, p. 67; Karbonski, *Fighting Warsaw*, p. 386.

be surprised if some of us grabbed rifles and fought both of them, Stalin and Hitler! I know it would be the end of us, but ..."

Those weeks brought great changes into their lives. After the initial euphoria, came disappointment when their street reverted back to German rule and the AK left the district. Ela moved to the country with her children, being convinced (after a night-long argument with her husband, an AK officer) that the Germans were bringing extra big guns to reduce the city to rubble, and the present incessant roar of their artillery was only a prelude to what was coming. Although safety was not to be found in the country either, it was believed that her sister's small farm might be healthier for the children than Warsaw. Mr. Lis went with them but, after discreetly inquiring of Jozek about the Ilski's food situation, promised to come back to see them quite soon. The black cat refused to leave, despite Lila's pleadings and now adopted the Ilski's cellar and learned to eat their meager food. Before their withdrawal, AK members blocked the entrance to the underground passage and Mrs. Sawicki, with two women friends, moved there after her house was taken over by the Secret State Police.

Back under the Nazis
Mrs. Amelia's Venture

So now, instead of their beloved Polish soldiers, the inhabitants of the street saw their oppressors again, but they were changed also. Nina noted with satisfaction that the German soldiers were terrified of everybody and everything. They walked in pairs on each side of the street, with their rifles ready, occasionally firing their weapons into the windows. The food became scarcer and scarcer. Mrs. Sawicki and her friends simply stayed at home, declaring that they would rather starve than face the 'unnatural vipers,' and subsisting on the charity of other people. The Ilski family did venture out, mother attending to her duties in the hospital where there was an influx of German casualties (Polish casualties were not allowed into the German hospital) while Krysia and Jozek now rummaged in the abandoned trash cans of the Germans who lived close by. Nina swore that she would never eat the 'Nazi refuse.' All became thinner, despite Mrs. Ilski's heroic effort to bring them her meager ration from work.

In this situation, as on many occasions before, the youngsters came to appreciate their elders' resourcefulness and courage. After watching Krysia and Jozek secretly repairing toward the trash cans, and coping with tearful Mrs. Nowak whose lamentations of 'poor, poor children' would invariably set off Violetta, Mrs. Amelia hit on the plan of trying to get to the abandoned vegetable plots in the city parks which had been exposed to almost continual bombardment, as was every wooded area in the city. "Of course they are afraid to enter parks, in case some of our units are there," Mrs. Amelia was telling her audience. "Therefore they are concentrating on firing on them. But they are shooting blindly, and at night would not be able to do much damage. This night, I will go to the park nearest to us and I will be surprised if I do not find something edible there. After all it is only September! No, you kids stay home till I come back and report," she added seeing that Nina appeared ready to accompany her.

"But you cannot walk that far with your crutch under a rain of bullets," exclaimed Violetta on the verge of hysteria, "and the very idea of going out without a pass is suicidal. Absolutely!" But Amelia was not to be dissuaded. "First of all, who told you that I do not have a pass? You do not think that our boys, who for years manufactured false papers, would not know how to make stupid German passes, do you? Secondly, my disability may be helpful here. Suppose they find me in the park, so what? I will tell them that I went there to listen to the orchestra. There are very many people who lost their senses because of what is going on around us, and the Germans know it. They may well believe that I am not only old and crippled but insane as well, and as such not dangerous!"

There were no arguments after that, and such was the need for relaxation, that all three children burst into laughter joined by the less robust tittering of Mrs. Nowak and Violetta. Even Mrs. Ilski evidenced a smile when, after coming home that night, she was greeted with a pantomime in which Nina was a stern German soldier with a gun (a broom handle) while Krysia imitated the machine gunfire and Jozek acted the role of Amelia who, pushing an empty baby carriage, was explaining in her high pitched German that she went to the park, in the middle of the night, in order to hear an orchestra.

Although Amelia's loot consisted of only two carrots and a few potatoes, she did find out where the vegetable plots were and proposed to go there on the next night with the by now famous baby carriage. As before, she absolutely refused to take any of the children. Mr. Lis, who came from the country to see how they were doing and brought with him some provisions, immediately suggested that he go with her, leaving it up to Amelia what to say if met by the Nazi patrol. He made sure that the carriage wheels made no noise on the pavement and despite the arguments of all present, both of them disappeared into the pitch-black street.

Some time later, Violetta's attack of nerves and subsequent fainting fit alarmed Mrs. Nowak sufficiently to knock on the Ilski's door. "Renata, please come," she whispered, appearing at the cellar window in her nightgown. "Violetta fainted while talking to me about this venture. I managed to resuscitate her, but she is still in a terrible state. Maybe she needs a doctor! Renata, you work at hospital, can you help? She may be seriously ill!" Mrs. Ilski and the three children immediately repaired to their friend's house. There on the floor of her salon lay Violetta, sobbing and moaning about the premonition she had received from 'above.' "I know they were being shot at," she moaned. "I feel it! You can call it a woman's intuition if you want! Oh God, oh God, help us!"

"Shot at? A pack of nonsense!" came Amelia's voice from outside. "We are both all right, there was no shooting, and the carriage is almost full. Come and see what we brought you." Still sobbing, Violetta began to embrace them, while Jozek counted the heads of cabbage and potatoes appreciatively. It was a happy time for all of them. "Now we will all go to sleep, and tomorrow we will have a big dinner," continued Amelia. "Violetta will fetch her friend Mrs. Sawicki and her two companions to share the food with us. Won't you dear?" 'Avec plaisir,' responded the latter, by now completely recovered.

It was on the way home that Jozek grabbed Nina's hand and made her touch the side of the carriage. "Do you know what it is?" he whispered. And Nina knew. "A bullet?" she whispered back, taking care that Mrs. Ilski and Krysia did not hear her. "Machine gun bullet fired from no very great distance," was his reply. "Perhaps Violetta's intuition was not far out after all."

United Front

In the middle of September, hopelessness enveloped Warsaw. Although individuals still hoped for Allied help, most of the population was coming to terms with the probability that victory had eluded them once more. Yet repeated demands for surrender were rejected by the AK leadership again and again, and Varsovians supported that decision. Was the wholesale destruction of life before them? They still clung to the hope that it would, miraculously, not come to that.

One evening, waiting for Mrs. Ilski with their meager meal (for weeks now millet, and little of it, was the only food available), Nina and Jozek recollected the words written in blood on a wall by a dying Greek boy after the disastrous battle of Thermopylae in 480 B.C.: 'A passer by, tell Sparta that here lay her loyal sons.'

"But whom shall we tell about our struggle when they begin to finish us all off?" Nina remarked morosely. Jozek, filled with despondency, added, "Nobody will hear us."

The heavy guns had already started their terrifying noise when Mrs. Amelia asked all three children to tea in Mrs. Nowak's house. Violetta was also present. The repast consisted of boiled water and pieces of potato and a nettle bread aptly called 'clay.' "I have to tell you that your father is out of the allied hospital in Sicily and is now in another facility where he will get specialized care," Amelia remarked, looking uneasily at each of them in turn, for by now Jozek was part of Ilski family. "He is doing reasonably well, but unhappily he lost his left leg and one eye acting as Polish adjunct to the Italian partisan unit in Italy. There will be plenty of time to find out about that period in his life. Meanwhile, it is enough to say that although severely wounded, he was luckier than many. Your mom knows about it and has taken the news in her stride. But she and you have to realize that he will need help in adjusting to life and that only family can do it."

The three youngsters sat motionless. "At least he is alive," thought Nina, full of compassion for that father of hers, so badly hurt, so far away and alone. "Of course he needs special care and he is going to get it as long as we are alive. But how on earth can we get together?" Krysia wanted to know if father wore a black patch on his eye like pirates, while Jozek cheered all of them up by relating stories he had heard as a shoe shine boy to the Germans. "Well, one leg is better than none," he announced sententiously. "And so is one eye. Hans's friend had two legs blown off at the Russian front and he is thankful that he is not dead. Don't worry too much, Nina. Nowadays they make wonderful artificial legs and with one healthy leg you can walk almost normally. He would not have to wear a patch, Krysia, they could fix him with an artificial eye similar to the one he has. Your mom knows about all that, for she is close to the medical establishment. So this is good news in a way, if you consider the circumstances."

"We have to think realistically," Mrs. Amelia continued, giving each of them a piece of bread. "As things look now, our forces must either die or surrender. But your mother and you must live! She has your poor father to think about, and you three and Kinga and Myszka are the future of Poland. How would our country look after the war if all its youth were missing? Because of Renata's underground press activity and even more because of her present position as head of the AK translation department, she will find herself in an extremely precarious situation when the Germans defeat our forces and start their revenge, and – this we know now – in equal danger if, after crushing the Uprising, the Germans were to retreat and the Soviets to take what remains of Warsaw. There is plenty of evidence that Poles who engaged in anti-Nazi activities will be considered 'hostile elements' by Russians and imprisoned or executed. I am in the same situation, but I am old and less important than your mom," here she was interrupted by a joint assault from Violetta and Krysia, who showered her with kisses and begged her not to talk nonsense.

"You are my first heroine among many," sobbed Violetta. "You are not old, not in the sense we understand, no matter what those low class barbarians think. Anyway a little touch here and there and a haircut a la Greta Garbo would take years off your appearance! If only you let me..." she finished weakly. "Therefore," continued Amelia, having patted both females on their heads and not having paid much attention to the latest suggestion, "you and your mom must leave Warsaw while there is still time and a way of arranging it."

"I am not leaving, and mom would not leave either," exclaimed Nina. "What, to desert Warsaw and behave like rats escaping a sinking ship! Never!" Jozek and Krysia repeated after her, "Never!"

A commotion outside interrupted those sentiments as a small boy appeared at the window. "Three of our people are running down this street," he stammered fixing his eyes on Violetta's pink turban and her tear stained face. "The Huns are going from house to house asking 'Wo sind die Banditen'? (Where are the criminals?) Mom sent me to tell you!" Those words were accompanied by a sound of shooting, perilously near.

"Good God, but the street is closed at this end," exclaimed Mrs. Nowak. "They established a Nazi precinct there soon after our forces withdrew. The escapees are in a trap!"

"What about hiding them in our place?" suggested Nina breathlessly, "Perhaps they could fit under our beds!" Even as she said it, however, she knew it was a stupid suggestion. There was literally nowhere to hide in their cellar, and the fact could be easily ascertained. Suddenly a harsh German voice through a loudspeaker announced death for anyone attempting to hide individuals running from the police, after which came another halting, strongly accented voice in Polish, "Whoever attempts to help the bandits…"

"If they come here, I will let them into my house," Mrs. Nowak announced. "But where, oh God, where to hide them?" A terrific noise drew them all outside soon after. There, a few houses from them, was a smouldering ruin of a building surrounded by the hateful uniforms. "They threw hand grenades into the house," whispered Jozek. "Our boys must have been hiding there. But other people were inside also…"

"So that is it," Nina thought wearily. "They killed the AK boys as well as Mrs. Koperski and her children. But maybe some of them are still alive?" She had very little hope that anyone would be permitted to approach the house, but she was on the point of calling Jozek to help her search for the living as soon as the Germans departed when three disheveled young men with tattered red and white bands on their jackets materialized in front of them as if by magic. They were still unharmed! Here they stood, gazing at them like terrified children who have lost all hope. "For Christ's sake…" whispered one of them. "Get in," said Mrs. Nowak in a trembling voice. But it was Violetta who astounded all of them by taking the initiative. She told the escapees in a shrill but relatively steady voice, "go into my salon; put on the pink overalls from the white cupboard; sit under the hair dryers; stick your heads well into them and turn the power on. Cover your knees and boots with towels, and I will put my rejuvenating formula on your faces."

"That could never work," Nina thought hopelessly when the three young men, suddenly energized, disappeared behind the door to Violetta's establishment. "How eagerly they started to believe that they could be saved! So now they will be killed and so will the three ladies! Perhaps, perhaps they will kill us as well! But God, coward that I am, I would prefer not to die yet! If it is all the same to you, God."

It took some minutes before the first military units arrived at their cellar, where they kicked apart the makeshift beds and threw a pail of water at the cat. "The Polish luxury apartment," a beefy soldier called their home, and the joke was greatly appreciated by others. During that time, Nina, Jozek, and Krysia were huddling together in the yard, listening with trepidation to the cries coming from across the street in the house once belonging to Mr. Lis, but now inhabited by Mrs. Sawicki and her two elderly friends. The ladies were apparently trying to persuade the intruders not to destroy Mr. Lis's furniture. That unfortunate suggestion provoked the Germans into smashing everything in sight, including the wheelchair and the family photographs.

Another unit, under the command of a corporal, arrived at Mrs. Nowak's house. "You go around," the officer told his three soldiers, "and I will enter from the front. Those three abandoned their weapons for lack of ammunition, so you are safe. Be ready to shoot, for we are not taking prisoners. GO!" He was, however, distracted from climbing the steps to the front entrance by the abrupt opening of its very door. In it appeared Violetta in pink overalls and matching turban. Her face, wet with tears, was marked by running mascara and some previous attempts with rouge. She kept one hand on the door handle, while in the other she held a flask of cologne which she kept spraying around her with uncertain circular movements. "Out of there," shouted the corporal putting his hand on the gun. "Out of there, you witch!"

"Mon capitaine," stammered Violetta looking with terrified eyes at the two straps on the soldier's collar. "The salon is for ladies only, 'nur Damen! Messieurs, – oh non! Oh non! S'il vous plait, Herr capitaine,…"

"Heraus," repeated the German, dodging the spray of perfume, but appearing somewhat amused and flattered by the promotion he had received. "Heraus you crazy monster!" Meanwhile Nina, acting as if under a spell, rushed into their cellar and, having retrieved from the bag of rice the first valuable that her fingers touched, moved speedily toward the two protagonists. "She is French, calls herself an artiste, and is mentally not quite…" she told the officer, each German word coming to her ears as if from a distance. "There are only women there, not quite dressed you know. You can see them through the window," as indeed three pink figures under the hair dryers were clearly visible. Meanwhile Violetta slowly descended to her knees, without however unblocking the entrance to the salon. The turban was now off, uncovering her sparse hair twisted around curlers in the shape of blue butterflies. "A case of female vanity, actually," came Jozek's voice from Nina's left in a carefree, conversational German. "Those ladies under the dryers have just had a massage and a beauty mask, and are in no condition to be discovered, if you understand what I mean. Typically, they would wish to appear at their best before a military VIP, as would no doubt the beautician under normal circumstances. Of course you would not be willing to wait till they are presentable again (as they would very much wish) now would you?" The German, looking puzzled, turned his eyes from Jozek to Nina and then to Violetta, who was now lying across the threshold with closed eyes, one hand placed in the vicinity of her heart, while the other still held the flask poised to defend the entrance to the salon with sprays of cologne.

"Please, please leave her and the salon alone, there are only three women," Nina whispered to the German. "We don't want our French friend here to faint, and her customers to get hysterical. This is a small memento," she continued, slipping into his hand the brooch which she only now recognized as one with rubies. "Thank you very much and good-bye."

After glancing to his left and right, the corporal put the brooch into his pocket without so much as looking at it. "Hey you," he shouted to the soldiers coming from the back of the house. "How are things over there?"

"Nothing interesting," was the reply. "Just two old creatures, one trembling like a jello!"

"Same here," remarked the corporal, "one crazy French woman and three other, old, ugly, and undressed!" The echo of their laughter stayed with Nina for a long time. But it became so intertwined with blessed relief that she could not even feel angry. For, despite everything, they were all still alive in this part of the street, and it was just possible they would stay alive! Life seemed very precious now, the most precious thing in the world.

"Do you think that he really believed us?" she asked Jozek, watching the soldiers disappear around the corner, "or was he bribed by the brooch?"

"He could have kept the brooch and done his German duty as well," Jozek pointed out. "Who knows what human motivations really are," he concluded philosophically. "But let's see to Violetta first, and then let's have something to eat, shall we Nina? Actually, there is still the bread your mom brought yesterday, and Mrs. Nowak's cabbage."

"Not till we've found out if there are any survivors in the house they threw grenades at," his companion reminded him. "Remember that if it weren't for me, you and Krysia would have eaten that rice a long time ago, and where would we have kept those jewels then? Answer me, please!" But Jozek pretended not to hear.

Chapter Five
Convalescence

Nina woke up feeling terrible. She felt nauseated, she was unable to move her left leg and her head seemed ready to split into a thousand fragments. It was a great effort to open her eyes. "If I am dying," she thought, "I want grandma to come and fetch me. I want her to use any influence she may have over there so that they glue the pieces of my head together to stop the ache." She was unaware that she had actually given voice to those sentiments. It must have been so, however, for immediately afterwards, some nearby sounds attracted her attention. "She is calling on her granny," exclaimed a tearful voice. "This, no doubt, is the end! Oh God, oh God, what shall we say to her mamma?"

"I know the voice, but I am too tired to remember who it is," Nina said to herself. After a while she realized that she could also hear some strange sounds coming from far away, friendly sounds, sounds that had nothing in common with artillery shells or bombs. Were there animals nearby? She could also see, although keeping her eyes open was difficult and she could not sustain this for long. But what she saw was puzzling. It certainly was not the familiar cellar arches, neither was it the ceiling in Mrs. Nowak's house. The surface above her was of white plaster, crisscrossed with wide black rafters. "It must not be the hereafter, then," she concluded without enthusiasm. "It looks like something we saw in the countryside before the war. Is it possible that I am still alive? I will consider this question once I've had some rest."

The next time she came to awareness, she realized that she was swallowing some liquid from a teaspoon. The broth, if it was a broth, tasted bitter and kind of salty and she was far from pleased to have it forced on her. Also, the person who was doing it to her must have been spilling some of the liquid, for Nina distinctly felt warm drops of something on her forehead and nose. Well, enough was enough. When the next spoonful came, Nina decided to open her eyes and take control of the situation. But on doing this she experienced a jolt of joy. It was the tearful face of Violetta that materialized before her, old Violetta who, between spoonfuls of soup, murmured the most extravagant endearments ever heard by Nina. "If I were better, I'd laugh like crazy," Nina thought. "What sense does it make to address a girl my age 'little lamb,' 'precious butterfly,' or 'dearest froggie?' Where am I?" she managed to ask, and immediately after that she added in a voice chocked with terrible anxiety, "Where are they?"

"Your mom and Krysia are safe. They are now in Western Poland trying to get news of your dad, Kinga and Myszka," this explanation came from another person who, judging by the voice, was Mrs. Nowak. "They left you in our care after the doctor assured them that you would recover. Jozek was lost for a while, but now he is safe also." Nina's heart expanded with happiness. "You have been ill for months, darling," continued the old lady. "It is a miracle that we got you out of that burning building. We are staying in a house abandoned by a family of farmers. The people in the village are friends."

Nina attempted to take all this in. "What about the Uprising?" she cried suddenly, trying to raise herself. "What about Mrs. Amelia, Mr. Lis, Ela, and others?" she ended weakly. But there was no answer from any of her gentle nurses. She closed her eyes again. There was no need for further questions.

Despite the gloom that stayed with her after her first communication with the world, Nina knew now that she was getting better, and she enjoyed the gradual cessation of pain. But the realization of her recovery filled her with disgust. "I must be a truly insensitive clod to be happy that pains are almost gone, and to feel stronger, when I know what happened in Warsaw," she told her doctor, an elderly parish priest who – because of the lack of medications – attempted to ease her suffering with herbs and talk. "It is all the doing of those two ladies who pamper me so," she added weakly. But the priest admonished her to get well as soon as she could and poo-poohed her scruples. "Remember that as a strong young woman you may be called upon to take care of others, to undertake some important mission, and for that you need health and determination. You have a future, my dear, a future that may be very demanding. What good would you do yourself and others if you stayed a weakling, physically and mentally? Remember God told us not to bury our talents!"

It was also he who – urged by Nina to tell her everything – briefly described the tragedy of Warsaw. No meaningful assistance came to the insurgents, although the Allies were already in France and were willing to help and the Red Army of the Soviet Union stood some twenty kilometers from the city. The main problem with obtaining help from the West lay in the fact that it depended on permission from Stalin to allow western planes bringing supplies to Polish fighters to re-fuel on Soviet territory. Without re-fueling, the aircraft faced great dangers; they could fail to reach safety on their way back without sufficient fuel. Yet Stalin repeatedly refused pleas from Roosevelt and Churchill to let Western planes re-fuel on Soviet bases. In fact, the Soviets deliberately held their offensive during the Uprising so that the Germans could destroy the capital.

The priest stopped his narration and looked at her uneasily. "Please continue," Nina whispered. "I want to know it all."

"In the cellars, pickaxes were used to break a way through from one building to another, thus creating long lines of subterranean corridors stretching from one part of the city to another," the sad story continued, "while the battles raged above them. The Uprising went on for sixty-three days. Most of the time, the military as well as the civilians suffered from lack of food and in the last weeks there was no water. Hundreds of wells were dug to alleviate this problem, but on the whole with meager results. When the last fighting Polish unit was eliminated, the Germans took the remnants of the military force into captivity and the civilians were ordered to leave the city. Immediately after that, Hitler ordered the total destruction of the capital, block by block; 97% of the buildings were gone.[53] Warsaw was left a heap of ruins."

Nina lay without moving with closed eyes. After blowing his nose, the priest took up the narration. "Your mother spent the last days of the Uprising with her unit, and there were tens of thousands needing medical care. Terrible news regarding the murder of the Polish wounded and the medical staff by the Nazi police in the Old City Hospital was communicated to Jozek. Without telling anyone, he went out to discover if a similar fate had met the hospital where your mother worked. He was prevented from coming back by the collapse of buildings on your street, but managed to get out of the city riding on a German tank, if we are to believe what he said."

"Oh, I believe it," Nina noted without surprise. "It sounds just like Jozek. It must have been his German friend Hans who helped him."

"Hans or another German fellow," the priest said with some distaste. "Not only gave him safe passage through the burning city but bestowed upon him some very valuable tins and other provisions. Very rare and valuable indeed! These, the boy shared loyally with all of us after finding you in this village, Rawa Maz, just about fifty miles from Warsaw." The last comment was made with the intention of erasing any uncomplimentary impression of Jozek which the previous

---

[53] Hitler ordered that Warsaw be "razed without trace," Davies, *The Heart of Europe*, p. 78.

communication had created. "Now he is with Sister Cecilia taking care of many Polish orphans in Piotrkow, not far from here. You will see him soon."

Despite Nina's pleas for more information, the priest was adamant in calling on her to rest, and there was nothing Nina could do about it. She knew better than to direct her inquiries to the two ladies, for such memories were too painful for them. Still, it seemed hardly fair that she still did not know how she got the cracked skull, a twisted leg, all these bruises and found herself in a farmer's hut on a strange bed. She waited impatiently for the clergyman's next visit and when he did, the rest of the family saga unfolded.

"You and Krysia were with Mrs. Nowak, Violetta, and Amelia when the incendiary bombs started falling on the houses on your street. It was a direct hit that caused the deaths of poor Mrs. Amelia and Mr. Lis, and injured you. Your pet perished also. There was, of course, no way to ask for medical assistance, as the whole street was on fire. By sheer luck, an ordinary wheelbarrow was found and was utilized to get you out of that part of Warsaw. Due to the efforts of the two good ladies, Krysia, and some strangers who came to their assistance, you are here today. Your mom was not with you at the time, and for a while poor Krysia was out of her mind worrying about her. It appears that Mrs. Ilski and other physicians and nurses were trying to evacuate the patients. At the same time, she carried on her other work, you know. She found you here but was obliged to leave, for news came about the opening of some of the Nazi camps by the allies. Your mother was determined to learn where your sister and her friend were, and Krysia insisted on going with her. Both left after you had been pronounced out of danger by me, although I was not too sure about it, may the Lord forgive me."

"So there was no news of Kinga and Myszka?" the agonizing thought made Nina shiver. "What about Father? Has he recovered?"

"Thanks to some arrangements by the surviving underground administration, your mother is not in an immediate danger," the clergyman was saying with a worried expression, "but it is only fair to tell you that both your parents cannot stay in Poland as things look now. The Germans are losing the war and becoming much less vigilant, but the Soviets are now in Eastern Poland and will be with us very soon. Although our Western allies want to believe that the USSR is now Poland's friend, we know better. The Soviets, like the Germans, do not like the patriotic Poles who were fighting for an independent Poland. They have already demonstrated their hostility towards the AK and the Poles who fought the Germans in the West. Furthermore, after the collapse of Nazi Germany, we may very well be saddled with a Soviet-sponsored government, which the West would probably duly recognize.

Our legitimate government in London now has no status among the allies. This is a sad truth and we have to cope with it. It seems to me that we have exchanged one hostile occupation for another."[54]

"So all our efforts were in vain?" cried the girl. "Then perhaps it would have been better not to fight at all, just to sit tight and let those two rogues fight each other instead of killing us?"

"Oh no, I do not think so," the priest affirmed with conviction. "The AK staged the Uprising for very definite reasons. In the first place, it would have been unthinkable for Poles not to contribute to a German defeat and not to liberate our capital, although nobody believed then that the Soviets would prove to be so hypocritical, so hostile to the whole underground movement. But the AK was also concerned about our image abroad. How would it look if Poles did not take part in pushing back the Germans from their native country? Soviet propaganda was already trying to convince the West that the Polish Underground movement was of no importance! Besides it had been rumored for months that Hitler intended to raze Warsaw to the ground and our people were determined to prevent him from doing it. Now, I have answered your questions, and we will talk about something else."

"Just answer my last question please," begged Nina. "How many... how many Poles died in the Uprising?"

"I do not know, and I do not want to speculate. A great many, no doubt. Now go to sleep."[55]

It would not have been surprising, if her dreams had been full of incendiary bombs and the Russians preventing Warsaw from getting help, but on waking up the next morning she was mainly aware of the image of Violetta pushing a wheelbarrow with her own prostrate figure on it! Terribly sad of course, but also extremely funny. She could not wait to tell Jozek about it. It certainly did not beat riding on a German tank but, as a visual impression, it possessed an allure of its own.

---

[54]   On January 11, 1945, L. Beria issued order Nr. 0016 instructing his commanders to dispatch "hostile elements." [Some 30,000 A.K. soldiers were arrested on January 1945 alone.] In April 1945, Beria's order Nr. 00315 called for the execution of the "hostile elements," Piotrowski, *Poland's Holocaust*, pp. 98-100.

[55]   An official estimate of the Polish victims of the Warsaw Uprising is between 200,000 and 250,000.

The New Life

With returning health, Nina became concerned with practical, down-to-earth questions for she could not but notice that the meals served by the two ladies with such loving care were unbelievably luxurious. It dawned on her one evening that her disgusting appetite must have been depriving her nurses, for no one appreciated better than she the difficulty of getting provisions under the occupation. That evening, when Mrs. Nowak came to her room to kiss her good night, Nina asked point blank, "How on earth do you manage to give me those fantastic meals when there is a war going on? Today I had two eggs, bread with real butter, and porridge with milk and yesterday there was a delicious chicken broth the like of which I haven't tasted for years. What about the apples that I devour every day? Does it mean that you both are going without in order to feed me? If that is the case, I swear to God that I will not eat the next morsel you give me, I mean it!"

Mrs. Nowak smiled gently as she attempted to calm her down. "Amazing though it may seem in this difficult time, we actually found people in this village, which by the way is only fifty miles from Warsaw, who were willing to feed and shelter us, and to get you a doctor (the priest who has since visited you daily). They even prayed for us. Then, Jozek arrived with the bounty from Hans. In recent weeks," here Mrs. Nowak started laughing, the first such sound Nina had heard from her in months, "it was Violetta who assumed the whole burden of taking care of us, procuring food, fuel, and other things. You will find it difficult to believe, I know, but this is the honest truth!"

She was right, this revelation appeared totally improbable to Nina. "Violetta taking care of us for weeks?" she stammered. "How?"

Mrs. Nowak seated herself more comfortably and embarked on a story which described the amazing activities of Violetta. "The woman not only has a heart of gold, but she also possesses talents for convincing others, especially females, of the superiority of what she calls 'an elevated life style,' which, in her mind, is closely connected with etiquette, hair care, manicures, and so on."

"Violetta was attempting to introduce etiquette and manicures among the village people?" Nina interrupted, not believing her ears. "Not among our people here, certainly not," Mrs. Nowak hastily replied. "They, the poor dears, have enough on their plates without worrying about such things. But she has done it, and done it successfully, among the Russian women, mostly officers' wives, who are now located not twenty kilometers from here." Seeing a complete lack of comprehension in the girl's face, the old lady hastened to explain. "Haven't you wondered during your illness why nobody around you talked about German police and German regulations? This is because the Germans have left this part of Poland

and the Russians have not yet arrived. We are therefore in a 'no man's land' and for the time being at least, we have not been bothered by anybody. The old head of the Polish village government is here, so is the priest, and the junior teacher (the headmistress was sent to a concentration camp). So far it is all to the good."

"How could I forget about the whole nightmare of the occupation?" Nina exclaimed in self-deprecatory tones. "Lying here in luxury, I let others worry about it. It must be the blow to my head that made me so dumb! But how on earth does Violetta manage to get to the Soviet military base and to communicate with the officers' wives? Does she have passes? Does she know Russian?"

"I do not think that she actually knows the language," the lady explained. "As far as I know she mostly uses French expressions. But she manages to understand the Russians. It is they, her present clientele, who provide the passes for her. Also, without actually telling them of her noble relatives, for she would never lie like this, she somehow induced them, unwittingly I am sure, to believe that she comes from an aristocratic family. They respect her very much."

"But even if they believed that nonsense, they would not respect her for it," Nina was still incredulous. "We know that they killed many nobles."

"True, but those Russian women who appreciate Violetta had contact neither with noble ladies nor with good hairdressers, beauticians, or style consultants. Their lack of consumer goods and their poverty was notorious. In Violetta they see a being from another world, a world of elegance and good manners, and it has great attraction for them. What is most important, however, is the fact that those women have nothing to do with the Soviet police. Their husbands are just army people. Violetta tells me that her Russian customers actually fear and dislike the People's Commissariat for Internal Affairs (political police). So please, Nina, do not blame our friend for what she is doing. She is just earning money for us the best way she knows how and she cares for your good opinion." But Nina was not convinced. "I still do not like it," she murmured.

She changed her mind due to the united efforts of Father Surman, the wife of the church organist, and a young farmer girl called Frania. All of them descended on Nina one afternoon bearing gifts of bread, cheese, and cabbage. "Having known you for some months now, I cannot conceive that you would harbor petty ideas about Miss Violetta's present occupation," the priest announced in his best pulpit manner. "What harm has she done? She is trying to earn a living, she is supporting an older friend and a young girl recovering from a serious illness. She is also providing, let us hope, those Russian women who had been living in a totalitarian society, with an insight into another world, not perhaps one of high spirituality or intellect, but certainly of civilized manners and customs." The girl Frania was even more explicit. "Miss Violetta is a sophisticated lady and she is also very clever.

Did you see the preparations she is making of herbs for creams, dyes, and such? She only managed to save scissors and combs from that burning inferno, yet she has already made curlers from small plastic bottles and acquired an electric hair dryer which my brother repaired for her. She is ever so sweet!"

That night, Nina dreamt of Violetta chasing the Russians with huge scissors. Now that she was so much better, she attempted to sort out all the information which had overwhelmed her in the last week or so. The new reality affecting her personal life, as well as the national existence of all Poles, boggled the mind! It appeared in her mind as a sequence of brief exclamations: MOTHER AND KRYSIA STILL UNDER THE GERMANS, LOOKING FOR KINGA AND MYSZKA! FATHER SOMEWHERE IN A MILITARY HOSPITAL IN THE WEST! JOZEK WITH ORPHANS! SHE, NINA, STILL AN INVALID, BUT GETTING BETTER, MEANWHILE SPONGING ON HER FRIENDS, WHO HAVE SHOWN HER SUCH TREMENDOUS KINDNESS! AND VIOLETTA, OLD VIOLETTA, TEACHING RUSSIANS THE 'BON TON'! Here Nina had to stop for she was seized with the desire to laugh, and she knew it would have been unkind.

But if her personal life had been affected to the highest possible degree, what about Polish affairs? Here again the sinister headlines, all printed in black letters, screamed in her mind: UPRISING CRUSHED DUE TO SOVIET RELUCTANCE TO HELP AND DUE TO WESTERN UNWILLINGNESS TO UPSET STALIN! GERMANS DEFEATED BUT SOVIETS VICTORIOUS, BEING LAUDED IN THE WEST! POLISH FAMILIES (HERS AMONG OTHERS) DEPRIVED OF THE RIGHT TO LIVE IN POLAND! This last statement was the most difficult to understand. The priest said that her parents would not be safe in Poland, and that meant that she, Kinga, Myszka, Krysia, and Jozek would have to go abroad. But where? Not that it mattered to her in her present state. She felt tremendous reluctance to even consider emigration from home (whether it was a from a cellar, the present room in the small hut, or anywhere else in Poland), away from her countrymen. In her sorrowful deliberation, she was even inclined to blame the clergyman for his unwelcome warning. "Father Surman believes that my parents cannot be safe in Poland, but what about him?" she asked her two friends. "Isn't it true that communists dislike priests and nuns and if, as he says, Poland may get a Soviet-sponsored government, he and Sister Cecilia might be in greater danger than my parents!"

"The clergy will never leave," remarked Mrs. Nowak, and Violetta, basking in her success as a liaison between the villages and the Russians, suggested that, "perhaps we could protect Father Surman."

On hearing about those comments the next day, the priest laughingly confirmed Mrs. Nowak's belief. "The Church will stay put, no matter who rules Poland. But I tell you Nina, after our experiences here under the Nazis, Soviet shenanigans are not going to impress me. Let Frania tell you about our experiences." Frania, who had just received a haircut 'a la garcon' from Violetta, began the story of their first encounter with the German police some years ago.

Village Stories
The New Order

"The German army," began the eighteen-year-old Frania, "was not the worst. Sure, we knew they were the enemy, and they were aware that we hated them. But besides announcing the curfew and the obligatory demands for food deliveries, they did not interfere too much. I mean, they did not throw the sick out from our temporary hospital nor did they close the school. That came some weeks later."

"It came when the Secret State Police arrived," interjected the outspoken wife of the village carpenter who entered with a bag of onions. "Those creatures were monsters, no doubt about it. Asking the pastor his pardon for using bad words, I venture to say that they were devils incarnate dressed in brown shirts and grey uniforms with death's head badges on their caps, exactly as the Holy Bible describes the evil one!"

Undaunted by a mild gesture of protest from the priest (which was repeated more than once), she gave further vent to her eloquence. "Did we do anything to spite them? Not us! There we were, most of us without husbands since the war had taken them away, listening to Father Surman. What did he say, non-stop, day and night? 'Do not provoke them, whatever you do,' he said. Do not deny it Father! What good did that do? None! It is those devils who showed the provocation when they grabbed old Edward Grala and hanged him on the tree in front of the church! If it were not for my seven orphans depending on me for every morsel of food, I would have showed the Nazis provocation, that I would!"

Taking advantage of the pause caused by the lady's running out of breath, Frania picked up the narration. "I had friends among the grandchildren of Edward Grala and we all cried, and his daughter begged them on her knees to spare her father, but to no avail. All this because they found a hunting rifle in the barn." Meanwhile, the previous narrator informed Nina with many meaningful winks that she herself had hidden the guns abandoned by the retreating Germans and had got quite a collection of them. "The devils have gone but the other scum is coming. Who knows what may come in handy?"

"That was only the beginning," the priest said with a sigh. "Some time later, the captain of the Secret State Police visited me and announced a series of misdeeds which would be punished by death, among them possession of arms, giving assistance to Jews, covering up for the people who possessed radio transmitters. These were just a few crimes to be punished by execution. We, of course, already knew some of them. The posters all over Poland announced death verdicts for anyone who helped Jews and only last May, in the neighboring village, an entire family, a shoemaker, his wife and two toddlers were shot together with the Jews they harbored.[56] Out of all Nazi-occupied countries, Poland alone had that law, but this did not stop those who harbor Christian feelings toward the unfortunate Jews. Our own have been provided for and are all right so far. But I do not think that in this village the people, including myself, knew much about the transmitters. It was only much later that we learned about the close communication between our underground forces here and the Polish government in London!"

Confessional Secrets

A break occurred due to Violetta's serving tea and honey, greatly appreciated by the visitors.

"I will never forget that Saturday evening when I was preparing to listen to confessions in our church," Father Surman began again. "The moment I entered our place of worship, I noticed two strangers in the nave. They had civilian clothing on, but I knew they were German, the new unit which had recently arrived to bolster the Secret State Police ranks. 'Well, all we can do is to carry on,' I thought, 'to the best of my knowledge confessions have not yet been forbidden.' But soon I sustained another shock. On my way toward the confessional, I was accosted by young Julius, son of our cobbler who whispered hurriedly, 'Father, there is a transmitter in the confessional! Be careful how you enter. Those two... you know...' after which he piously joined the people waiting for confession. This sudden information floored me. I knelt before the altar to give myself time to think. Needless to say I was feeling exceedingly upset and angry. Putting this thing in my church was risking death, not only mine, but in all probability those of other people as well! But then, on reflection, I had to admit that the church was not mine, that it belonged to all the people in the parish and that whoever had placed the transmitter in the confessional must have been desperate. Weren't we all indebted to those men and women who were trying to establish communication with the free world? These charitable thoughts were soon replaced by more selfish ones regarding my role in all of this. Should I cancel the confessions? That, in itself, would alert the unwelcome visitors. Well, I knew that I could not stay before the altar indefinitely, so I proceeded toward the confessional with the litany for the dying on my lips, for I was sure that I was done for." His audience listened with attention but without any outward signs of surprise or horror. "We are so used to their atrocities that such stories are common, not to say normal," thought Nina.

---

[56] The Polish population at large lived under the formal threat of instant execution for the entire family of anyone found sheltering, feeding or helping Jews," Davies, *The Heart of Europe*, p. 72.

"Of course the question now was whether that transmitter and I could fit into the confessional," the clergyman continued. "I must tell you that even before this event I experienced discomfort in our confessional, which must have been built for pygmies! It had a low ceiling, walls closely surrounding a small chair in front of the grate, and a sliding door. It was my custom, while listening to confessions, to leave the door slightly ajar to allow for air circulation, as the confessional was some feet removed from the public benches. But I knew that it would have had to be shut now, and was waiting with great trepidation to see how I and the transmitter could share such a small space together, always aware that the eyes of the Germans, and indeed the congregation, were upon me. The first thing, of course, was opening the door to the confessional. I did it while hiding any view of the interior with my person, but when I saw the transmitter, my heart sank. It was a huge, uneven metal box sitting on the seat, hardly leaving any room for me! I can only tell you that after squeezing myself in, the only possible posture I could assume involved my becoming prone on the uneven surface of the box, with protuberances jabbing my stomach, and keeping the door shut with my feet. It was sheer martyrdom, apart from being very undignified for a father confessor!" Here the narrator assumed a tone of self pity and injured dignity. He looked with approval at the three older females, whose demeanor manifested commiseration and empathy, and he intentionally directed his disappointment away from Nina and Frania, who were unsuccessfully trying to stifle giggles.

"When the first supplicant addressed me through the grate," Father Surman explained, "I told her that the confession was off, that the Germans were in the church, and I begged her to stay for a while as if she were listening to my teaching. Thank God she understood all this and even alerted some of her friends to do the same. I had to remain on that blasted structure for an entire hour, the normal time designated for confessions, very uncomfortable in body and soul, and expecting every moment to be physically hauled out by evil forces! Most of the supplicants immediately grasped the danger of the situation and behaved very well, pretending to go through the whole ritual of confession. Yet, at the end of the hour, I had a terrible time trying to explain things to a lady, who, after peering through the grate, demanded to know why I was in the position I was, and had the effrontery to ask whether my posture was adopted as penance for my sins! Upon my mentioning the words 'Germans,' she literally shouted: 'Germans? What Germans? There is nobody in the church but I and Julius! Are you sick father?' It was only then that I ventured to move my aching body and after verifying her statement, emerged from confinement. On doing this, I met Julius' eye who, even while appearing to listen solicitously to how I spent more than an hour in that confessional, was actually smirking. It did not improve my mood when I saw that his hilarity began to infect the old lady, who should have known better at her age. 'How dare you use the house of God for such a purpose,' I thundered. 'whatever purpose it was! Who told you to do so?' But of course I had to add that I did not want to know who that was, not for anything in the world! I always believed that the less one knows in such circumstances, the better. I told Julius with great firmness that the thing had to be removed that very night, or else. Of course he knew that I could not do anything if it were not."

"Oh Father, you behaved beautifully on other occasions also!" Frania was trying to make up for her previous weakness. "Do you remember your encounter with the body that was not a body?"

"That I shall remember to my dying day," intervened the carpenter's wife. "What with this war, the killings, and many illnesses due to all the deprivation, we had to manufacture a lot of coffins! For you must know that my family is known in the whole county for making beautiful caskets, and although my poor husband is in German captivity now, my brother, my oldest, and myself are giving satisfaction in this field to all our customers. The pastor here will attest to the truth of this."

The entrance of a boy called Jan with a message for the priest caused a temporary interruption in the narration. The lady carpenter used the time to tell Nina that during the latter's sickness, a beautiful coffin was being prepared for her, for everybody including the priest himself believed that she was doing poorly. "As soon as the casket was finished, I told your mom about it in order to ease her worries," the coffin maker announced proudly. "'Ready for your little daughter and a feast for your eyes,' I said, which was the gospel truth. May God punish me this moment if I am lying!'"

Not a Real Body

On coming back, the priest was prompted by the assembly to embark on another story. It was supplemented by the comments of the two female parishioners, who were eager to refresh his memory when necessary. "The Secret State Police, apart from spying on my movements and demanding to be given summaries of my homilies, [that they never received] also took an interest in funerals. They scrupulously noted each death in the village and ordered us to provide a photograph of every adult buried by me. At first, I could not comprehend what prompted them to do so. Then I learned that they may have been after some people who, while alive, had been formally regarded as deceased for security reasons at the instructions of the Underground. It was a gruesome task to tell the grieving family that they had to provide a photo of their dear one for the satisfaction of our enemies."

"Just what the devil himself contemplated, no more and no less," was the comment from the lady carpenter.

"The event I am going to relate occurred in the winter of 1944 when the units of the AK fought the regular German Army no more than twenty miles from here," the priest resumed. "We knew that some of our own boys and several girls, were involved in it and had a terrible time waiting for news from the battlefield. Apart from worrying about any dead or wounded, we knew that once the Germans established the connection between the Polish units and our village, they would impose harsh sentences on us, perhaps even burn the whole village as they had done with the township in the neighboring county. The next morning, the news came to me delivered by a twelve-year-old girl from a nearby village. The AK officer informed me that five of our young people sustained light wounds in that skirmish and were being taken care of. Unhappily, one boy, the son of the blacksmith, was dead. His body was left in a certain designated place in the forest. The AK commander believed that his family would have liked him to have a Christian funeral and hoped that I could help in this task. It apparently did not occur to him that our occupiers were watching all funerals and once they found that the poor boy was from our village..." The priest made a hopeless gesture, upon which Violetta rushed to replenish his cup of tea.

"Not surprisingly, the family of poor Richard insisted on his being buried in the village with as much ceremony as possible. They understood that it had to be done in secret and suggested that the body could be brought over by night, and after the funeral, be buried not in the cemetery, where a new grave would attract attention, but close to the rectory grounds. I cannot say that I was enthusiastic about this plan! It seemed to me full of grave risks. Carrying the body some miles, digging a grave close to my house, and finally having the whole ceremony at night, had the potential for disaster. But how could you argue with the bereaved? His mother, and your aunt, Frania, begged me to accede to their wishes and reluctantly I did. You know what happened, next, Frania. You were there. You continue now."

"Yes, I was there with my auntie on that snowy night," Frania went on. "The grave was dug properly and Mrs. Duda had the coffin ready. It was about midnight. Father was there too, telling us to be absolutely quiet. He insisted that the moment the body arrived, the funeral must proceed speedily. Soon we saw four of our boys carrying the body of Richard on a stretcher, all of them breathing heavily after the long journey but glad to see that everything was ready. Auntie helped them to put Richard, frozen stiff, into the coffin and Father had just approached him with holy water when..."

"What I saw was some movement of his lids, but I thought at first it was the light of the lantern," the priest took up the narration. "It was his mother who, after falling on him and tearing apart his blood-saturated jacket and shirt, whispered, 'God Almighty! He is alive! After staying there frozen for a day and more, he is alive!' Under her touch, the solidified blood started melting and Richard's mouth opened in a groan. I must admit that I was in no state to reach any decision as how to deal with this unexpected development. Here was a wounded AK soldier, whom the Germans considered their mortal enemy. He needed all the care he could get, he needed to be hidden from the authorities, and I was the only medical person available! While the others hurriedly filled the grave and the coffin was being taken back to the carpenter's shed, his mother raised her eyes to me and I shall never forget that moment! She never uttered a word, she just looked. 'The rectory is the house most frequented by the Secret State Police,' I found myself saying. 'It is virtually impossible for me to have him there. But,' and here I listened with amazement to my own words, as if somebody else delivered them, 'the basement in the rectory is dry and warm and the windows are still covered with plywood, from the time of the blackout when we stayed in the basement during the bombing. A bed could be put there.' After I said it, it was too late to go back. I only impressed his mother and aunt with the importance of keeping him absolutely quiet, as messages from the authorities arrived in my house almost every day. I think that deep inside me there was a conviction, not to say hope – may the Lord forgive me – that the boy would die very soon, and this overwhelming new problem would be taken away."

"But Richard did not die," exclaimed the lady carpenter triumphantly. "The boy was in the pastor's basement with his mom when, during the day, some of the evil ones saw the freshly overturned earth, and the whole squadron of them kept digging for hours hoping to find something. They called on the pastor, but he simply said that the boys were looking for water, taking advantage of the thaw that night, since the well in the rectory yard was going dry. Good for you father, and may God bless you!"

"One practiced lying so often, that it almost became a habit," the clergyman commented sadly. "I also informed the authorities that Richard's mom was my housekeeper. That she occupied the basement, that her friend Mrs. Duda here came to help her take care of the rectory and I do not know what other lies. All I could think about day and night was the state of my patient, who developed a high fever and raved for days. His poor mother had to muzzle him, and keep him from tearing his bandages away. She was the only one who could do it, for he resented others trying to help her. The herb tea that we gave him would keep him quiet for perhaps two hours a day at most. The rest of the time you had to watch him every minute, as his cries could have had terrible consequences."

During the interval that ensued, the company expressed their opinions as to the consequences of such a happening. They quoted examples from other villages, while Violetta, shivering and keeping fingers in her ears, sat mum, not wishing to hear.

"I got a heavy cold that winter, and managed to persuade their mailman to let me have some sulfa. I used it for Richard," Father Surman reminisced. "Not that there was any sign of recovery for weeks on end, and we wondered how long he and the deception could last. The climax came when two German officers moved into my house, leaving me only my study and the kitchen. Then I really believed that it was only a matter of time before we were put in front of a firing squad. Sometimes I thought that the sooner that came about the better. Also there was the issue of punishment for the whole village, once they verified who Richard was. Thank God they did not use the kitchen for their meals, which they took in their restaurant. On coming home, they mostly listened to records, and that might have helped to camouflage the noises from the basement. The barking of Azor, my dog, which started as soon as he saw them coming and continued for a time after they actually got in, might have been a useful signal that the patient had to be exceptionally quiet. It only lasted a short time, however, because they managed to befriend the animal, and he developed a great affection for both of them."

"Christ himself was tempted by Satan, so it is not surprising that a dumb animal found no strength to resist their evil machinations," Mrs. Duda interjected knowingly. "I myself, I must admit, was affected when the two Germans complimented me on my racuszki which, having been moved by Christian charity (they were both so young, just out of their teens and far from their families), I offered to them for a late collation." Her racuszki were indeed known to all assembled, and they surpassed one another in voicing their praise, while the creator of that delicacy sat quietly with modestly lowered eyes.

"It was in the middle of the night when that poor boy opened his eyes in a normal fashion and recognized his mother and myself," the priest concluded. "From that time on, his progress was astonishing. When he was better, he took control of things by contacting the Underground authorities, to whom he had access. After a while, a certificate from the Warsaw hospital (where Richard had allegedly gone in late fall to look for work in construction) testified that he was badly mangled while working, and had to stay five weeks under medical care. His return to his mother's house for recuperation was simply an ordinary consequence."

Thus, there was a happy ending to this story as well as the previous one and all of them felt immensely relieved. Violetta, after kissing each of them, produced some more tea and honey. Mrs. Duda retrieved from the folds of her copious cape a mysterious bottle, the contents of which she kept for 'medicinal purposes.' She proposed to use it now to drink to the success of similar endeavors.

"The thing that is the most impressive in all this," Nina thought happily, "is the behavior of the people. Everybody in this village knew of Richard's experiences, adults as well as children. Yet, it did not even occur to the pastor or the two female parishioners that there was any need to worry about betrayal, despite the danger to them all. That is what is so fantastic!"

The Spring of 1945
Political and Other Anxieties

The spring of the year 1945 brought with it many conflicting impressions and expectations in Nina's life. For a long time now, she had become used to separating national events and developments from those relating to her family and friends, to living as if on two levels; one life related to national issues, another to the people around her. But she was now becoming aware of a third dimension: a new level of interest which related only to her personal existence. Her health had improved tremendously, and apart from occasional headaches she was completely recovered. The coming of the new season suggested new hope and new beginnings, despite the terrible past and gloomy present. It seemed to her that the spring this year was especially beautiful, at least it was so in the country, with warm winds blowing the winter weather away and the first flowers timidly raising their heads. Contemplating such phenomena often led to a feeling of intense joy and hopeful expectation. The world was beautiful and she was young, now healthy and ready to exert herself in any worthwhile activity! If only... often after such emotions, the stark reality would emerge again and the temporarily forgotten anxieties would resurface and squash the light-hearted mood.

She could not believe that the events which came rushing one after another were anything but disastrous. On the national level alone they could hardly be worse. The echoes of the Treaty at Yalta among the Big Three (President Roosevelt, Prime Minister Churchill, and the General Secretary of the Communist Party of the Soviet Union, Stalin) effectively ended pious hopes that the Allies "would do something" and that the obvious designs on Poland by her eastern neighbor would be restrained.[57] The experiences of Poles under the Soviet occupation, the revelations of Katyn, and the present hostility of Stalin's government towards the Polish underground authorities were too real and too ominous to permit anyone to entertain hopes that the present occupation would be better than the previous one. What complicated the matter was the attitude in the West, where Poland's allies insisted on calling Stalin 'a dear and democratic friend' and appealing to Poles in Poland to establish friendly and workable relations with this new power, which was now in possession of the entire country.

---

[57] "...the Home Army [the A.K.] broken by the Warsaw Rising... the hopes [of Poles] brutally dashed by the Yalta agreement... the whole Poland prostrate beneath the Soviet Army ... Poland had been handed to them [Soviets] on a platter [by the Allies]," Davies *The Heart of Europe*, p. 97. Similar comments in Korbonski, *Fighting Warsaw*, p. 422. Seton-Watson, *The East European Revolution*, p. 157.

In the village, the only two-story building (which before the war had hosted a school and later became the Secret State Police headquarters) now sported a red flag and was the seat of the infamous People's Commissariat for Internal Affairs, the Soviet security police. "They are no better than the Nazis and I believe that they may be even more difficult to deal with," was the comment of Ewa, a young Jewish teacher who had been sheltered by the village community and had recently befriended Nina. "More difficult because, in the first place, they are now fighting the Nazis and who remembers that only several years ago they supported Hitler's war effort and were friends of Germany? Secondly, the West is tired of the war and grateful for the Russian war effort – Russia being more important than Poland. Thirdly, because even among our own people there may be some who believe that fighting for independence is at present hopeless. Can you blame them? Any reasonable person would agree that Poles cannot start a new war with the Soviet Union. That would be national suicide. Some people believe that 'if you cannot fight them, join them.' Is it really the worst we can do? I myself am inclined that way."

Nina's vehement denials that embracing the enemy is never an option, were supported by her Warsaw friends. Still, coming events confirmed the pessimistic views of the Jewish girl. The Soviets, ignoring the fact that units of the AK had greatly facilitated the Red Army's advance in Poland by their valiant struggle with the Germans, proceeded to demand that the remaining Underground forces come into the open. In this, Stalin was strongly supported by the Allies. Some Polish units heeded that 'friendly' request, but when they did so they were surrounded by Soviet forces, disarmed and arrested. No appeals to the now emasculated Polish government in London[58] or to the British and American governments brought any improvement in the situation. The final blow came when sixteen members of the Underground – under the pressure of the Allies – agreed to reveal themselves to the Soviets in order to negotiate with them. They were arrested, tried on charges of treason and condemned. The condition, however, specified that the AK leadership were to be given an opportunity to fly to London first, in order to talk to the Polish and British authorities prior to negotiations. This request was accepted by all concerned and assurances were given by Soviet authorities of safe passage to England. However, instead of taking them to London, the Soviet plane took them to Moscow. There they were tried on charges of treason and condemned to many years of hard labor.[59]

---

[58] Western allies withdrew their recognition of the Polish Government in Exile and gave it to the Soviet-sponsored communist government in Poland in the summer of 1945.

[59] Among others, Seton-Watson, *The East European Revolution*, pp. 117-118.

"So we cannot do anything now," Nina exclaimed in desperation. "God, what a fate! All this effort for six years only to be saddled with another enemy, and this one favored by our friends." But she was by now too mature not to understand the Real Politik (practical politics) of the time. In the present situation, there was little the Poles could do. Their government had lost its support, for the Allies shifted their recognition to the Soviet sponsored "Government of National Unity" in Lublin. Poland was devastated, with her capital in ruins and another contingent of foreign troops on her soil.

Among the older females, the reaction to such bad news was varied. Mrs. Nowak looked totally disheartened and depressed. Violetta cried her eyes out, supported in her grief by her new friend, a Russian woman, whose opinion of the Soviet government, and particularly of the People's Commissariat for Internal Affairs, was almost identical to theirs. The woman, was in fact one of Violetta's customers who appeared ready to offer her friendship to Poles. Born after the revolution and raised in a collective, she retained memories of a father who had vanished into a Soviet prison, a mother dying of appendicitis with no help available, harsh working conditions, abject poverty, and all-embracing fear of the authorities. Her husband, an army officer, shared her views but "would rather die that reveal them to anyone but me." Less timid than her spouse, Tatiana was wont, when excited, to curse the entire Soviet leadership, which she did in a hushed voice but with a towering passion.

Violetta's new friend paid her first visit one evening, dressed in a nightgown purchased in the market place which she had mistaken for evening wear. Even after six years of war, Poland appeared to the Soviet people as a land of plenty and they did their best to acquire clothes, watches, and other consumer goods with shouts of wonder and delight. Tatiana loved to draw out Violetta's reminiscences about pre-war Poland, particularly if they related to a sophisticated life style. Still, her visits were not very frequent. She openly stated that much as she wanted to be with them often, she knew that frequent meetings "were not good for you and not good for me either. We are under a bell jar, darlings. We are being watched and frequent unauthorized get-togethers are not appreciated by the party."

After an initial wary period, Nina came to believe that the woman was obviously sincere and friendly. Her influence among Violetta's Russian customers contributed to giving the latter recognition as an expert on good manners, feminine sophistication and everything Tatiana considered to fall under the general heading of 'culture.' Since only Nina had studied the Russian language in the underground courses, she was often called upon to interpret more difficult phrases. At times she was driven to helpless laughter trying to translate Violetta's lady-like sentimental reflections and the far less elegant, but highly colorful, epithets used by temperamental Tatiana once she got going about life in her native country.

"I feel the need," Nina noted on one occasion when a small group including Father Surman and the girl Frania gathered around supplies of bread and cherry tea provided by Violetta, "to know what to think about our people who say that we have to accommodate the new order. I wish to know what developments in our country we should accept and which we should reject. I think that it would do us good, every one of us, to know. I mean, we must be clear in our minds what our perception of our national situation is. For instance, how do we approach the present government that calls itself Polish but is working under the Soviets? Are they traitors? Frania agrees with me," she added, although she noticed anxiety on Mrs. Nowak's face and apprehension on Violetta's.

"I am all for calling them traitors," exclaimed the girl. The priest suggested that they should first examine the meaning of "traitor," "collaborator," and "quisling" (derived from the name of a Norwegian official holding high rank under the Nazis).

"It is easy," argued Frania. "It is a person who works with the enemy to fill his own pockets or to get other privileges, for instance a high position and influence." There was general agreement, with the acknowledgment that although no Pole had ever achieved honors under the Nazis, there might have been some who were bribed to collaborate. "We must not forget, however," the priest remarked, "that some people might have been forced to go with the Germans either by being blackmailed (either you report on your neighbors, or you and your family will suffer) or by being deprived of badly needed products, i.e., penicillin for a sick child. Would such people be called traitors?"

A discussion ensued in which there occurred a split among the assembled, the younger portion of whom insisted on the label "traitors" for the people giving in to threats of violence, while the elder appeared to see extenuating circumstances in such cases. "I would condemn such behavior but would not punish such a person with severity, although I know that the AK did," declared Mrs. Nowak while Violetta embarked on vague musings regarding a civilizing influence to which the Russians, if not the Germans, would eventually succumb.

Sensing irritation in the two girls, the priest started talking about the theme of revenge, now called for by many Poles, but especially the new "Polish" government. Forbidden for obvious reasons to talk about Soviet crimes, the members of this puppet government exceeded even the most zealous members of the AK in their inflammatory remarks calling for retribution on the Germans. Father Surman was strongly against such sentiments. "Once the monsters have been defeated, they are no longer so terrible and we should feel for their human condition. Did you see the German wounded? Did you hear what happened in Dresden?[60] Since when is a collective punishment justified? A harsh campaign of revenge should not appeal to us."

---

[60]   In the Spring of 1945, the allied bombers turned the city of Dresden into a fireball.

Against the backdrop of all those events, a persistent fear for her mother, her sisters, and Myszka remained with her day and night. There was no news from them and, with the advance of the Red Army, communication with the German side did not exist. Was it possible, Nina asked herself, that Mother and Krysia were now in Germany, looking for Kinga and Myszka among the inhabitants of the Nazi camps? The last address of the two girls was within Germany proper, but Germany was slowly approaching capitulation and rumor had it that some of the prisoners had been released by their captors with the view of finding favor with the Allies. At the same time, a different unconfirmed report suggested that systematic liquidation of prisoners was being carried out by Nazi prison guards before the oncoming date of surrender. As all of Poland was now under Soviet rule and the Red Army was pushing toward Berlin, it was possible that Mrs. Ilski was now living under Soviet occupation. Whether it was better or worse, Nina did not know. The Germans, close to defeat and eager to favorably impress the western allies, might perhaps have shown some leniency toward her family, but the Russians? Nina well remembered the priest's remark that her parents could not be safe in Soviet-occupied Poland.

Jozek's Reappearance

It was a great joy to her when one day, a clean, well dressed and self-confident Jozek appeared at their door with a huge bag of provisions. Both Mrs. Nowak and Violetta shed tears of joy and Nina herself was deeply moved. "I never thought that I would see you again! Even when we heard that you were all right, I did not believe it." she whispered.

"Things being the way they are, one had to adjust to circumstances over which one had no control," Jozek declared, after being hugged and kissed by the three females. "My present position as a vice director of the Robertow Orphanage," he continued, speaking through his nose as he used to do when trying to impress his listeners, "my present position requires unrelenting attention to every small detail concerning the administration of the institution. Sisters Cecilia, Teresa and I share the burden of leadership in this case," he continued. "Still, due to the sensitive nature of their vocation, I alone deal with the Russkies. They have not yet heard of Jesus, you know, but that may change. Indeed it may," he added importantly. Watching the respectful demeanor of Violetta, who now seemed to regard Jozek in the new role of a missionary, Nina experienced a sudden desire to giggle. Good old Jozek, same as always! At least he did not suggest that it was he alone who would bring Christianity to the Soviet Union!

Meanwhile, satisfied with the impression he had made, Jozek was embarking on further details about his contacts with the Russians. "So far, they have left us in peace, but I know that they have an eye on the building we occupy at present. If they order us to leave, where would we go with fifty-five orphans, all below ten?"

"God save us," groaned Violetta. "Is it worse for those children than under the Nazis?"

"It is and it isn't," was the reply. "It is worse because the supplies are hard to get, the country now being throughly devastated. But it is also better because the Russkies are more inclined toward transactions of various kinds and it is easier now to obtain necessary papers and to get permission to do things that were previously considered illegal, if you know how to approach them. Of course, one has to exert himself, but so far I have not found obstacles that are overwhelming." Both Mrs. Nowak and Violetta proclaimed their boundless trust in his ability to provide for the orphans. Even Nina looked at him now with appreciation. The biblical command "feed the hungry" never seemed more appropriate than now. Also, Jozek's free conversation with Tatiana in Russian convinced her that German was not the only language he was able to pick up on his own without regular schooling. "He is without a doubt the best possible vice director, or whatever title he has, for that orphanage, despite the fact that he is only sixteen." Nina admitted to herself. "And the nuns know it. Living by his wits is nothing new to him, and it comes in handy now when he has all those children under his care. Obviously, no nun could hope to deal effectively with the present authorities." Then she suddenly realized that taking Jozek out of Poland might be far more complicated than she had thought. "So how can we pressure him to leave Poland with us, should the scenario described by Father Surman materialize, and my parents have to emigrate? What would happened to all those children if he were to leave?"

"Far be it from me to extol the military ethos," Jozek began again and his audience knew from experience that the tone of voice and the boy's face indicated that they were about to be treated to an expression of sentiment that Jozek held to be as profound as it was well-articulated. "For being a civilian, I am a firm supporter of democratic values which cannot but prevail in a civilized society. But this Red Army of theirs is simply a disgrace! Pieces of rope instead of leather straps! Burst boots and torn coats! Dirty, unkempt, smelly (this last word was uttered in an undertone), and I have heard from a reliable source that the aroma is due to the use of an anti-lice potion popular among the warriors. And the way they march! I do not believe that there is an army in the world, including the Nazis, which would not be ashamed to look the way our Russian 'liberators' do."

"It may not be their fault entirely," interrupted Mrs. Nowak. "How can they be clean if they do not have soap? Do you remember, Nina, how your aunt wrote to you from Siberia saying that there was simply no way to obtain soap or any other cleaning materials. As to the matches, they had to resort to the Crusoe method of rubbing pieces of wood together." Fastidious Violetta, although she shuddered on hearing about the lice cream, came to the lady's aid. "Absolutely true, as I have found from my clientele," she asserted. "It was only last week that a Russian client, Ludmila, told me that her mother – who is with her children in Russia – suffered a nervous breakdown after she accidentally broke a needle. Apparently there are no needles in the Soviet Union. They are commodities which you could hardly manufacture at home and are impossible to replace. Ludmila," she continued heatedly, "is trying to be clean, although the only soap she possesses has been purchased in Poland and she uses it very sparingly, always afraid that the supplies will not last. In the USSR, consumer goods appear seldom and their availability lasts a very short time. Of course, she believes that these conditions prevail elsewhere."

"You know," mused Nina, "after what happened to us, I did not think that I could be surprised by anything. But this new reality with the bedraggled people who have descended on us in order, as they say, to 'liberate us,' is simply bizarre. If anybody needs to be liberated it is they!"

"Well," remarked the teacher Ewa, who had just entered the house and stood unnoticed at the door. "What their government is doing to them is their business! The question that concerns us is what they are going to do to our country. Though the army is hardly Stalin's forte (please remember that he may keep the military units underbudgeted for fear of revolution), there is no doubt that the police network is very efficient indeed and that is their strength. Police and terror tactics. So are they as bad as the Nazis for us? This is the question we have to answer for ourselves."

"As bad as," whispered Nina, and Jozek agreed with her. But the ladies were not so sure.

"Their police may be as bad as the Nazis' but their civilian population, the wives of the military and the children, are not," Violetta said pleadingly. "Can you imagine what their lives are like in that police state? Apart from political oppression there is a terrible lack of basic consumers goods, like soap, toothpaste, diapers! As to the finer things in life, such as coiffures… they can only dream of them."

"If this is so, then why don't they revolt?" asked Nina. "Why do they follow orders like sheep? Why did they allow their government to sign the treaty with Hitler and to invade us? What did your Ludmila do when that happened?"

"She might not have been able to do anything," Mrs. Nowak interfered soothingly. "You have to remember, Nina, that the police terror in that country is simply unimaginable to us, considering that it is their own government which is doing it. But the question that is at present before us is this: is our eastern neighbor as bent on our extinction as the western? Our leaders must be trying to settle this question in an effort to make an assessment for which the whole nation is waiting."

"But if they are as bad as the Nazis, how can we oppose this new threat after all the devastation?" Nina cried in despair. "Who can fight the Soviets, now the darlings of the West? The remnants of the AK? A civilian population which has been decimated? Maybe we should commit collective suicide."

Here, Jozek, hitherto rather subdued, assumed his previous pose. As usual, Nina was never quite sure if the arguments he issued arose from deep conviction or if his inclination to make an impression prompted the rebuttal. In this case, the presence of two visitors, the clergyman and Ewa, might have leant weight to his eloquence. In preparation, Jozek cleared his throat twice and proceeded.

"I cannot even imagine," he announced loftily, "What Mother Superior would say to the kind of diatribe we have just been exposed to! Shame on you, Nina, for contemplating a coward's way out of our dilemma! Don't you know that many people were in circumstances far worse than ours? Consider, for example, Saint Bonifacia…"

"OK, OK, spare us your lecturing," Nina interrupted impatiently. "You should have known that I did not really mean what I said about suicide. Of course we are more important to Poland alive than dead. However, we have to decide how to treat this new menace. Do we accept them conditionally or reject them outright, as we did the Germans?"

"We accept them conditionally, for to start a full-scale conflict would be sheer madness," the priest noted quietly. "We should, however, preserve and consolidate the strength that is left to us for future use. For the time being, let's give this new Polish/Soviet government the benefit of the doubt. Perhaps even there, there might be individuals who joined the new regime in hopes of softening harsh policies and helping the people. Let's wait and see."

"'To strike when the great clock of history strikes,' as our great poet Mickiewicz put it," Jozek added with pathos.

"I do not believe that Mickiewicz ever said anything of the sort, although he was thinking about an uprising when he organized the Polish legions in Turkey," Eva corrected him good-naturedly. "However, I, for one, vote for Father's suggestion to consolidate and wait. What do you say ladies?" The two ladies agreed with alacrity that to grab weapons (here Mrs. Nowak looked uneasily at the kitchen knife) and attack the Soviet forces would be premature.

"Perhaps," Violetta whispered in ingratiating tones, "we could meanwhile conquer them on the field of Haute Couture, of sophistication and refinement? I wholeheartedly offer my humble services for this purpose." The reactions to this surprising comment were varied. The priest smiled kindly, Mrs. Nowak proceeded to busy herself with tea things and Nina, Jozek, and Ewa, now united, excused themselves hurriedly and collapsed in convulsive giggles outside the door

Good and Bad News

On May 1, 1945, the Soviets announced their entry into Berlin. This brought to Nina's mind distant pre-war scenes when young Polish soldiers, eager to show their vigor in the approaching war, parted with 'Do widzenia w Berlinie' (See you in Berlin). How utterly ridiculous it sounded today after all those staggering defeats! But at least the war was now formally over and Germany was divided into occupation zones, some of them controlled by Western Allies.

Then came news, from a letter written to the priest by one of his parishioners, that Mrs. Ilski and Krysia were indeed in the British zone of Germany, reunited with their husband and father, respectively. Father Surman brought this wonderful news late at night inducing Violeta to scream her head off, convinced that burglars were after her beauty products. Although the hand-delivered note was short and cryptic, it did state that one Captain Ilski, staying in the British military hospital in Winsen near Hamburg (the sender worked in the hospital as an orderly), was in touch with his wife and daughter who had just arrived at the Polish refugee camp. This event opened a whole new vista before Nina. Father was alive, although still under medical care. He would recover, for, as Jozek indelicately put it, "people either recover from wounds, or die, but no one keeps dying for months." Mother and Krysia were now re-united with him in a free part of Europe, among friends. Although Nina blamed the British and Americans for the Treaty of Yalta, even she could not consider them foes; mistaken, for certain, blundering and misjudging, yes, but not foes. Yet a persistent anxiety penetrated all the euphoria brought by the note from Germany. There was still no news about her sister and friend. She told herself not to dwell on it, for everybody knew that at that particular time, lack of information regarding relatives incarcerated in Nazi camps was not unusual. Not all of them were liberated by the Allies, and even if they were, the very task of collecting data about the inhabitants was a monumental one which would presumably take months. As the International Red Cross was now involved in putting together lists of survivors, the information would be available before long. At least this was what the press of the new government proclaimed, so there was still hope.

The next week dashed her hopes completely. It became a nightmare which was to stay with her all her life. It happened one morning, when she made ready to start knitting a new sweater for one of Violetta's Russian women (a skill that she had acquired under the direction of Mrs. Nowak). She entered the kitchen silently and caught Mrs. Nowak listening in obvious agitation to a tearful Violetta. Upon seeing Nina, the latter stood for a while as if paralyzed and then fled, murmuring something about her client. "She knows something bad," flashed through Nina's mind, "it is either father, or Kinga, or perhaps..." Fear, the like of which she had not experienced even during the bombing, made her speechless for a minute or two. Then, trying to control her voice, she turned to a pale Mrs. Nowak and said, "Please tell me what you heard. I am an adult, I am healthy, do not try to spare me. Who is it?" Mrs. Nowak's reply was far from reassuring, although she tried to present the information she had received as nothing more than a rumor, a probably unsubstantiated rumor. There were people in the village, she reported without further procrastination, who on visiting the newly established Red Cross facility situated in the neighboring town, apparently saw a list of the people liberated by the Western allies from the camp which contained the two girls. "And," whispered Nina through a tight throat, "they are not on it?"

"The name of Myszka Stein/Ilski is on it, but Kinga's name is not," stammered Mrs. Nowak. "This is what Ewa told Violetta, after warning her not to tell you, as it may all be a mistake, and…"

"I am going to see the list," interrupted Nina, grabbing her jacket. "I am going to see for myself." At the same time, she was conscious of only one thought, "why should Myszka escape when my sister…"

The priest met her in the yard. His demeanor verified the news. "There is no need for you to go there, my dear," he said, embracing her. "It is true that your sister's name is not on the list. Perhaps it is a mistake, perhaps she is not among the survivors. When you remember how many people died in recent years, you must realize that it is almost impossible to see any Polish family intact. And look at the Jewish people."

"But I want to know how she died," cried Nina wildly. "Was she shot, was she hanged, was she guillotined?[61] How?" The priest explained that in that particular camp there had raged a typhoid epidemic and many slave laborers succumbed to the disease. "She was not alone," he tried to console all three sobbing females later in the afternoon. "There was her friend Myszka, and other Poles. What you should do now is to use the channels made available by the Red Cross to contact your parents. The moment you verify their address, you must be prepared for a new venture in your life, for which I believe your health is now adequate. You must conserve your strength, physical and mental, and go to them as soon as possible while it is still warm, before October. They are your family and you should be with them. The Soviets have not yet managed to control the traffic of the refugees, and although they have put check points on the roads and there are patrols guarding the borders between zones, those problems are not insurmountable. There is no other way for you, Nina. We know now

---

[61] Some young Polish girls were guillotined by the Nazis. See Stefania Tokarska-Kaszubow, *Nenia* (girl's name), Poznan, Wydawnictwo Miejskie, c. 1999; also Irene Tomaszewski, ed. *I am First a Human Being: The Prison Letters of Krystyna Wituska*, Montreal, Quebec: Vehicule Press, 1998.

for sure that your parents, especially your mother, must not come back to today's Poland. Unbelievable though it would seem to our western allies, these AK activists who greatly contributed to the victory over Germany are, in fact, on the Soviet enemy list. There is evidence of it. Those lucky enough to find themselves in areas under British or American control must stay there."

"But for how long?" moaned Mrs. Nowak. "How long will they be separated from their families in Poland?"

"Nobody knows how long," sighed the clergyman. There was a long pause during which Violetta retrieved a handkerchief the size of a bed sheet from her bag and offered to share it with the rest of the company.

Nina sat speechless during this exchange, stunned by what it implied. She wondered how in all her expectations regarding her future life, she had never envisioned anything like this, for she was always trusting that things would get better, that they would all be reunited in Poland! How totally naive she must have been! So now she was to put away her grief and undertake a journey which might end badly, for she had no illusions about Soviet border guards! Her family was now banished from their native country, perhaps forever. She had to bid farewell to her friends here, whom she had come to love dearly, who had tended her with such devotion during her illness. Yet, not for a moment did she consider any alternative. "Of course, I will go," she said calmly. "I will go as soon as I can. I will have to have road maps and things." But the two ladies had by now sufficiently recovered to voice their arguments. For a young girl, a teenager, who had just recovered from a very serious illness to undertake a journey to the British zone of Germany, to cross a frontier alone, unprotected, this did not bear thinking about! "You cannot be serious, Father!" Mrs. Nowak burst out. Violetta, after agreeing wholeheartedly that the project was utter folly, suddenly changed sides and offered to accompany Nina herself, as "a mature woman of the world." She also made dark hints about the weapon she was ready to obtain from her Russian friends to defend Nina and herself on the way. It was Tatiana who was to teach her how to use it.

Without paying much attention to the two ladies, the priest continued. "Of course Nina will not go alone. Jozek has volunteered to go with you and, knowing him, he is actually looking forward to it. He will get the use of my bicycle and we will get another bike for Nina. I will give you the address of a party who conducts passages from the Soviet to the British parts of Germany. It is better that you two pose as brother and sister and use Jozek's surname instead of your own as a precaution. He already has new papers and will explain, if called upon, that you have not had a chance to obtain yours. With all due respect to your ingenuity Nina," he continued in a lighter tone. "I believe that Jozek's eloquence and shrewdness will be a great asset on the way. He can hardly find an equal among the Russians."

The Journey
Getting Ready

"But what about the dear boy?" asked Mrs. Nowak after digesting the information. "Is he going to stay with Nina's family in Germany?" Here Father Surman revealed he had already discussed with Jozek the possibility of such a development. The teenager was to escort Nina to her parents and come back. In no way could he be persuaded to leave his post at the orphanage. Also, things being what they were, there would be no problem with his coming back to a Soviet occupation area. "The Russians allow free entrance to their zone to anyone who has the inclination," he said. "There are even trains going from western Poland toward the East, just not many going the other way. What the Soviets do not like is that there are (not surprisingly) many people who desperately want to get to zones under British, American, or French control. The Soviets make it difficult to reach such areas without violating the law."

"Absolutely true!" cried Violetta. "Tatiana told me the very thing herself. Entry to the Soviet Union is wide, very wide," here Violetta spread her hands, "but the exit from the USSR is very narrow," her hands came close together, leaving only a little space between them.

Nina listened to all this in silence. "I may consider allowing Jozek to accompany me, but only if he never leaves the Soviet side of the border," she announced with determination. "I will not expose him to the danger of crossing a border guarded by Soviet troops. No way."

There were no comments from her listeners for a long time, although accusatory glances from the two ladies appeared to undermine the priest's confidence. "It is much too early to decide anything now," he finally said. "The first priority is to receive a message from Nina's parents. I will try again to get in touch with Frank, the guide. He is a solid, reliable man and I hear that he conducts groups through those crossings routinely, though illegally, I am afraid. Nina will be safe with him. But all this is putting the cart before the horse. That journey cannot be undertaken after September. Any later will prove far too rainy for such a project." The two ladies brightened up perceptibly. "Even September is sometimes rainy," noted Mrs. Nowak, while Violetta entertained them with a vivid description of Septembers so cold that they necessitated the wearing of woolen underwear (which she coyly referred to as *dessous*) and made plans for even short trips out of the question.

The priest had suggested that she would be wise to pose as Jozek's sister during the journey. She tried to visualize the moment when she would have to reply 'Nina Poplawski' instead of 'Nina Ilski' when asked for her name. She asked Jozek to show her the papers which he had wisely accumulated for himself when dealing with the Russian authorities on behalf of the orphanage. It was quite an impressive array, including identity cards in German and Russian, forms in Russian and Polish testifying to his position in the orphanage, and a certificate in Russian attesting to his proficiency as a truck driver. The latter had a recent stamp. As exclamations surfaced regarding his ability to drive and his age, he calmly explained that a genuine Russian document describing an employable skill of a non-political nature could come in handy on their forthcoming journey. He was quite blasé about the fact that he had never driven even a car, let alone a truck. "You remember Hans, my German friend? On one occasion, some three years ago, he gave me a lift in the truck and I observed what he did. It did not seem too complicated. In fact it was a 'piece of cake,'" he said, proudly demonstrating his command of colloquial English, which he was now studying with Ewa's help. "The certificate cost me a bottle of vodka, purchased in the village," he continued. "I admit I did it with the greatest reluctance, for I abhor the stuff. But Ivan, the guy in the Soviet military vehicles office, would not give me the certificate otherwise. Beggars cannot be choosers," he concluded, savoring the impression his English made on Violetta.

Nina did not think that this was the time or place to object to his obviously far-fetched optimism. If driving a truck, which neither of them had ever attempted to do, was what Jozek envisioned, she thought with resignation, then they would attempt it. What worried her now was the fact that she had no documents other than the old German Karte which would be accepted by the Russians as legitimate. There were efforts by the occupying force to register the village people, but it was mostly ignored. Would all those papers Jozek so proudly exhibited cover her as his sister? He thought such concerns were of little significance. "You can just say that you lost your i.d. in the public bath," he suggested "and they will believe you. Yuri told me that there are public baths in most Soviet communities because this is what their constitution prescribes. However, there are no towels or soap and the water is seldom plentiful or heated. What is worse is that many of those establishments are controlled by thieves who get your clothes before you enter the bath and claim not to have received them when you demand them back. Or they put your things in a 'delouser' to kill the vermin. But the delouser shrinks all your things terribly and you cannot wear them. Consequence in both cases: you run home naked! Shivering! Without your wallet, naturally."

All this took some time to sink in. Before Nina decided to reject the account as sheer fantasy, Violetta came to Jozek's aid testifying that theft in public baths was indeed a common occurrence in the USSR. "That is why they, poor dears, often prefer to keep their clothes with them when bathing, although the things would, of course, get wet and be very uncomfortable to put on afterwards. Tatiana was quite angry about it."

While trying to familiarize herself with her new identity, Nina became acquainted with Jozek's family secrets. "Poplawski is not the name I had when I was born," Jozek confided in her one evening when, in the absence of the two ladies, they were poring over the map on which Ewa had drawn their route west. "I only acquired it later."

"Oh," remarked Nina cautiously, aware that there was some mystery concerning the boy's father. This, however, proved not the be a factor in the name change. "Mom was not happy with her name," mused Jozek stretching luxuriously in the armchair recently acquired by Violetta. "Being an actress, she considered it inappropriate. Neither did she appreciate her first name, although grandma believed it to be romantic. By the time of my arrival, mom decided to change them both, but did not act on this decision for several years."

"So you were not Poplawski?"

"Not originally. My initial surname was 'Ryj' (Snout)," Jozek informed Nina. "Inoffensive in itself, but not what you would call melodious."

"I agree," admitted the girl, telling herself that if she started giggling now, she would lose his friendship forever.

"As to the first name, it was Roza (Rose), which I believe was enough to counteract the prosaic meaning of the surname. However, mom thought, and possibly rightly, that 'Roza' and 'Ryj' (rose and snout) do not go together too well."

"She was right," murmured Nina unsteadily, busying herself with the tea things.

"That is how Papeta Poplawski was born," came next.

"But what kind of a name is Papeta?" exclaimed Nina incautiously. The moment the question was out she regretted it.

"As good a name as Nina," retorted the boy. "And why not? Mom was always interested in clothes, and there were certain materials before the war which were called 'pepita.' Mom liked both the fashion and the name. To be on the safe side, in order to avoid possible manufacturer jealousy, she decided to call herself Papeta, which I believe is even nicer."

Nina remained silent. After pouring himself a mug of cherry tea, Jozek embarked on further confidences. "The name 'Poplawski' came by accident," he continued. "It happened one night, when I fell asleep in the cemetery where I played. Being a very caring parent," here the boy's eyes filled with tears, "mom looked for me even though she could have left me there for the night. She found me. The name on the grave on which I slept was Poplawski. She liked the name and so did I."

"But," remarked Nina overwhelmed by all this information, "weren't there, well… legal problems?"

It was revealed by Jozek that soon after the cemetery decision, his mother had approached the orphanage and explained that her son prevented her from achieving self-fulfillment. "I understand it," Jozek said defensively, "A talented actress such as she could not be encumbered by a kid of six. You cannot quarrel with that, can you?"

Nina murmured her consent although she was overwhelmed by sudden anger at that silly, selfish woman, who could give up her little son, a son like Jozek, for self-fulfillment! She forced herself to listen quietly to the sequel of the boy's separation from his parent. She learned that the orphanage agreed to accept the child and to arrange for his papers under the name of Jozef Poplawski, name of mother Papeta, name of father 'Antoni.' ("He could have been Antoni, for all I know, but mom was not certain," was Jozek's comment.) During the next four years, up to the time of her death in a bus accident, his mother managed three visits and three postcards. Her son kept the cards wrapped in pink tissue paper bound with a pink ribbon.

"It is a wonder," Nina could not help but remark, "that your mother agreed to give you such a name as Jozef. Didn't she consider it lacking in melodiousness?"

"Oh, that! It was my grandma Ryj," came the eager reply. "She was Jozefa and prevailed on mom to call me after her. Actually, mom wanted to name me Litavor."

"The name of Mickiewicz's protagonist in *Grazyna*!" exclaimed Ewa, coming into the room with a new roll of maps. "Are you both reading Mickiewicz?"

"Not right now. I was simply telling Nina that my mother wanted to call me Litavor," explained Jozek. "She was a very educated person," he added proudly.

It was shortly afterwards that the news came from Krysia. On seeing her writing on the envelope, Nina wondered with apprehension whether it contained another piece of bad news. Are all three of them all right? Had they heard anything of Kinga? Were they in touch with Myszka? Finally, after crossing herself and saying a short prayer to St. Jude, she opened the letter. It was a short sorrowful note. They knew about Kinga. They were told that both she and Myszka succumbed to typhoid at the same time, but only Myszka recovered. "It had something to do with Kinga's weak heart, apparently," Krysia wrote. The effect on the parents was devastating. "Father sits in the hospital chair for hours without saying anything. His one eye is still bad, so he cannot read. Mother did not eat anything for at least a week, that is, up to the time of Myszka's arrival. Yes, Myszka is with us, but how changed! She is totally bald and looks like a skeleton. Myszka also has problems. She has frequent fainting fits, always succeeded by sobbing, and only mother can calm her down. I am glad that she is with us. This at least relieves me from caring for mother, because mother is taking care of Myszka and I can give some time to reading to father," Krysia wrote.

"That's it," Nina said. "I will leave as soon as possible."

The next few weeks embroiled the whole household in feverish activity. The older ladies threw themselves into the preparation of foodstuffs, blankets, and other paraphernalia that they considered indispensable for the journey. In between such activities, they severely censored the priest for suggestions that endangered the two 'infants.' This was inevitably followed by the employment of some of the huge handkerchiefs favored by Violetta. Jozek was seldom seen during this time. He was overwhelmed with preparation for the operation of the orphanage in his absence. The priest's bicycle was duly refurbished and the search continued for a woman's cycle of strength and durability. Because of lack of success in this endeavor, all cycles found being pronounced not sturdy enough, it was decided that Nina would also ride a man's cycle. It was a big, strong bicycle that was one day triumphantly produced by Violetta. "Without telling Ludmila about your intended trip, my dear, I purchased the machine from her after I found from Mr. Zawada, the blacksmith, that although it was of Soviet manufacture it was very solid indeed. In fact, Ludmila told me that it used to carry her husband (a large man) plus two boys, one on his back and another in front, to their school in another village and back. He is now being promoted, and hopes to get a motorcycle, so the bicycle is not wanted. Don't you worry your darling little head about the cost. I can easily pay for it with my hairdressing sessions."

"But how can I return the machine to you?" asked Nina.

"You do not return it at all," was the eager reply. "You give it to somebody who is in need. God knows there are many such people around nowadays."

That night Nina could not sleep. "I am leaving, perhaps forever, people that I have come to love, people who are so good, so noble," she thought. "Mrs. Nowak, Violetta, Jozek and others also: Ewa, Father Surman, Frania. If I were a poet, I would say that a part of my heart will stay here, that by wrenching myself from them and from the country where I belong, I shall never be complete. Also, by going away, I automatically preclude the possibility of ever doing anything for them, and for others. As Professor Rylski (not his real name) told us in those secret courses, 'after the war, Poland will need a lot of building up. But you cannot do it staying abroad.'"

It appeared that, slowly but surely, some good things started to happen. Ewa got admitted to the graduate school of Warsaw University, which had opened near the ruins immediately after the end of the war. The university announced grants and accommodation for the students in the new academic year. A group of old professors started remedial courses for the youth whose studies had been interrupted by the war. The Polish puppet government, perhaps in order to get a modicum of support from the population, was actively trying to help widows and orphans. Jozek's orphanage got assistance that even several months earlier would have been beyond their expectations. Polish officials took positions in the village and the uniformed Russians became far less visible. Hospitals and medical centers were being opened and although they were still woefully inadequate, the sick and the handicapped now had at least a place to turn to. There was a heart-warming resolve to rebuild Warsaw, to have it exactly as it used to be!

Of course the immediately apparent sore point in the situation was the new police force, called the Militia. The people did not trust them and carefully avoided their headquarters. It was believed that the new security people were tightly controlled by the communist political agency, that they were under the thumb of "the Party." "Whatever they are," Frania said, "they are certainly not 'ours.'" And the community agreed.

Meanwhile, many of 'ours' who had gained the love and admiration of the nation were still hiding in the forests, refusing to accept the new reality, even engaging in sporadic battles with Soviet forces. Exposed to hunger and cold, devastated physically and psychologically, they were desperately hoping that the allies, whose soldiers had for years been their comrades in arms, would see the USSR for what it really was and create a new political situation in which they, the Poles, could again be useful. "Realization of the Soviet menace must penetrate the western governments' consciousness," they kept telling themselves. "They must come to see the truth eventually. When that happens, they will find us here, ready, embracing with gratitude any sacrifices the new struggle will demand from us."

Finally, the two teenagers were ready. Blankets, in addition to raincoats and sweaters, were attached at the back of each saddle. Two rucksacks were packed 'scientifically' with: changes of underwear, canned food and biscuits, small jars with tea, sugar and coffee. Nina's backpack had a small kettle and Jozek's a small pot. A large umbrella was affixed to the frame of Nina's machine. They both were to wear slacks, cotton jackets over shirts and heavy shoes. Money, which by some miracle was obtained for them by means of common clerical and secular endeavors, they secured in the belts created for that purpose by Mrs. Nowak.

Long sessions with the priest and Ewa told them how they were to proceed. Ewa, who had graduated from the Warsaw University's geography department before the war, took them step-by-step through the territory they were to cross. "Going northwest (roughly in the direction of Hamburg, ditto the British zone), you cross terrain good for bicycling, a plain without large forests (one exception, Puszcza Kampinowska, could be avoided), hills or marshes," she lectured. "You have to memorize the route, for I do not think you should have my detailed map on you. Officially you are going to Stettin, which, with other counties to the west of the old Polish border, is now to be under the administration of the Polish Socialist Government. We hear that an office for refugees has just opened in the city. I estimate that your journey will take five days. I will leave it to Jozek to explain why you want to go northwest, should you be asked. However, since thousands of people are moving around due to the eastern Polish territories being incorporated into the Soviet Union, it is unlikely that you will be interrogated while in Poland. Still, you have to remember that there are allegedly some nineteen Soviet divisions in our country and they often behave like an occupying force. I would advise you to avoid large towns. Villages are less damaged and the people there more stable emotionally. They will help you to find shelter for the night and to acquire food. Frankly, you both look too innocent for anyone to suspect you of anything bad."

The session with Father Surman proved to be less comfortable. The priest was now by no means sure that he had done right in encouraging Nina to join her family. "I will say mass for you every morning for a week," he promised in a shaky voice. "I trust in God's mercy, but I know I will not have a good night's sleep until I hear of your safe arrival. Please be careful when proclaiming your identity. Remember that you are brother and sister. I am especially concerned with the part of your journey beyond the river Oder on the way toward Hamburg. There is no doubt that the Soviet checkpoints are more frequent there and the border is heavily guarded, for we know that many Germans try to get to the allies, including, as I have heard, the soldiers who have not yet surrendered to the Russians. For heaven's sake, avoid any contact with them. New complications may occur because you are Polish. Of course, I do not mean that all Germans... of course I don't. I told you the name of the place where you are to meet the people who are expecting you, and I gave you the password. Never, never let it be heard by others. I hold you to your promise that in case of any difficulty, you will both come back to us without hesitation. No silly heroics, please. Remember you swore to it. Jozek, don't think that you should return my bicycle. I do not really need it. Walking is good for me, I shall enjoy walking."

To mitigate any ill effects of Jozek's absence, both Mrs. Nowak and Violetta were to move to the orphanage to help the nuns. The evening before their departure, Violetta pulled Nina into her room. Shutting the door behind her, she proceeded to tell the girl that she, Violetta, was ready to go to any lengths to take care of Mrs. Nowak, the priest, Ewa, and others, including the children in the orphanage. "I will manage, do not worry. I will defend them," she assured her again and again, ceremoniously putting two fingers on the English grammar book which she had mistaken for a bible.

The Witch

With a heavy heart Nina prepared for the journey. Notwithstanding her height, she soon found that the bicycle she was to ride had been made for a person much larger than she and that her feet could barely reach the pedals. Beside her, Jozek, despite his recent growth spurt, looked diminutive on the priest's bicycle. Both of them said good-bye to their village friends in front of the church. A tearful parting with Mrs. Nowak, Violetta, Father Surman, and Ewa took place in the house.

Despite their recent emotional experiences, both of them perked up considerably when the village was left far behind and the unspoiled early autumn landscape unfolded before them. Old scout songs from her school days came back to Nina. She started to sing and was soon joined by Jozek in his occasionally cracking baritone. The long forgotten words sometimes escaped them, but they invented their own, each attempting to surpass the other in poetic creativity. They were happy. "I must really be quite heartless to feel like this," she thought with compunction. "I have suffered a grievous loss recently, the loss of a sister. I don't know if the rest of my family is all right. I have left my dear friends behind, have undertaken a journey Violetta compared to a voyage through a sea of sharks! Yet I enjoy singing and laughing with Jozek. At my age, too! Shame on me!" But the lightheartedness did not leave her. There was a challenge before them, an adventure full of risks, but they had two good bicycles, some food and some money; above all, they had youth. They felt equal to it.

The evening caught them close to a dilapidated village, where a majority of the houses had barred windows and doors. The rest of the homes were guarded by ferocious looking dogs. Nobody seemed interested in discovering why the animals were barking. "This is the proverbial hospitality of the countryside that Ewa mentioned," grumbled Jozek. "Why is it that the people with whom we lived were different?"

"This village must have suffered some terrible atrocities," Nina guessed. "At least two-thirds of the houses are uninhabited. Did you see the burnt buildings behind the school?" Yet, despite the unprepossessing look of the village, spending the night in the open held little appeal for them, especially since dark clouds began gathering in the east, a menacing sign of the coming storm.

They arrived at the other side of the village, where there stood a small house in whose window appeared a meager light. Immediately, a huge Doberman began barking furiously, straining at the rope around its neck. They stood there for several minutes when, finally, responding to Nina's energetic calls and the unceasing noise made by the animal, the door opened slightly and an old, bedraggled woman put her head cautiously out. "We are traveling to find our parents," shouted Nina over the ferocious barking. "We have nowhere to spend the night. Could you help us, please?" This simple request appeared to be unintelligible to the woman. She leaned out further scanning the scene behind them intently and after a while made as if to shut the door again. "Please," persisted Nina, "can we spend the night in your barn? We mean no harm." It had an unforeseen effect. This time, the witch, as she appeared to them, emerged with a rifle under her arm. "Nobody is going to take me alive," she screeched, "not like those women and children dragged away by the uniformed devils. Try to come near me and I'll set Burek on you and I will shoot you too. Just try me!"

"Let's go away," urged Jozek, but Nina did not move. The realization that she had just seen the consequence of some terrible war tragedy dawned on her.[62] "We are no black devils," she shouted. "Look at us! Do we look like them?" At this moment lighting illuminated the whole scene, showing the two youngsters attempting to cover their heads with their jackets. "The barn is open," came a distinctly reluctant grumble. "But remember, nobody, but nobody, enters my house."

"Ask her to calm down this horrible dog, and where we can find water," urged Jozek, by now convinced that he should leave the initiative to Nina. The request was made. After a long time, the witch spoke a few words to Burek, who immediately stopped his noise and withdrew into his doghouse with the expression of a dog fully aware that it had done its duty. From the indistinct muttering of his owner, they learned that they could stay a short time in the barn, provided that they did not assume the appearance of devils.

In the ever increasing rain, both of them moved speedily toward the building close by. It was indeed a barn, whose interior contained a tractor and bales of hay. It was dark and stuffy inside, but warm. "Better than nothing," commented Jozek. "At least it is dry. But we still need water. You make the beds out of hay and blankets and I will go and investigate the terrain. Can you give me that paper bag our sandwiches were wrapped in?"

"What for?" asked Nina. "What do you need the bag for? Going out when nature calls is one thing, but shuffling through somebody's yard in the rain, at night, is another. You want water? I already put two of our pots out, we shall have plenty of rain water." Jozek, however, was not compliant. When the rain eased a little, he ventured out and came after a while bearing a bag bursting with apples. "I noticed the orchard close by when we were on the road. I think it belongs to the

---

62   "The well known fate of the one Bohemian village of Lidice, where 143 men were murdered by a Nazi reprisal order, was visited on Poland not once, but hundreds of times over," Davies, *The Heart of Poland*, p. 70.

witch. I only gathered the ones that were on the ground and were sure to spoil in the rain. No Christian would blame me for it," he explained. Although somewhat dubious about the extent of the old woman's Christian feelings, Nina joyfully consented to consume the fruit.

"Get up," whispered Jozek early the next morning. "Have some bread and an apple and let's be on our way. Who knows what kinds of ideas that mad woman concocted during the night. We are not psychiatrists, trained to deal with something like this, are we? Let's go."

"But it is still frightfully early, and I did not sleep very well," complained his partner. "It is not true that hay is soft. It is very hard. I suspect there are fleas here. Something kept biting me all night."

"It may be worse for us when she realizes that we are apple eating devils," was the reply. "The apples were hers! That will add insult to injury! Let's go." Convinced of the truth of this, Nina splashed water over her face and hands and followed Jozek out of the barn. Only Burek, now in a tolerant mood, said good-bye, giving them two wags of his tail.

Back in Rawa, before leaving on the journey, they agreed that Nina would deal with the Polish authorities and Jozek would tackle the Russians. But the first test involving a Soviet road-block failed before it began. Seeing a group of high-ranking Russian officers from a distance, Nina panicked and, without waiting to consult Jozek, made a sharp turn toward the trees at the side of the road. Behind them, and behind a ditch, a path led into a forest. Having gone through the ditch at high speed, splashing water on all sides, she reached the path and, pedaling furiously, disappeared from view. Jozek caught up with her a mile or so later, looking disgusted. "There is something to be said for avoiding the Soviet road checks, but circumspection should always prevail over raw emotion," he lectured. "To wildly enter an unknown forest (I believe it is called Puscza Kampiniowska) at twilight, to put miles between oneself and the road is not what a reasonable human being should attempt. What is the result? We are now stuck, with night fast approaching. If we were to go back, it would look very suspicious to the Russians. They saw your performance and are probably thinking that you hid something in the forest. On the other hand, we cannot go forward. The path is practically invisible now."

"I know, I know," Nina was now penitent. "I should not have panicked, but when I saw that komandier (commandant) with a chest full of medals, I thought he must be from the People's Commissariat for Internal Affairs. You were scared also, do not deny it."

"To be perfectly candid, I must admit that I experienced a touch of uneasiness," Jozek said graciously. "But it was not the medals, it was the car, 'Volga.' This vehicle is used only by the elite and members of the People's Commissariat for Internal Affairs are the elite." They both agreed that it was better to be safe than sorry and that there was a silver lining: neither the Germans nor the Russians liked to penetrate into the forests of Poland.

Lesniczowka

There was nothing for it but to spread blankets on the moss and try to sleep. After a snack of bread and cheese, the sandwiches having been eaten long since and the canned food being considered inviolate except in high emergencies, they lay down. "Just as well that Ewa lent me her compass," Jozek murmured. "Tomorrow, we will go northwest and regain the road again beyond the check point." Unused to sleeping in the open, Nina stayed awake. Various scenes from her childhood, the war, the Uprising, rose before her eyes. By now, it was pitch black, with a starry sky above them. There was a constant rustling around them and the wind made the tree branches assume fantastic shapes. "I have no reason to be afraid of nature," she told herself. "The trees, the noises, all this is nature, benign, not like people. It is only a matter of self-control." But when she was just on the point of sleep, Jozek's strained voice jerked her wide awake. "What is it?" she whispered, sitting up.

"I only asked if, during your geography talks with Ewa, she mentioned the existence of wolves in this part of Poland," he said in a low voice. "She never talked about wolves," Nina asserted vigorously, although she was aware that the subject simply had never come up. "Why?"

"I was simply speculating about a wide range of possibilities," Jozek sounded now like his normal self. "It seems to me that I heard something like howling, far away, a minute or so ago. Just as a point of interest, have you ever climbed a tree?"

"What nonsense," she exclaimed, "climbing trees, indeed! What tree will you pick, I wonder?"

Conceding that he had already given some thought to the question, he switched on his torch and its light fell on a large oak tree with low branches about eight feet from the ground. "In case of an emergency, we'll put your bicycle against that tree, climb it, and pull ourselves up," he remarked in a conversational tone. "It should not be difficult for you Nina, for your long legs would put any giraffe to shame, and..." The rest of the sentence was lost on the girl, who suddenly experienced a sense of extreme alertness. She now heard howling, and it was by no means very distant. "Good God," she whispered. "Could it be a dog?"

"Unlikely in the extreme. A dog in the forest? There was no human habitation in this forest as far as we could see. Maybe it is a jackal?" saying this, Jozek was already tugging her bicycle to the tree. "I do not think that there are many jackals in Poland, and they usually do not attack people unless... they are very hungry," she added weakly. Then came a noise identified by them as 'something' tearing through the bushes. Both sprang to the tree. "You first. Climb on the first branch and give me a hand," he whispered. Nina managed the task without great difficulty, but when she extended her hand downwards, it did not meet Jozek's. Ready to jump down to help him in his struggle against 'something,' she heard his chuckling and soon after that, a joyous yelping. "It is a dog, and a friendly one," Jozek's laughing voice came to her from the darkness. "He is happy to be with us." Indeed, in the light of the torch, a big yellow dog was now clearly visible, wagging his tail and inspecting their backpacks. After reaching the ground, Nina joined Jozek in patting and caressing the animal. It was very thin and muddy, a sign of its having been in the open a long time. Although they had promised themselves that their cans of meat could only be used in a great emergency, Nina handed the boy the can opener and he proceeded to render accessible the contents of one can. The dog received the greater portion of the goulash, plus a biscuit. They divided the rest between themselves. "He has a collar around his neck," Jozek, who was now sharing the blanket with the animal, announced. "Do you think that he could lead us to somebody's house?"

"If there is a house he lived in, why did he leave? Is it because his owner was taken away?" Among these speculations she fell asleep to the tune of Jozek's breathing and the animal's light snoring. Fear had no access to her now.

What awaited them the next day was tedious trekking through the forest following the dog, who appeared confident of the direction he was taking but remained unaware of the problems his new friends had with their bicycles in the thick undergrowth. After an hour or so, they saw a clearing in the woods, only to find that the animal, obviously thirsty, had led them to a small lake. "What now?" they asked. Obviously relieved of thirst and inclined to be frisky, the dog rushed ahead of them through the undergrowth and vanished. Not for long, however. He came back and barked at them with impatience. "I hope that this dog is not another specimen of madness, this time in animal form," groaned Nina. "I do not think that I could go on in this fashion much longer. We are now completely lost."

"He should realize that leading us astray is not the best way to repay us for the goulash and biscuits," Jozek continued in the similar vein. "What if he thinks that it is some kind of a game?" But another quarter of a mile showed how baseless their suspicions were. Before them, in a meadow, stood a white house of nice proportions surrounded by smaller buildings, a vegetable garden, and fruit trees. There was no sign of life, however, and the doors to the stable, the chicken coop, and the barn were wide open. "This is what used to be called a 'Lesniczowka' or a forester's house," Nina recollected from her pre-war trips. "I visited one of them with my scout group. It is obviously empty. I wonder what happened to the owners?" Cautiously, accompanied by the dog, they approached the door and knocked. There was no answer. Encouraged by the animal's scratching at the door, they opened it, and entered a hall.

There were several doors leading to different rooms, all opened except the one toward the back. One of the rooms proved to be a bright spacious kitchen with a modern range and a variety of utensils neatly stacked on the counter. Another was a bedroom with a complete bedroom suite. The third was an impressive library with books filling the shelves from floor to ceiling and a grand piano. "It is a beautiful and a very well-kept home," breathed Nina. "Like the houses we used to see before all this ugliness started." Meanwhile, Jozek opened the closed door and stood for a while as if transfixed. On a sofa, under the window, lay the body of an elderly woman, or rather a female skeleton. Her eyes were closed, and there was no sign of life. "She must be dead," whispered Nina, but the more perceptive Jozek shook his head. "She is still breathing," he noted. At that moment they were joined by the dog, who, having jumped on the sofa, started to lick the emaciated hands of the woman. Her eyes, suddenly alive, focused on the two newcomers and the pale lips formed a question with difficulty. "Who are you?" After a stunned silence, Nina managed to introduce herself and Jozek. "But why are you laying here, are you ill?" she asked. "I am not ill," answered the weak voice with determination. "I just want to die. Leave me in peace, but otherwise do what you want."

They withdrew from the room silently, taking the dog with them, and closing the door. Only then a heated exchange took place. "She wants to die from starvation," whispered Jozek, horrified. "She let all the animals out, including the dog, to find food for themselves in the forest."

"There is plenty of food in the house, sacks of flour and cereal, also fresh vegetables in the garden," sighed Nina. "So this is an entirely voluntary food deprivation. What do we do?" But it was not difficult to know what should be done. The answer was plain. They had to convince the lady to give up the idea of dying. As she told them to do what they wanted, they decided to stay in the house for a day or two, longer if necessary, and to cook nourishing meals for the lady, the dog – and themselves. Hadn't she given them carte blanche? The most important thing, of course, was to save her, and seeing how terribly emaciated she was, it did not apear to be an easy task.

"If Sister Hermencia were here," was Jozek's nostalgic remark, "she would know what to cook for such a person. She would have her on her feet again in no time."

"Not if there was a determined refusal to eat," Nina retorted. "Though I am not equal to your Sister Hermencia in my culinary talents, I can cook pretty well too. Mrs. Nowak said so."

Jozek was conciliatory. "OK, no offence intended. Think about those nourishing messes Violetta prepared for you when you were sick, and try something like that. Of course, we will have to convince her to eat it. Do you think she wants to die because of Poland's fate?"

"She wants to die because something happened to her children," she said with conviction, "and I am going to find out what."

But when they looked into the foods available, they found that many of the ingredients normally used for the sickroom were missing. There were no eggs, milk, or butter. In the cool cellar they found dog food, salted pork, some herbs, mushrooms, and rice. Their own 'iron rations,' the greasy cans of goulash which the dog and they had enjoyed so much in the forest, were obviously not suitable. They had one can of condensed milk, however, and with plenty of fresh vegetables, and a sliver or so of salted pork for flavor, Nina thought she can acquit herself without dishonor. She suggested to Jozek that she would make a minestrone soup of fresh vegetables, mushrooms for the aroma, a handful of rice, and a tablespoon full of condensed milk. Salt and pepper were to be used in moderation.

From the very beginning of the cooking, Jozek stayed in the kitchen as a consultant and the dog in the character of an interested observer. What a pleasure it was for them, after three days of rough picnicking, to be able to have a large clean kitchen at their disposal! Jozek brought wonderful vegetables from the garden: potatoes, onions, carrots, spinach, and green beans. There was all this bounty available, not counting the fruit in the orchard! He informed Nina that in the barn there was cattle fodder in huge quantities and that the whole household had been well-managed, buildings taken care of, garden and orchard obviously attended until recently. They wondered who it was who did all this, surely not the old lady! What had happened to the animals?

But there was no time for such speculations, for every time Nina tip-toed to the sick room, the patient looked worse. She kept her eyes closed, did not react to the girl's gentle questions, seemed to be lethargic. Having no experience with sick people, Nina had no idea if those symptoms indicated approaching death and felt panic rising within her whenever she approached the sofa. Jozek, however, was more optimistic. "I saw people, who after spending months in a concentration camp, had been smuggled out by the Resistence and stayed hidden in Sister Cecilia's convent before its liquidation. They looked and behaved in every way like this lady. But under the nun's care, they fully recovered."

"But they had a will to live, and she doesn't," Nina pointed out. This of course was the problem.

They agreed that it would be Nina's task to induce their hostess to eat the soup, or at least drink some tea, which Jozek prepared with a drop of condensed milk and some honey he had found in the cupboard. "When one of our orphans got sick, Sister Teresa fed her with a teaspoon every half an hour or so," he told the girl. "Cheer up, Nina! We have faced other challenges before. This is different and more difficult, but it is not unbeatable."

With a beating heart, Nina entered the sickroom bearing a steaming bowl of the soup and a glass of tea on a tray. Sitting herself on a chair close to the sofa she asked for the lady's permission to feed her soup. "Just open your mouth a little," she begged. The patient opened her startlingly blue eyes and looked surprised. "But I do not want to eat," she whispered. "I want to die."

"Why?" stammered the girl. Slowly, interrupted with persistent coughing, the sad story unfolded. Mrs. Latowicz, that was the lady's name, lost her husband at the beginning of the war. He was executed because he knew the forest and the Germans looked at forests as a potential hiding place for the resistance. One of her sons died as a soldier of the AK, another vanished in a Soviet 'gulag' (Soviet concentration camp). The third child, Irena, stayed with her throughout the war, but last month went to the city to inquire if the just-opened public library would be interested in purchasing her books. Irena was a writer specializing in literature for children and she knew that the new library was to replace an old collection which had been destroyed. She went on horseback, promising to return the same day. But a day passed, then a week, then a month. News on the radio mentioned a speech by a Comrade Vyshynski, a member of the Soviet government. It indicated that diligence was necessary to protect the working people from the 'insidious and harmful influence of Polish writers.' "I tried to tell myself that although under Soviet influence, our country was still Poland, that it figured on the map as such," sighed the lady. "But after this long agonizing waiting, I could not be optimistic. I believe that she is in a Soviet prison, as is my younger son. So I now have nothing to live for," she concluded, obviously exhausted.

Nina listened with tears in her eyes. "I am a religious person," added Mrs. Latowicz with an effort. "I did not want to commit an outright suicide, but food deprivation is nothing radical ..." Her attention turned now to Nina. "My dear, have I upset you?" she breathed, putting her skeletal hand on the girl's sleeve. "I did not mean..." But by now Nina was sobbing uncontrollably. "There have been too many deaths," she cried wildly. "My grandma died, my sister died, our relative in Siberia died, and others, many others. If this goes on, who is going to stay? Who is going to take care of Jozek's orphans?"

"What orphans?" whispered the patient, but Nina, busy trying to stem the flood of tears, was too far gone to answer. There was a long silence, the lady lying motionless with closed eyes. Then the blue eyes looked at Nina with a kind of sad resignation. "Give me some of your soup, my dear," she heard the faint voice say, and her heart jumped for joy.

So it was a victory! "Four spoonfuls of soup and a cup of your tea," she reported to Jozek. "I believe that if I get her to eat even a little, very often, as did Sister Teresa with the orphan, she may recover. God, what an achievement we may pull off yet." Discounting his role in all this, Jozek was generous in his praise. "Apart from the psychology which you obviously used very successfully," he said, "that concoction you created was first class, absolutely first class. It was not really a soup, I would be inclined to call it a stew in its more condensed form. Sister Hermencia herself would not have been ashamed of it!" The dog, whose name was Lolek (it was painted on the doghouse) was apparently of a similar opinion. He preferred the soup to his old, dull dog food.

The night brought a well-deserved sleep. After being induced to eat more of the soup and drink several cups of tea (Nina had the patient drink a little every half an hour or so until late, modeling herself on the orphanage), Mrs. Latowicz slept peacefully. The newcomers spent a luxurious night in separate rooms, after a thorough wash in the scullery where a primitive but useful arrangement had been made for bathing. They were both awakened very early in the morning by the joyful barking of Lolek. They ran to the window facing the yard and saw a black and white cow slowly crossing the yard, with the dog joyfully dancing around her. When, after hurriedly dressing, they rushed out, the cow was still there in the middle of the yard glaring at Lolek with disapproval. After staying there a while and meditating, she looked back, uttered a gentle moo and took a few steps toward the barn, only to stop and look back again. Suddenly, from the bushes outside, a small black head peeped out. Soon the body of a tiny black calf emerged, shy and trembling, on thin legs. Jozek grabbed the collar of Lolek and the three of them stood there motionless. Encouraged by repeated moos, the bovine offspring staggered toward its parent. When both of them were finally in the barn, Jozek released the dog. "I will go and feed them and you let Mrs. L. know," he cried excitedly. "Imagine, she came back! There are now two of them!" Nina sped to the sickroom. Mrs. Latowicz lay there looking no better, although her color may have improved a little. On hearing the news, a spark of interest came to her eyes. "So Zhenia has calved, already? Nina, my dear, in the cellar there are salt cones specially prepared for cows. She used to love them. Both of them will need a lot of fluids."

"So do you," the girl firmly responded. "You simply cannot die now, you cannot. What would happened to Zhenia and the little one in winter if they have no home?"

Later, Nina confided to Jozek her ambitious plan to milk the cow. "I have used the only can of condensed milk we had, and there is no more. Yet milk is vital for the patient. Do you think Zhenia will allow me to milk her?" Jozek was skeptical, convinced that the cow would view milking as an effort to deprive her offspring of nourishment. "She will show you her attitude, see if she doesn't," he hinted darkly. "Did you see her horns?" But although the first effort could not be seen as an unmitigated success, a pint or so of milk was obtained and Nina brought it triumphantly to the kitchen. She served porridge with milk for lunch. They ate it at the table in the sickroom, with Mrs. L. reclining in the armchair, swathed in shawls. She listened intently to their reminiscences and actually smiled at Nina's vivid description of Zhenia's antics during the milking.

That afternoon, two grey hens arrived, enthusiastically greeted by Lolek. They positioned themselves in front of the chicken coop expectantly, and received their feed from Jozek with gratitude. "The animals are coming back," he said with great satisfaction. That night, accompanied by Lolek, they went around the household looking at it with pride. The yard was swept clean, the ripe vegetables gathered and stored in the cellar. Above all, the animals were fed and happy. They looked into the barn where the cow was resting with the calf at her side. Mrs. L had urged them to give a name to the little female and they called her Carlotta, because of her 'Spanish look' (Jozek's choice). In the chicken house, the two hens slept on the raft designated for them and there was every hope that the ducks (there used to be three) would also come home before bad weather, as well as a tabby cat, Fibcio. Lolek now had an old pillow in his dog house, of which he was very possessive. "When I am old and rich," mused Jozek, "I will have a house like this with animals, in a forest, far from the war."

"Perhaps there won't be any war when we get old," Nina remarked. "Perhaps the world will be at peace."

"Perhaps," he sighed longingly.

Despite the joy of Mrs. L.'s recovery and their satisfying work, the question of the length of their stay weighed heavily on their minds. Nina was eager to see her family as soon as possible, Jozek had his duties to attend to back in Rembertow. Yet, although Mrs. L. was no longer at death's door, her health was still in a precarious state. More important, psychological and mental well-being had not yet been achieved. She was always loving to them; she even smiled when they described their exploits. But whenever their future plans were mentioned, she invariably grew very quiet. "What if she descends into depression again after we leave?" Nina asked anxiously. "We cannot leave now without endangering her," Jozek was positive. "Let's wait another couple of days. Perhaps something will come up."

And something did come up.

The unusually loud barking of Lolek, reaching a high hysterical pitch, drew them out of doors on the next day. "Another animal is returning," they thought. At first they did not see anything unusual, but a couple of minutes later, a rhythmical thumping could be heard. "It is a horse, galloping," Jozek remarked. "It must be one of hers." The horse emerged, sweating and breathing heavily, coming to a sudden stop in the yard. But it was not alone. On it sat a young woman in a very dishevelled state, her long hair flying around her head, her face beetroot red. She had on a peculiar jacket reminiscent of the Red Army uniform, a rather short dilapidated scarlet skirt, and on her feet were dirty men's 'valonki' (woolen boots worn in Russia on snow) several sizes too large. She tumbled from the horse and then stood motionless regarding them with terrified eyes. "Mother?" She stammered. "All right, Mrs. Latowicz is all right," they cried in unison. Upon hearing this, the newcomer rushed toward the house, fell over the dog whose emotional greeting was partly directed toward the horse, gathered herself up and after gasping by way of explanation, "have just come from jail," disappeared behind the door.

"This must be the writer," concluded Jozek. "Those types, you know, tend to be somewhat eccentric, immensely sensitive, unusual in behavior, inclined toward unorthodox clothing. It is said that the literary muse..."

"Oh, stop it, Jozek," interrupted Nina. "Didn't she said that she just left jail?"

"Even in jail, nobody wears valonki in September," was the sobering comment.

While Jozek took the horse to the stable to relieve him of the saddle and give the animal water and fodder, Nina slipped into the kitchen, pondering on the forthcoming dinner. It had to be extra good. Washing the vegetables and preparing noodles she heard fragments of the conversation between mother and daughter. Phrases like 'guardian angels,' 'wonderful young people,' 'incredibly mature' made her both highly gratified and ashamed. She knew they did not deserve such praise. When after an hour or so both women emerged, Nina could not but be amazed by the change in the older lady's appearance. Although still painfully thin, she was rejuvenated and fully alert. Gone also were shawls and old slippers. She had on an elegant dressing gown and Nina saw traces of powder on her cheeks. Her daughter, although not improved much in appearance (she wore the same shocking clothes she had arrived in), won their hearts with her straightforwardness. After embracing each one in turn, she made a very short speech. "I know very well what we owe you, but I am not going to say it," she cried. "If it weren't for you both, my mom... but I am not going to think about it! Now may I help you in whatever you are doing? I am at your service!" She suddenly remembered to take care of the horse, but when Jozek told her it had been done, she decided to explain the costume at which both young people looked with wonder.

'Independent' Judiciary

"We got word of impending release this morning, after five weeks of sitting in that filthy jail," she began. "But that beast of a guard, threatened that he would hold us there longer if I did not sell him my boots (remember my black riding boots, mom?). I did not know if he could actually do it, but in cases like this, when every minute counts, you do not want to risk anything, do you? The reason for the transaction he proposed was personal and romantic. His girlfriend, Natasha, did not want to marry him (and who can blame her!). He thought that my boots would bring her to the altar, or rather to the place where the Soviets marry. So I sold him the footwear for this horrible jacket and he threw old valonki into the bargain since I had no other shoes. The skirt, however, came from a different source, namely from the cell next to us," she continued looking ruefully at the scarlet horror. "The girl there, Nyura, fancied my riding breeches to such an extent that she was willing to go to any lengths, including her clothing and the food ration, to obtain them. 'Let me have those breeches, dushenka (dear soul),' she begged. 'They are going to send me back to Rostov and release me there, since I am not political. These breeches, they will be much in demand, the People's Commissariat for Internal Affairs ladies will be ready to fight like mad over them. I need money for my little sister, dushenka...' Well, I let her have them, but of course I had to have something to put on. This red skirt was the only thing fairly respectable, others were far too short and slit at the side up to the waist."

"Please wash and change into something less eccentric," smiled her mother. "Dispose of those things you are wearing now as soon as possible."

When, after some time, Irena reappeared, this time in her old clothes, her help in the kitchen was not needed. Nina, with the loyal support of Jozek, managed to produce a dinner 'fit for a queen' as she herself called it. There was a fluffy omelet (the grey hens obliged with spotted eggs) with creamed spinach for the invalid. For general consumption, a casserole of mixed vegetables, onions, potatoes, turnip, beans, carrots, celery, and cauliflower was served with fried noodles. There was barszcz, a clear beetroot soup with mushrooms. For people with a sweet tooth, Jozek prepared pancakes with honey. "You wizards," cried Irena. "How on earth did you manage all this?"

During the happy dinner hour, Irena recalled her experiences: "After it was announced on the radio that the Polish local government was taking over the administration of the city from the hands of the Soviets, I decided to take the books I had written to the county library, to find if they might be interested in purchasing them. The previous children's collection was burnt during the bombing. I took Sivek (the horse) with me, for to cross this forest on foot takes an awful lot of time. By the way, Sivek and Zhenia stayed with us during the war. On the two occasions when the Germans penetrated here, they were on the meadow and escaped seizure. Our other horses and two cows were appropriated. Well, I rode Sivek to the town hall and asked the clerk where I could talk to the major, a Polish man newly installed. She ushered me into his office. I cannot say I was impressed by him. A short man with an unfriendly manner and shifty eyes, he informed me that the present is not a good time for reading novels. When I explained that my books are for children, for whom the present 'Polish' government pretends to care, he referred me to the library budget committee. It consisted of a renowned poet, an elementary school teacher who had come from a village on horseback, and one person from the Ministry of Education. The latter had a manifestly foreign accent. He was very ill at ease and complained that it was too hot in the room, no air to 'dychac' (the Russian word for breathing). Well, it was during this meeting in the library, when we were discussing the budget for the new building, that we were all arrested by the Soviet police. This is how far you can trust the national news about a Polish administration replacing the Soviet. We, the two women, were sitting in a jail with a Russian guard behind the door and Russian women of unsavory reputation in the next cell. The poet was put in another part of the jail, sharing his fate with criminals." Here Irena stopped to refresh herself with tea. "We were totally flabbergasted, of course. After a week of that, during which any communication with family was forbidden, we got news that we would be tried for 'deviations.' What the word implied, we did not know. The teacher was worried about her father abroad, who was probably considered 'polluted' by capitalism and I about my two brothers because of their AK involvement, for as you know the Polish anti-Nazi resistance is being viewed as hostile by the Soviets. We were both getting desperate to find way to notify our family members, I my mother, she her children. There was no way, of course, to find what had happened to our horses, which had been left tied to the library fence.

During that time the Russian soldiers guarding the jail were not too bad. Some of them liked to talk with us, when the officer was not there. They told us about the villages they came from. Spending time in prison seemed to be a normal occurrence there, and political deviation apparently very common. When asked about our trial, they just looked surprised. 'I believe our constitution guarantees speedy trial, but it does not mean that it is so,' one of them explained. 'It is up to THEM when you get your day in court.' The word 'them,' that is, the political authority, figured prominently in the discussions. All in all, I do not think that they wished us ill. If it were up to them, their country would never have invaded us."

"Then the trial came and we were informed about the charges against us. All three of us (the poet was also there, although the government representative was not) were accused of 'influencing other people through writing and teaching in a manner hostile to the USSR.' Before we even attempted to object, two prosecuting attorneys in uniform appeared and we were ordered to be silent. The poet, looking much the worse for wear after a four-week sojourn in captivity, was the first in the dock. Being told that he spread capitalist propaganda through his poems, the man objected vigorously. 'I am not interested in politics and my writings do not include it,' he said.

'Is that so?' queried an unpleasant red haired lieutenant. 'So what do you write about?'

'Oh, about nature, landscapes, the sea,' replied the defendant.

'And ships?'

'Yes, occasionally, tall ships.'

'Occasionally tall ships, low ships, perhaps submarines. The question is WHOSE?' thundered the prosecutor, putting his face close to the defendant.

Shocked and confused, the man leaned back. 'What country do the ships you described belonged to, eh? Skazhy. (Speak.),' persisted the officer.

'I do not know,' stammered the prisoner. 'He does not know,' repeated the prosecutor sarcastically, looking around the hall. 'Vot imienno. On nye znayut. (Exactly. He does not know.) Did all of you hear it? He does not know what country owned the fleet he wrote about, he does not know what flag was there. This is enough to make one laugh.' After roaring with laughter, he sat down triumphantly. 'No further questions,' he announced. The matter was clinched.

After watching all this," Irena was saying, "I thought I knew why there were literally millions in Soviet prisons and I lost all hope. My case and the teacher's were to come up after a few minutes' adjournment, which in reality lasted over two hours. During that time, all three of us descended into the depths of despair. The fact that salvation would come, and in the figure of this unimpressive major with shifty eyes, would have seemed in those hours of hopelessness impossible. But this is just what happened!

When the court assembled again, the judge was so tipsy that he had mistook Zuzia (the teacher) for some unknown Svetlana Rozkova, who had been accused of bringing death to three of her husbands, (fortunately not party members, but still human beings and Soviet citizens, according to the judge). After being told by the female prosecutor that ours was a different, potentially even more significant case, the judge announced that he had no time for details, for there were important official matters awaiting his attention.

The shifty-eyed major had the good luck to approach the bench then. To see a Pole, however unprepossessing, take our side before this Soviet court in his role of 'native element,' was wonderful. He was stupendous! Never will I distrust shifty eyes again! It is only now that I fully appreciate the skill of his defense and blame myself for previously criticizing him to the other two. Having asked for and received permission to speak, the major embarked on the most effective defense that could be had under the circumstances! He attempted to stress the 'friendship angle' between the Soviet and Polish governments. I remember only fragments of that speech, delivered in relatively good Russian. 'Here you are, our friends, our comrades in the war with the fascists, but how do you show your friendship?'

he cried. 'Not only do you detain our people (innocent though they are) but, what is more important, you strip our stores bare and,' he raised his voice in moral indignation, 'you drink our vodka!' I believe that these last words made the intended impression, for the judge looked, if not exactly guilty, at least willing to consider the right and wrong of the accusation. After a short nap, he awoke with the verdict: 'Dismiss the case.' The previous prosecutor was luckily not there, but the woman who was to interrogate me and the teacher, raised some objections. 'The case had not been heard, yet,' she said. 'You be quiet,' he snapped. 'Dismissed! All three of them. I have to have time to rest, don't I?!' After saying some obligatory phrases praising the Soviet government which 'looked on Poland with friendly eyes' and mentioning 'peace-loving comrade Stalin,' he staggered from the room supported by the clerk. For a minute or two we could not believe this wonderful escape.

Outside, we met with the major. He waved away our thanks and advised us to leave town immediately after reporting back to jail and getting our dismissal formally acknowledged. 'Otherwise, you will be hunted as refugees from justice,' he warned, seeing our reluctance to go there. He also mentioned to the teacher and me that our horses were in the Red Army compound and gave us a note to reclaim them. 'It may help, it may not,' he remarked. 'Won't hurt to try. Good luck.'"

Irena stopped again to attend to her mother, who during the narration had her head in her hands.

"This is how I got my clothes," she was now eager to conclude. "After we bribed the soldier to let us go (although we were pronounced innocent of 'deviation,' he claimed he could hold us in jail longer) we said good-bye to the poet. Then Zuzia (the teacher) and I repaired to the horse compound. There was a moment of anxiety when the soldier rejected the major's note as not valid. But Zuzia, without objecting, took her medallion off her neck and offered it to him 'for your mother or grandmother.' After a reverent inspection of St. Jude's features, he let us collect our horses, gave us two old saddles (ours were gone) and I galloped home and so did she. End of story."

Another Parting

It was then their turn to recall their past experiences. It was after midnight when they all finally bid one another good-night. Nothing was said about their departure, Irena insisting that they should not 'spoil things' by doing so. Yet departure was inevitable. They were warmly urged to stay another week or so, but had to refuse. Nina thought that two days after the happy re-union was a suitable time for saying good-byes and Jozek agreed.

The day before their departure, they spent hours discussing Jozek's proposed arrival in the company of orphans, who would stay in Lesniczowka recuperating, playing, and reading. Mrs. Latowicz mentioned the possibility of having two sets of siblings in rotation. "There is certainly food, we have plenty of vegetables, flour, and rice. There is a small village not far from here, where Irena can always get more. With Zhenia and the hens, they could have a healthy diet. I am already looking forward to seeing Jozek again. Not that I would not miss you terribly, my darling girl... But it makes no sense to be sentimental. Family you have, and to family you must go," the lady said firmly.

The last evening was to be spent in a manner they had not foreseen. On that occasion Mrs. Lachowicz laughingly announced "a musical evening, like those we used to have in the old times." She told them that Irena, before she became a writer, had been thinking about a singing career. They were invited by both ladies to be their audience, for Mrs. Latowicz was now strong enough to accompany her daughter on the piano. Of course, the young people agreed, although without enthusiasm. "Musical evening? It sounds too old fashioned," thought Nina, and from Jozek's expression she deduced similar sentiments. But when the performance began, it was a revelation of such power that it hit them with unexpected force. Irena sang arias from internationally known operas, and she sang beautifully. Unexposed for years to any serious music, this new experience gave them a delight that was at the same time painful, uplifting, and soulful. A world, up to now unknown, was opening to them. A world where borders, sectarian differences, conflicts had no place. "This, this is the most important division between human beings, and animals. This creativity is surely divine," Nina thought, and Jozek told himself that if he ever lost faith, he would turn to music to regain it.

At the same time, a terrible feeling of deprivation overwhelmed them and this feeling again was new. Questions like "Why did we lose our country? Why have so many people died? Where is international justice?" were replaced by others. "Why had Polish youth been prevented by the war from listening to such wonderful music, from enjoying moments of bliss? Why were other people prevented also?" Moved to tears of which they were heartily ashamed, they became fully aware of another, hitherto unknown loss that fate had meted out to them. To their own surprise, they did not mind at all, when together with Polish, French, and English songs, Irena included German and Russian, for they were delightful also. "Is it possible that the power, the tremendous impact music can have, may further brotherhood and prevent wars?" the girl thought. She promised herself to ask Jozek if such an idea seemed crazy to him.

Although Irena, mindful of the major's warnings, did not want to be seen in the town for a while, she insisted on taking them to the suburbs by way of a shortcut, using a path suitable for bicycles. She also gave them the address of a man who, as she'd heard, had business connections in Stettin and was known to make trips there in his lorry. Utilizing the lorry would shorten their journey immeasurably. "I do not know this man, but mom says that he comes from an honest family," Irena advised. "I propose that all three of us go to town: I on Sivek, you on bicycles, and I will just point out the road to his house. I shall do it from the safety of the forest, so there will be no danger to me at all. But for heaven's sake, do not confide in this man or anybody you meet. Remember what happened to me!"

Thus they parted again from friends who had become very dear to them in a relatively short time. Irena equipped them for the road with sandwiches, while her mother found some ripe apples. They now had clean clothes and spare pairs of clean underwear in their knapsacks. All in all, it was as if they had again lived through the loving preparations made for them by their old friends just over a week ago.

After taking a warm leave of the ladies, and almost equally warm leave of the animals, they got on their bicycles and followed Irena, who rode Sivek. Nina could not but compare the latter's appearance now, in a smart riding habit (second best) with how she had looked on her arrival to Lesniczowka. It was not only the clothes that made the difference! Then, Irena personified extreme anxiety. Now, she looked hopeful and content.

Their trip was indeed quite short. Irena had been brought up in the forest and it had no secrets from her. On its outskirts, close to the main road, they insisted on saying good-bye. But before they left her, Irena had sketched for them a short map of their way to the man with the lorry, whose name was Edek. They were to keep their new identity (brother and sister, name of Poplawski, looking for parents in Stettin) when meeting him. They had to avoid any unnecessary contacts on the road.

We Are All Comrades

Their first impression of the owner of the lorry was far from positive. Although not shifty eyed as was Irena's major, Edek shared with the latter a definite lack of charm. Morose and suspicious, he asked them many seemingly irrelevant questions. When he finally agreed to take them and their machines to Stettin, he quoted an exorbitant price. After a short consultation they agreed to it, for to speed up their journey was now a priority. Pocketing one half of the fare, the man informed them that the Soviet road blocks would become very frequent on the way west, and that their journey would by no means be pleasant. "You will sit on the truck in the open. Don't expect me to take you into the cab when it rains. And let's understand one thing," he added in a loud voice. "I am not going to stick my neck out for anybody! Clear?"

"Rotten manners on top of extortion," was Jozek's comment on the side.

Having been told to stack up their bicycles on the lorry and to sit on several muddy tires which lay on their sides, they took comfort in assessing the situation. The speed of the lorry was such that the time it would take to traverse the distance still before them would be reduced to no more than eight or nine hours, much less than it would have taken them on bicycles. Also, although dusty, the ride was more comfortable than when pedaling. "Let's be grateful for small mercies," murmured Jozek, promising Nina and himself a veritable feast once they got to Stettin. "Did you watch when Irena and Mrs. L. made those sandwiches?" he could not suppress his curiosity. "What did they put in them? Can you refresh my memory?" So Nina gave a recital of all the good things placed by their new friends in the freshly made rolls. Things like 'skwarki' (cracklings of pork) with pickles, cheese (Irena had retrieved it from the underground cooler) lettuce and radishes, dry sausage with green peppers, hard boiled eggs and mustard, all of them neatly wrapped in a moist cloth and wax paper. Jozek heard all this with his eyes closed in pleasurable expectation. "Knowing my proclivity toward all forms of sophistication," he began, reclining on the dusty tire, "you may well have thought, Nina, that only gourmet food would meet with my approval. Not so. A modest egg, fresh and hard boiled, with mustard, is fully acceptable to me. Of course the secret lies in the mustard."

"Is that so? Thank you for relieving my deep-seated anxiety," Nina exclaimed, but soon she desisted from teasing. So Jozek had his peculiarities. So what? No reason to bug him.

Talking about the sandwiches made them look back on the happy week behind them, the two ladies, the animals. "Carlotta is still very young and will need plenty of milk," mused Nina, "but I do not think Zhenia will object to the orphans. Some of them may even play with her calf."

"After your milking, the poor cow is bound to welcome a change of hands, so to speak," was the unkind reply which precipitated Nina's retort about people who, without ever attempting to face a challenging task on their own, love to criticize others. She did not finish her rebuke, because the truck came suddenly to a screeching stop. "Road check," hissed the driver through the small window in the back of the cab. "Get down with your things!" When they obediently jumped down with their backpacks, they saw three Russian policemen approaching in a menacing manner. To show their lack of concern (the Underground directive: never show anxiety), Nina bent to lace her shoes, while Jozek took a mouth organ from his pocket and started to play a lively folk tune. They observed, however, that the effect on Edek was devastating. He leaned against the truck, pale and shivering.

Meanwhile a corporal came closely to Jozek and shouted to him "Who the hell are you and what do you want here?"

"Here I am, in my own country, being accosted by a Russian who wants to know who the hell I am and what my business is. Wouldn't it be more to the point if I asked him these questions?" Although these sentiments passed through the boy's mind, they were not reflected on his face. He calmly replied with a pleasant facial expression that both he and his sister, were going to Stettin where their parents were supposed to be. "So they are in Stettin, eh?" barked another. "Not on the other side of the border?" Appearing to find the question puzzling, Jozek begged to be informed, what border the officer had in mind? Ukrainian?

"Stupid twit," was the comment of another soldier who, turning toward Nina, ordered her to remove the contents of their bags, one by one. "What are these?" he exclaimed looking at the meat cans. Put them there, against the wall." Both of them stacked the eight cans of goulash as directed. "Get away," shouted the policeman and drawing his pistol he fired a series of shots into the cans while two others roared with laughter. The shock the youngsters suffered passed quickly, replaced by helpless anger. Having observed with satisfaction the brown gravy flowing from the smashed cans, the corporal turned to Nina. "Papers," he ordered. "I do not have papers," she replied struggling to keep the voice lighthearted. "I lost them in the public bath. They were in my jacket and it vanished. A good jacket, too," she added with a sigh.

"Now I, for instance, have everything in perfect order," interjected Jozek, displaying his array of documents one by one. "But then I never go to the baths. Don't believe in bathing. Too much of it, I keep telling my sister, and you may turn bourgeois. The same goes for goulash, decadent Hungarian food, not like our kasha! But can you expect sense when you talk to a girl? No way! Me, I am for the toiling masses," he concluded with a flourish.

"He is talking so much because he wants to divert their attention from Edek," Nina guessed, for the driver was, to all appearances, close to fainting. "What is the matter with that man?" She thought irritably. "He has all the papers required, yet he is shaking like a jelly. If he behaves like that, he will get all three of us in trouble!"

Mercifully, after inspecting the driver's documents, the policemen did not pay much attention to him. They were now absorbed in looking through the cab, whose seat they slashed open, and in carefully tapping each of the eight wheels of the truck. Finally they waved the travelers on. "Get your things and scram. The packages stay," the corporal said pointing to the food parcels. "We have to inspect them." Jozek was on the point of objecting, but he got a nudge from Nina's elbow. The driver was already starting the motor. "The liberators," murmured the boy when they were on the lorry. "The cheek, the incredible cheek! There was no need to prevent me from commenting on their behavior, Nina. All I wanted to say was 'if our sandwiches were to be eaten by great Stalin, we would die happy!'"

"Jozek," Nina admonished him with great seriousness. "You are good in these encounters, you are very good. But don't let your impudence go too far. They are not all a bunch of idiots, you know." But Jozek did not pay attention. He was mourning the lost food.

Regained Territories

When after a long bumpy ride they entered the suburbs of Stettin and got down with their bicycles, Edek for the first time demonstrated some concern for them. "I hope that you find your parents soon," he remarked, pocketing the rest of the fare. "I am sorry that I charged you so much and even more sorry for exposing you to danger. But believe me, I did not do it for selfish reasons."

"What danger?" commented Jozek contemptuously, "you mean that silly shooting exhibition?"

"Danger, because both of you were sitting on explosives," was the staggering reply, "and those stupid policemen did not even look at the tires on the truck."

He was already in the cab when Nina approached him "One last thing," she asked. "Who will benefit by your activity?"

"Who else? Poland," he shouted.

He left them somewhat confused. Pondering on the ramifications of all this, Nina observed thoughtfully. "Such activity does not have any chance of success now. How can they fight alone against the Soviets? Also, I do not think that people like Edek, despite their best intentions, would be very good at it. There is an obvious lack of training."

"Definitely not AK material," the boy agreed. "Number one, he went to pieces at the check-point, no trace of self control, no preparation. Number two, he really put us at risk with those explosives. The AK would never do it unless there were an emergency. He will probably cause more problems than solutions." On that somber note, both of them became depressed.

The next three days brought nothing but misery. The Polish Resettlement Committee in Szczecin (as it was called now) had moved to another place, and they had trouble finding it. After locating the office, they saw a long line of bedraggled people stretching over five blocks. These were the Poles who had been kicked out of their homes in Eastern Poland, which was now integrated into the Soviet Union. They were now to find a new life in the West. The German families who had lived there were being sent westward. This forcible resettlement of both Poles and Germans was due to the directives of the victorious allies, among whom the USSR played a dominant role. Although the 'regained territories' represented the oldest Polish land, the intent to give it back to Poland was not dictated by considerations of justice. The Poles lost the eastern part of their country in order to please the USSR, while the extension of Poland's borders to the West, was meant as a punishment for the Germans.

"At least the Germans are not being sent to Siberia, like our people were," said Nina. "They are staying within their own country."

"It is still grossly unfair to them," objected Jozek hotly. "No Christian should accept the idea of collective responsibility. Although Poles suffered terribly, treating Germans like this does not help. Two wrongs do not make things right, you know."

Indeed there was very little joy among the Poles assigned to German homes. "I hate it here," complained a buxom lady from Polesie, located in the eastern part of Poland, whom they stopped on the street to ask for help. "Back there, I had a little house with a garden and three fruit trees. It was my great grandparents' house! There were family graves in the local cemetery. Now all that belongs to this horrible Soviet Union! They tell me to 'take a German apartment' instead, but it is not mine! It belonged to a German lady who left it last week, crying! I feel awful about it!" Out of the goodness of her heart, she allowed the teenagers to spend a night in the basement. "Nobody knows to whom this basement belongs," she informed them. "But you are welcome to it and I will try to get you some food. This is now the main problem. There is very little food in Szczecin." As indeed that proved true. After a day in Szczecin the young people decided that the best they could do would be to leave it as soon as possible.

After saying good-bye to the woman from Polesie, from whom they got some bread, they proceeded on their journey toward the river Elbe and the longed for melina (a hideout; a safe house). Their previous information regarding the traffic proved only too true. Apart from the military vehicles, there was very little traffic moving westward. Even the railway carriages ran predominantly eastward. It really felt spooky to be alone on the road west.

"If I were a truly noble person," mused Nina while pedaling after Jozek, "I would persuade Jozek to leave me here and go back east. He would have no problem finding accommodation on one of those vehicles." But she did not say it. She knew that he would have rejected any such suggestion and she was secretly grateful.

"Do you have a road map to the melina in your head?" he asked after an hour or so of heavy riding. "No matter if you don't, I believe I am clear about it. Let's put it on a piece of paper and compare. We will destroy it afterwards, of course." But when they attempted to recall all the directions painstakingly prepared for them by Ewa, they found out that some details had escaped them. "Didn't Ewa say that a village by the name of Torgelow was not far from the freeway towards Hamburg?" asked Nina. "But we have been riding at least three hours and there is no such village in sight. Perhaps we should ask?" So when they saw a lonely bicyclist making leisurely progress, they decided to ask for directions to the village of Torgelow. "Torgelow?" he replied. "There is no such village. "

"What happened to it?"

"It probably got another name," he responded angrily. "I myself am going to my native town and have no idea what name they have given it now. This is happening in my own country, mind!"

"But who is doing it?" Nina wanted to know. "Who else, if not the verdammen Polaken (damn Poles)?" After which he sped away.

Upset, disillusioned, and hungry, they pushed ahead. They found some potatoes in an abandoned field, which they attempted to bake. Jozek congratulated himself for taking a small penknife and a package of salt on this trip, things which would have never occurred to his partner. Still, they learned that baking potatoes in an open field was not easy, and being very hungry and disinclined to wait, they ate most of them half raw. "I have never before eaten raw potatoes and I do not think that Sister Hermencia would have wanted me to do so," Jozek complained with a trace of self pity in his voice. "Gastric distress seems a virtual certainty. A total lack of the satisfaction which normally accompanies an acceptable meal can only prove debilitating. I wonder if this hospitable land has any drinkable water anywhere."

"What I think we should do is to knock on any respectable door and ask if we could spend the night somewhere under a roof. We could ask them to sell us some food. We still have some money."

"We are no longer in the 'regained territories' after having crossed the Oder river, although we never noticed the difference. I remember Father Surman telling me that the Russians do not think it necessary to bother about the newly negotiated Polish/German frontier. Since the Soviet occupation extends over Poland and far into Eastern Germany, they are only concerned about borders between their zone and the British and American zones. This is when Frank comes in."

"I know all that. I don't think that Father Surman only talked to you. I still think that we have to approach somebody about food and shelter, although we are now in Germany proper."

"And risk being called 'damn Poles,' again?" But even he realized that a night in the open on an empty stomach was a poor option.

A New Uncle?

A large white house, seen from a distance, was their target. However, when they negotiated a sharp turn in the road, they were suddenly faced with a Soviet checkpoint of large proportions. The road was closed by a steel barrier and next to it stood two soldiers with rifles. A machine gun was placed on the side of the road against the wall of a large barrack in front of which stood a group of soldiers, fully armed. "Here we go again," groaned Nina, contemplating the gloomy scenario. The moment they were seen, several soldiers hurried toward them holding rifles 'at the ready.' "One would like to inquire of these warriors, what is the use of screaming 'postoi' (stop) at the top of their voices, when they see that we have already dismounted and are unlikely to run away on foot?" the boy whispered. "Patience, Nina." She responded with a nod of understanding.

They were conducted to the barracks and ordered to wait for the comrade colonel. Meanwhile, their backpacks were searched and their bicycles taken away. Their interviewer proved to be an elderly man of some dignity. He listened with a smile of disbelief to Jozek's fervent appeals to let them join their parents. "Where are these parents of yours?" he inquired gently. "Not far, we hope," replied Nina but it sounded woefully unconvincing even to her. Jozek's further attempts at explanation were peremptory dismissed by the officer. Turning to Nina, he said, "Look at me girl, and note what I say. I have a daughter your age and believe me, I do not wish you ill. You have chosen a dangerous mission and you must give it up before you suffer for your naiveté. Do you think that you have a chance of getting through the border? Do you know how many people languish in prison for such attempts? What you will do is to get on those bicycles and go back east as fast as you can, before you get interrogated about your real intentions. Poniatno? (Understood?)"

"So here is a man who cannot be duped," she thought desperately. "But to be so close and to give it all up? It is horrible, just horrible." From the expression on Jozek's face she learned that he, too, thought the game was up.

Meanwhile, a commotion of sorts occurred outside and the orderly reported an emergency meeting at the Elbe Center. "Will Comrade Colonel attend? Other officers had already been notified and the car was on the way."

The officer addressed Nina again. "You will spend the night here. I want to spare you a nocturnal encounter with our guards. Tomorrow morning you get your bicycles and push east, back toward Szczecin. Nothing bad will happen to you here. It is not a prison, you know, although you will be locked up for the night. I instructed the orderly to bring you some food."

The orderly took them to a room which contained two beds with blankets and had a door which led to a lavatory. There were bars on the windows and the door was solid steel, so it was obviously used to detain people. Yet the accommodation was luxurious from the Soviet point of view and it was easy to believe that the whole building had once been used by the German road patrols.

In this new environment, Jozek perked up considerably. Seeing Nina crestfallen, he made efforts to cheer her up. "In the first place, we now have a roof over our heads for the night, two beds, and wonder of wonders, a lavatory. Certainly not what detainees in Soviet hands are used to," he remarked counting on his fingers the benefits which had accrued to them. "Secondly, we get some food. After those jerks stole our goulash and sandwiches, we only had raw potatoes. Thirdly, we have a whole night before us and who knows what may happen during the course of it?" As usual, she believed him to be far too optimistic. "If you are thinking about escape, you had better give it up," she told him. "Even if we managed to get out of this building, we would be immediately apprehended, if not shot. The whole barracks is surrounded by soldiers. Did you see the poster in the entrance hall? 'Try to escape and you are dead.'" Her pessimism grew when the orderly, a huge youth in a rather dirty uniform, placed before them two small pieces of bread and some water.

Jozek, however, did not appear despondent. After trying to engage the soldier in a discussion on the relative merits of white and brown bread, he proceeded to cut a piece with his pen knife. The soldier watched him enviously. "This is a weapon," he announced. "You are not allowed to have it here."

"I will be happy if you confiscate it in the name of law," the boy responded, "but would it be too much to ask for something better to eat? After all, we are not prisoners, you know. More like guests and should be treated accordingly. Your comrade colonel's words exactly. A fair exchange, may be in order. My penknife is yours and more bread, sausage, and whatever else you have, are ours. Vodka not required," he added humourously. The orderly needed time to think. "No sausage," he finally declared. "Bliny (pancakes)."

"Very nutritious, I am sure," noted Jozek encouragingly. "Bliny, dumplings, cabbage, potatoes," continued the orderly. "The officers' supper, but they gone. Cook says we can have it."

"Prekrasno! (beautiful)," cried Jozek, offering him the knife. It was accepted with respect and the new owner left them, locking the door from the outside. "But will he really bring us the food?" Nina was torn between hope and scepticism. "He already has the knife, you know."

"Must you always distrust human nature, Nina?" her partner reproached her. "He will be back with bliny and other things. You will see."

He was right. The orderly reappeared with the previously mentioned viands, plus two smoked herrings. "You may just as well know that the herrings are extra, from my own ration," he informed them with an air of generosity. "Eat fast. I have to get them dishes away." After accepting their grateful thanks, he departed and they threw themselves at the fare. The quantities were generous, but they ate everything including the herrings, whose quality Jozek estimated as 'passable' but not up to the standard to which he was accustomed.

"I remember my grandmother telling us a long time ago that the old Russia, I mean Russia before the revolution, had been famous for 'yezda i yeda,' which means comfortable travel and good food. The latter still emerges today occasionally. Those bliny were excellent!" Although more restrained in his praise, Jozek agreed that he had had worse.

"It is strange how a full stomach influences one's mental attitude," Nina meditated, stretched out on the bed. "You feel more optimistic when you have eaten your fill. Wasn't it Napoleon who believed that 'an army marches on its stomach'?"

She awoke refreshed early the next morning, but became immediately aware that Jozek was already alert and not looking very well. "It must be either the herring, or a delayed reaction to raw potatoes," she thought. To her inquiry, he simply replied in a low voice: "Am thinking." Then, pulling a small notebook from his pocket, he wrote on one of the sheets and handed it over to her. "The room may be bugged," it said. "Jozek, do not fantasize," she retorted, but seeing his serious mien, wrote on the back of the sheet. "If there were bugs, the orderly would not have been so free with our supper, would he?"

"Non-political offense. Besides, he – not a brain. Might not have known," the message came back with the word "destroy" underlined at the bottom. Deciding to humor him, although she still regarded this as a game, she tore the paper into small pieces and dropped them into the lavatory. When she came back, another note was on her bed. "Was in the lavatory last night (herring!!). Heard two soldiers discussing decorations. One decorated officer was general POPLAWSKI. Destroy."

"So?" she scribbled feverishly. Jozek's expression indicated impatience with the slow-thinking female. "Suggestion: adopt him as our relative, preferably uncle," he wrote with a flourish. "Destroy."

"How?" But further communication was impossible, for there was already somebody unlocking their door. Nina fled to the lavatory where the last note shared the fate of the previous ones.

The same slovenly orderly brought them only bread and tea, mentioning that the hawk-eyed cook had berated him for eating too much last night. He also told them that they must be on their way back east soon. A new officer, a sergeant, was going to give them instructions. Comrade colonel was needed elsewhere.

"A sergeant in place of a colonel," murmured Jozek on their way to the office. "We are coming down in the world."

The new C.O.'s behavior was far from welcoming. "So because of comrade colonel's good heart, you spent the night here in elegant quarters instead of prison where you belong," he thundered. "Thank your lucky stars for it. Before you go east, write here in legible characters your confession. Both of you." Warned by Jozek's glance not to say anything, Nina kept silent.

"What exactly should we confess to?" the boy asked pleasantly.

"Write that you deeply regret that you stupidly came here and caused problems to the forces of the glorious Soviet Union," suggested the officer.

"Gladly," agreed Jozek accepting the pen. "But, you know, the family ties being what they are, I would be reluctant to talk about stupidity... Genes, you know, and all that. Some people may say like nephew, like uncle, general or no general. But as to the regretting..."

"Your uncle, a general?" inquired the stupefied sergeant.

"Recently decorated for unsurpassed bravery and logistic genius! Inordinately fond of us both, but especially of my sister," Jozek confided unabashedly handing him his documents. "He is forever sending her letters. 'Ninochka, my little pigeon, come to me when the war is over,' he pleads. But when we try to do just that, we find obstacles," he ended in a wounded tone.

"So this is why you are trying to go west? To meet the general?"

"Where else would he be? Didn't he liberate Berlin?"

"Did he? I heard that it was Konev," was the officer's comment.

"Where would Konev be without Poplawski?" exclaimed Jozek with conviction. "Nowhere!"

"Well, it changes the picture. Do not write the confession now. But, why didn't you tell this to the colonel?"

"We wanted too," said Nina who thought that Jozek deserved some respite after his exhausting performance. "We were on the point of doing that, when he was called away. But we were planning to tell him this morning and ask him to connect us with our uncle by telephone. Do you have the general's personal number?" If Jozek could be impudent, she could too, she told herself.

"No, I don't," he admitted. "But I tell you what you should do. Go to our Information Center some two miles north along the Elbe river, and ask the people there. They have all the numbers, including personal, and will be glad to oblige you. Tell your uncle that you have been treated well here. Harasho? (OK?)"

After taking their leave of the CO and waving to the rest of the soldiers, who waved back, they proceeded on the road west. Surprisingly, while Nina was jubilant, Jozek appeared less so. "I do not think that such experiences are good for me," he said in a subdued voice. "It is the exaggeration which it is occasionally necessary to employ that goes against my nature. My modesty, my disinclination to depart however slightly from the absolute truth, hamper my talents of invention. Intellectually, I am equal to the challenge, but emotionally I hesitate, I agonize, I waver. I understand that such inner struggles were undergone by Slowacki."

"Of course, he had to compare himself to the one of the greatest Polish poets," she thought irritably. "A narcissist, if there ever was one." Aloud she said, "I have never yet seen you overcome by modesty and hesitation, nor agonized when it came to lying," but, pricked by conscience, she hastily added, "and I am glad of it, because circumstances required it." Jozek brightened up perceptibly and gratefully acknowledged her good opinion.

Frau Lange

The next few hours proved uneventful. Nobody stopped them on their way toward the river Elbe. It was just before it was reached that the road split in two. Their instructions had directed them to take the left fork of the road, when it faced a large bridge. After a mile or so, a second, much smaller bridge would appear. Opposite it was a path into the woods, not far from their destination. But an unexpected obstacle, this time having nothing to do with politics, stopped them. The second bridge was not there. "It is now more than two miles from the crossroads, and there is no bridge," Nina noted with concern. "What on earth could have happened to it? Do you remember how old Ewa's map was?"

"It must have been new, for Poland was not on it," replied Jozek. "The only conclusion that comes to mind is destruction by bombing. The allies probably destroyed it."

"But surely, some fragments of a large bridge would have remained, even if bombs had hit it,' insisted Nina. "I have seen nothing that looked like the ruins of a bridge." Neither had he. Yet, it was vitally important to know which of the many small paths leading into the extensive forest they should take, a virtually impossible task without the bridge. Their instructions warned them against making mistakes. They decided to try to find the remnants of the bridge by walking along the bank of the river.

Part of the problem, was their mode of transportation. The bank of Elbe was covered with thick undergrowth which was unsuitable terrain for bicycles. Their backpacks, although much lighter than before, were very inconvenient to carry. Nina suggested that the machines and backpacks could temporarily be left in the trees and bushes on the other side of the road. Then, they could look for the remnants of the missing bridge, unencumbered. Jozek voiced his reservations at first, (what if they get stolen?) but eventually complied. They had to find the bridge. Without it, they would not know where to turn. They would be lost.

They parted at the bank promising each other to be back in, at most, forty minutes. Moving along the edge of the river and looking intently into its grey, dirty waters, Nina began to have doubts about the wisdom of her plan. "Even if there are some posts left, we could never see them in this sewer," she thought. "Perhaps it would have been better to inquire." Yet, she was aware that they had received instructions not to talk to strangers. Wouldn't it look silly if not suspicious, to ask for a non-existent bridge? What rotten luck that it should happen to them at the end of the journey! The blasted bridge was to be the point from which the detailed instructions began. Without, it they would never find the melina! On top of all this worry, she was tired and hungry. The meager breakfast they had eaten hours ago was simply a distant memory. The night was not far away.

These pessimistic thoughts were suddenly interrupted by a gentle voice speaking in German. "My dear, you are not contemplating suicide...?" It was a frail elderly lady, looking at her anxiously, bearing a surprising physical resemblance to the grandmother she had lost at the beginning of the war. It was the shock of this encounter that made Nina behave in a way she later described as idiotic. With tears in her eyes she stammered: "I am not. I am looking for a bridge." In spite of this lunatic explanation, the stranger remained sympathetic. "There is a large bridge perhaps a mile or so from here. You cannot miss it." It was then that the girl decided to accept the woman as friend, though she was sure that Jozek would have considered such behavior risky.

There, on a bench close by, she began by asking the German lady if she could tell her something in confidence. When she got gentle assurances that she could do so, she told her, in her halting German, the gist of their saga without going into the more damaging details. However, looking into the intent blue eyes of the stranger, she had a feeling that the latter had a fairly complete picture of their dilemma. "Let us not go into the Kleiningkeiten," (details) remarked her new friend. "What I propose to do is this: we wait for the boy Jozek here, and then I take you to my modest abode for a supper and a warm bed." Oh, how wonderful this sounded! "Thanks awfully, but we have to retrieve our things first," Nina exclaimed. "You do it and I will wait for you here," was the calm reply. "Please do not say one word more about gratitude, my dear. Believe me that many of us Germans are aware of what our country did to yours."

Jozek arrived, looking with apprehension at the lady. "No need to worry, we have found a friend," Nina told him while introductions took place. (The lady's name was Frau Lange.) "Now, all we have to do is find the bicycles." But this apparently simple task proved unexpectedly very difficult.

"Where exactly did we enter the woods?" they asked each other anxiously. "Was it before we passed that huge oak, or was it closer to that poster saying 'Achtung'?" Having left the old lady on the bench, they dived widely into various portions of the wood only to emerge with disheveled clothing and torn and bleeding hands. The bicycles could not be found. To make things worse, it now became much darker and a slight rain started falling. "We cannot possibly ask Mrs. Lange to sit there in the rain," Nina whispered. "Perhaps we should leave the search for tomorrow and go with her now." Jozek, however, was dubious about the idea, although the vision of the supper exercised a powerful influence on his imagination. His reluctance to accept defeat received support from the lady, who urged them not to give up. "In the first place, do not worry about me," she said putting a folded newspapers over her head. "Secondly I would not recommend leaving things in the bushes close to the road, as there are now many unsavory characters roaming there. What I propose is to tax your memory. When you pushed your bikes under the fence in order to enter the wood, did the fence have one horizontal wire, or two?"

"One," they cried. "We did not really think that fence meant much, and it was easy to drag the bikes under the wire."

"Then, it could not have been anywhere here," the lady remarked. "This fence has a double wire. What you have to do is to find the spot where it changes into a single wire and start your search from there. It will not be far. Also, look for disturbed grass under the wire; the bicycles had to leave their imprint on the ground." Of course she was right. Full of admiration for their new Sherlock Holmes ally, they retrieved the bicycles and backpacks and were ready to go.

While getting ready to accept her hospitality, Nina kept observing Mrs. Lange in a speculative way. "You seem very thin and light and my bicycle will easily carry both of us," she declared. "We place the folded blanket on the bar in front of me, like so, you put your hands lightly on the handles, and off we go. I can even hold you with one had if the road does not prove to be too bumpy." This well meaning suggestion did not seem to impress Mrs. Lange. "My dear, to sit in this way on the pipe, at my age? It would make history!" But Jozek was also for it, and the rain was by now falling with a vengeance. "No problem," cried Nina and after firmly placing the old lady on the frame, jumped on the saddle and rode down the road in a cavalier fashion. "Do not show off, Nina," Jozek shouted behind her.

Directions for reaching Mrs. Lange's home were given by her passenger in a quivering voice. They arrived there with only minor mishaps, having been accosted on the way by two dogs who considered a pair of females perched on a single bike too much to tolerate.

The house was a small cottage surrounded by a beautiful garden. Having quickly revived from the bike trauma, the lady took charge. "First a hot bath, then a hot supper and bed," she announced to the delight of her guests. After some time elapsed, clean but now somehow shy, they sat down to a supper of fried potatoes and yogurt. It did not need much penetration to realize how poor the household really was. That the meal was part of Mrs. Lange's meager ration of food, Nina had no doubt. "How strange life is," she meditated, lying in a clean bed under fluffy blankets. "For the second time now, we have been fed by people of hostile countries, people who are certainly not happy or prosperous. So why did their leaders start the war? If only a few days ago, somebody told me that I would hold a German woman in my arms with affection and gratitude, I would not have believed it."

Breakfast was a joyous occasion for all three of them, although it consisted only of porridge with a scant quantity of condensed milk. Consulting a new map of the area, Mrs. Lange found the actual place where the bridge had been located before its destruction. A large cable sticking out from the water was thought to mark the spot. She insisted on accompanying them to the place – this time on foot, since the weather was fine. Before leaving, Nina noticed several family photos displayed on the cupboard. Black tape surrounded the frames of two, which showed an elderly man and a young boy in uniform.

"My brother and my nephew," the lady said, noticing Nina's interest. "You?"

"My grandmother and my sister. We don't know about the relatives in Siberia."

"We live in horrible times," sighed the lady.

Opposite the cable on the other side of the road was a narrow path leading south. They supposed that this was where they should turn. So now it was again time to say good-bye. Turning to Mrs. Lange, Jozek said rather formally, "Auf Wiedersehen, Frau Lange. Vielen Dank." But Nina threw convention to the wind and grabbed and hugged the old lady with a passion. The latter stood at the head of the path for a long time. They waved to her with feelings similar to those they'd experienced when parting with friends in Rawa and later in Lesniczowka.

The Melina

They knew that they had to travel two miles down the path before the sign described in their instructions was to become visible. "Given the rotten luck we had yesterday with the bridge, I would not be surprised if the sign has fallen into the bushes, or has been burnt or destroyed," Jozek grumbled. "Where is it? We should have seen it already." It took two more turns before a small green post with a red sign reading "Tourists" appeared. "Thank God, we are almost home," sighed Nina.

Their instructions specified that they were to follow the path to the left of the sign. They were then to stop and seat themselves on a wide flat stone some way down the path. Once stationary, they were either to sing or to play on the mouth organ a particular folk tune. Jozek became quite breathless playing his harmonica again and again and was about to tell Nina that they better start singing, when a black haired girl of eleven or so appeared before them with an accusatory expression on her face. "Where on earth have you been? We expected you last week," she said. Both of them remained silent. "Well, there is no help for it," remarked the kid, "follow me."

"So this is our contact?" murmured Jozek, and Nina wondered what kind of security arrangement Frank's organization had, if a pre-teen child was used as a lookout. They followed the girl for about an hour ("it would have gone much faster, if it were not for those nasty machines of yours," complained the infant guide) until she stopped them. "We are home, and high time too. I am starving." But home was nowhere to be seen. Standing there with their bicycles, they gazed at the jungle of trees and bushes surrounding them on all sides. The girl disappeared and in her place a young man emerged from the bushes with the question "what date?" After getting a satisfactory answer (the date of the battle of Plowce), he said, "Welcome. You are just in time for lunch," and he led them through a cleverly concealed passage to the melina.

The way to the safe house was hidden behind the cleverly arranged branches of young trees. After a short passage, they saw a large green tent with a chimney under a green hood, its doors rolled up. Ten cots were arranged along the walls of the tent, and a large table with benches around it stood in the middle. Toward the back there was a kind of a kitchenette, with several primuses on a small table and pots and pans on a makeshift shelf. A large stove, unlit, completed the furniture of this shelter.

A young woman with red hair hurried toward them. "So here you are, darlings," she cried. "We expected you a little sooner, but it does not matter, does not matter at all! Well, I do not even know your first names and am not going to ask for them. Frank believes that real names should not be used here, and of course his real name is not Frank either. He is not here now, by the way. Had to leave for a few days. But perhaps there should be an introduction of sorts? Otherwise you will think we are exiles from civilization. This is my husband whose present name is Jerzy. I am Iza, although last month I was Julia. The lady you see reclining on the cot, we call Mrs. Z. She is the mother of the girl we sent to look for you, whom we christened Ala. Her little brother is called Baby. You, I think, will be called 'A,' for the girl and 'B' for the boy. Two more people will arrive tomorrow and then we will leave. We cannot have more than ten. The barge will not hold more."

From that time on, everybody was very friendly including Ala who, after having shed her official function of lookout became a normal pre-teen girl. Mrs. Z, a sickly woman with a beautiful head of hair, greeted them with a smile. The baby, a ten-month-old vivacious boy, made a wobbly journey toward Jozek with outstretched arms. Then they all sat down to a lunch served by Iza at the picnic table. Now it was time to have a better look around. But for the table, the cots, the benches, and several makeshift shelves for pots and pans, there was no other furniture. Despite the primitive conditions the tent was clean and orderly. The food, too, was surprisingly good – noodles with mushrooms, flat bread with honey, luscious black-berries. After lunch, Iza showed them the makeshift bathroom and lavatory. "We have plenty of water. The stream is near and we bring water each day in shifts. Generally, once a month I go to buy supplies, every time to a different store. I have a little wagon attached to my bicycle. Also once a month, bulkier supplies – flour, powdered milk, butter in cans, rice, soap, and kerosine for the primuses – are brought to the spot where the sign is and left. This is Frank's arrangement, we do not know with whom. Otherwise, we get a lot from the forest: mushrooms, nuts, berries, honey, and occasionally a rabbit. Neither my husband nor I like to kill animals and we do it only if there is a serious shortage of food. This can happen in winter. But do not imagine that we are the important people here. The melina is Frank's baby."

Nina suddenly remembered that Jozek would probably have to leave the next day. She tried not to think about their parting, which was to be another among the many she experienced in recent days. Seeing him asleep, she decided to let him rest and to wash his clothes. After doing it she hung then on the bushes to dry, so that he should begin the journey back by assuming what Violetta used to called a civilized appearance. She also began repairing Jozek's jacket, torn in two places. After so many years of sharing sorrows and joys, they were to say good-bye, perhaps forever. But she would have never tried to keep him abroad. His place was in Poland with the orphans, or possibly in one of the emerging high schools and later at a university. Father Surman thought that was the boy's future and she had no doubt that he would do well there. It was different with her. Much as she would have wanted to join Ewa in Warsaw (or in what remained of it), her place was with her family, especially now when Kinga was gone.

"Jozek, I want to talk to you," she called to him. Jozek was playing the role of a bloodthirsty dragon who lived under one of the cots. The shrieks of delight from the little boy prevented her from being heard. Thus she turned to Iza, who was sitting on the cot near her and said. "My co-traveler will be leaving us very soon; the sooner the better, in fact. He has his return route well marked and we do not anticipate difficulties."

"First assumption incorrect, second true," came unexpectedly from the dragon.

"So you are not going back?" inquired Iza.

"But of course he will," cried Nina. "Everybody knows that. He will go as soon as his things are dry."

"He is not going back before crossing the border," Jozek called from the dragon's cave. "He also does not like it when other people make decisions for him and talk about him as if he were not in the room." There was a trace of irritation in the voice. "But Jozek," Nina was at a loss for words. "Didn't you promise to go back as soon as I met Frank's people?"

"Nothing of the kind! I promised to go back, but did not specify the point of departure. Sister Cecilia, for one, was fully cognizant of my plans. I was going to tell you today, but seeing how eagerly you washed my things I decided to let you proceed. Why should I deprive you of your pleasures?" A missile in the form of a small pillow was intended for him but hit Mrs. Z instead, causing her two offspring unmitigated delight. After apologizing to the lady, Nina pursued the matter further. "Jokes apart, I do not think you should do it," she said. "It is one thing to penetrate the guarded border an then to stay on the other side, another to expose oneself unnecessarily to being captured or shot."

"If I get shot on my way west, I shall be in nice company – yours," he answered flippantly. "It is unlikely that such a misadventure should befall me on the way back, since the Russkies welcome everybody into their zone. However, if they detain me, I will simply tell them that I could no longer stand capitalist oppression and want to join the socialist brotherhood. They will probably think me looney but they could hardly hold it against me." Much as she pretended to be angry with him, Nina was in fact delighted that they would be together several more days. She was also moved by his confession that he wanted to see her mother and Krysia and was eager to make the acquaintance of her father and Myszka. "How could you think that having come so far, I would give up the chance to see them?" he asked reproachfully and thus effectively rendered her silent.

The next day brought unwelcome news. Frank was 'detained' at one of the Soviet check-points, managed to escape, and was now in hiding. Iza and Jerzy were under orders to conduct the present party across within two days, and then to come back, close the melina, and resume their previous identities in Poland.

Chapter Six
The Crossing

Two men arrived the next day on foot, one elderly the other a youth of about twenty. They were introduced as 'C' and 'D,' for the initials 'A' and 'B' were already assigned to Nina and Jozek. "This is in case some of us get apprehended," Iza explained with her unfailing good humor.

"So that we cannot reveal the real names of our friends here, even if force is used."

"But surely you are not envisioning anything of the kind?" quailed Mrs. Z. "Surely you are confident that my children and I can make it safely?"

"You mean one child, Mama, for I am no longer to be classed with the baby," interjected Ala. "Oh, we are bound to be fine," Iza attempted to cover up her previous frankness. "It is only a precaution Frank wanted us to adopt."

Another of Frank's instructions, however, elicited strong words of disapproval not only from Mrs. Z but also from the newcomer, 'C.'

"We leave tomorrow in the evening," Jerzy told them after supper. "This means that your backpacks must all be ready at about 8 p.m. The child has to be got up too, and before we begin our journey you will give him the drink we prepare."

"A drink you prepare? What drink?" exclaimed the anxious mother. "A drink to make him sleep for at least eight hours," was the unrelenting reply.

"Surely you cannot expect the lady to follow your instructions blindly," interceded C. "Ridiculous!"

"Either the child takes the drink, which is absolutely safe, or the three of you stay," declared Jerzy in a tone allowing no protest. "We cannot be exposed to danger because of his yelling."

"But I have never heard of anything so outrageous," lamented the lady. "How do I know what is in that drink?"

"How do you know that Iza and I are not Soviet agents who had enticed you here in order to deliver you to the People's Commissariat for Internal Affairs?" was the harsh reply. "You have to trust us. There is no other alternative."

"You know that they cannot stay," began the old gentleman argumentatively. Jerzy simply turned and left without paying any attention to him or to a now tearful Mrs. Z. Aware that his mother had been made unhappy, the baby embraced her and started whimpering. His sister was trying to console them both by patting the little guy and offering her handkerchief to her distraught parent. "They cannot risk his crying aloud when we cross over," she argued gently. "Iza would not give him anything bad to drink. She is a medical expert."

Nina's reaction to the scene was mixed. Of course Jerzy was right about the danger of smuggling a young child through the enemy border and Mrs. Z should have thought about it. On the other hand, the man's behavior toward the distraught mother was inexcusable. Was he perhaps becoming overly anxious, fearful of the new responsibilities dumped on him by Frank? As if her thought had a telepathic powers, Mr. C's next words voiced her concerns. "I am not going to comment on the appalling rudeness of this young man because I believe that it has been caused by his feelings of inadequacy, closely related to his role in our coming adventure. It is indeed highly unfortunate that he is now our guide instead of Frank. However, we have no choice but to go ahead. For my son and me, remaining under Soviet rule would be suicidal."

"We must also go ahead. Mom is not well and her brother is waiting for us there," whispered Ala. Seeing a questioning look directed toward them, Jozek gave a nod for himself and Nina indicating similar sentiments.

Iza appeared with food rations soon afterwards and tried to sooth Mrs. Z's fears regarding the drink. "There is nothing to be uneasy about," she urged. "Baby will be as right as rain after his long sleep. And the drink has a pleasant taste. Children love it. We have used it several times before without any ill effects. You must trust me! After all, I had three years of medical school before the war. Though the Nazis prevented me from finishing my university studies, I did get a diploma as a registered nurse."

They knew that they should spend the next day resting up before their departure, but none of them could relax except for the little boy, who fell peacefully asleep at his usual time of 7 p.m. By 8 p.m., they had their backpacks packed with simple food rations. Jozek was helping Jerzy to stack up the cots, bring their bicycles into the tent, and in a general way prepare the melina for his and Iza's absence. Jozek was to return with them. After retrieving his bike he would go home by a different route from the one he and Nina had taken. All three promised to dispose of Nina's bicycle as best as they could.

At about 8 p.m., Mrs. Z approached Jozek timidly and inquired in a low voice if she could ask a favor. It concerned her little son. "He is asleep now, but has to be awakened in order to take the potion that caused me so much anxiety. He will not like being roused from sleep and he most certainly will sense my apprehension and react by crying. Even Ala, whom he adores, may not be able to control him. You have this wonderful ability with children, Mr. B. Could you oblige me by trying your luck with him?" she ended pleadingly. "Will try," promised Jozek, flattered by this appeal. After getting under the table on which the baby's cot was placed, he began uttering gentle murmurs and suppressed roars, interspersed by a narrative explaining that the dragon had had a good nap but now wanted his supper. The baby woke up and, after some hesitation, joined in the game, offering the dragon sundry objects to eat, such as his mother's purse and the pillow from his cot. Meanwhile Ala managed to get the milky drink inside him. After that, the boy fell asleep peacefully to the tune of the dragon's singing.

By voluntary consent, the boy's cot, which was actually a carrier with two handles, was to be carried by two different people in rotation. Ala was to attend to her mother, who was now becoming quite hysterical, so much so that Iza was obliged to get her a tranquilizer.

Punctually, at 9:15 p.m., they left the melina. According to their guides, it was most unlikely that they would encounter any difficulties on the way to the river. "We know this part of the country well," Iza told them by way of consolation. "Problems may arise on the river and later on, not before. I crossed over once, when Frank wanted me to attend to a gentleman with a weak heart. I always have my kit with me, you see. Jerzy went over with Frank two times, so of course he knows how to proceed."

"I wish I was sure of it," murmured Jozek, and Nina simply crossed herself.

There was a sheltered place in which they found a large flat-bottomed boat. How Frank managed to have it there when needed was not divulged to them. The problem that faced them now was sailing across the river without being exposed by the searchlights periodically illuminating sections of the water. The searchlights, each mounted in one of two distant towers, did not meet and left a dark passage across. It was their object to travel in that dark area, careful not to stray into dangerous illumination. Before they pushed off, Jerzy gave them a short lesson how to row. He instructed them one by one, ignoring Mrs. Z whom he placed in the middle of the boat with the baby's carrier next to her and telling Ala, "we will let you know when we need you." They were told to row in pairs. Jerzy and 'D' in the first two seats, 'C' with Iza in the second, Nina and Jozek in the third. They had had the important task of keeping the vessel 'stable' by changing their seats from the right side to the left, and rowing on either side as circumstances demanded.

The beginning of their venture was not auspicious. The boat, resting with its bow on the shore, appeared reluctant to leave it. Jerzy was trying to push it free and, after vain attempts, asked D for help. Their efforts proved successful, but while the boat disengaged, the two of them were soaked to the waist in slimy water. Iza was especially concerned about 'D.' "Jerzy is used to it and it is a warm night, but for a newcomer the wet underwear may be unpleasant," she declared solicitously. "Do not hesitate to change your clothes if you have dry ones in your backpack. No need to feel bashful, it is almost dark and we cannot see much. Still, we promise to close our eyes if you insist." As he admitted he had no extra clothing, she continued helpfully. "I have a spare pair of underwear and quite clean extra slacks. The latter may be a little short, but what does it matter? Please do put both of them on! You do not have to return them, you know." The recipient of this generous offer appeared horrorstruck. "Thank you, I am all right, in fact excellent," he stammered, dripping water all over Mrs. Z's legs on his way to the front seat. "Many thanks. Much obliged." Close by, Ala burst into suppressed giggles and both 'A' and 'B' had a hard time controlling theirs.

For the first ten minutes or so, the voyage proved uneventful. The steady rhythm of the rowing moved the barge across the Elbe without undue oscillation toward the northwest, the direction of the current. The searchlights, when they came, swept the water to the left and right of them. It was as if they had a safe passage before them, between two precipices threatening extinction.

"We are doing all right. The opposite shore is not too far," whispered Iza.

Then – unexpectedly and terrifyingly – they got stuck. The vessel quivered and came to a full stop, lodged on some invisible underwater rock "Oh, God, we must have gone too much to the east," groaned Iza. "Damn this filthy river," her husband swore in a low voice. "At least there is no puncture in the bottom that I can detect. We must get her off, but the oars alone will not do."

"Look, since we are both wet anyway, I propose that you and I get into the water, stand on this underwater boulder, and push. It cannot be too deep," proposed 'D.' Jerzy complied readily, but when they got into the water up into their necks and pushed, the bow of the liberated boat suddenly swung toward the northwest and proceeded to drift with the current at an alarming speed. The two men were left behind. "Grab the oars and row back," cried Iza. "With all your strength row back. We have to stop her before she gets into the danger zone and becomes visible." They all, including Mrs. Z, started the difficult, arm-wrenching rowing back. Nina felt as if her arms were being pulled out of their sockets at the shoulder, at the elbow joint, and at the wrist. Close to her she heard the heavy breathing of Jozek and the gasping sobs of Mrs. Z. "Harder, do not rest," hissed Iza. After what seemed a very long time, the boat slowed down and stopped. Then Jerzy's figure, covered with river slime, scrambled into the vessel, followed soon by that of 'D.' With them aboard, the boat became obedient again and turned its bow toward the bank. "It is wonderful that you ladies, my dad and Jozek here managed to stop the barge in time," said 'D,' throwing some river weeds clinging to his hair overboard. "The current here is quite strong. Congratulations."

"Oh, it wasn't really too bad," was Iza's response. Jerzy sat there rowing powerfully but saying nothing. "He feels guilty, as well he might," thought Nina. "I am sure that Frank would have never allowed the vessel to get stuck." Her eyes went to the huddled figure, opposite Jerzy. "At least one of the two young men has manners," she thought appreciatively.

During the next leg of the journey, Nina became better acquainted with 'D' who, together with Jerzy, had plunged into the polluted Elbe and now resembled a creature dragged from the sewer. Both young men took the experience in their stride, although 'D' periodically apologized for the terrible smell which emanated from his soaked garments.

While acting as his partner in transporting the carrier with the baby and while resting and having a snack, Nina began to appreciate him. She liked his lively intelligence and his carefree attitude to danger, although in truth all of them, with the exception of Mrs. Z, displayed the same unconcern when problems arose. She also found that his background, with a brother in a Soviet prison and his family in Kazakhstan, was not much different from hers. Like Nina, he had attended underground courses but at a more advanced level. There were other, perhaps less important attributes – he was good looking and well-mannered.

Although asked not to do so, they revealed their real names to each other and engaged in long discussions about their plans. Here, there was a difference in their thinking regarding the future. Marek (for that was his name), believed that he and his father could find a niche in the West from which they could contribute to the well-being of their native country. He thought that the Poles who had left Poland in recent times would become beacons spreading knowledge of Polish history and culture among the peoples in the West. He saw British, American, and French citizens conceding that a terrible mistake had been made in allowing the USSR to have supremacy over other nations in eastern and east central Europe, and thought that they would try to rectify it. Nina was more skeptical. "Suppose you do convince them," Nina remarked. "There may be no reaction on their part. Even if they believe that the Yalta Treaty was horribly unfair – and I am not sure that most of them believe that or care about it – they may still accept it as 'one of those things.' Injustice does not hurt if it involves others. The westerners have been used to injustice. Look at their colonies! Why should they care about us?"

Still, it was very pleasant to have somebody other than Jozek with whom to exchange one's views, to compare observations, and to laugh. "If we lived in normal times," she told herself, "I might fall in love with him and we would go to dances and to the cinema and be entertained by Grandma at her 'podwieczorki' (a five o'clock reception) as it was with cousin Jadzia and her intended before the war. We would both attend the university and possibly marry, with smiling families attending the church ceremony. But," she sighed, "it is not for us. He has a monumental task before him, if he is to exert some influence in a foreign country. I have my family to support, materially and morally."

During rest intervals, which Jerzy called every hour or so, he was seen consulting his compass and various pieces of paper which had the appearance of official communications. It was Marek who discovered the secret behind the innocuous instructions issued by the authorities about the gathering of mushrooms, leaving litter behind, carving one's initials on trees and other sundry prohibitions. "I wondered what possessed Jerzy to look at those lines again and again, when all of us were violating far more important ordinances," he confided to Nina. "Then I noticed that there were barely discernible signs among the letters and I am convinced that these were the instructions on how we should proceed. In other words, it was a map for us." Both of them sincerely hoped that there would be no mishap in reading those hieroglyphs.

As the border grew nearer, apprehension affected them all. They knew that, beside heavy arms, the Soviet border guards had dogs with them. These ferocious animals represented a great danger to people crossing the border illegally, since they were trained to discover the presence of human beings from a distance. In order to avoid detection and its tragic consequences, the group had to adopt certain precautions. They were to cross over at dawn, a time when the animals were allegedly less alert. Secondly, Jerzy was to lead them through a part of the forest where animal life was very plentiful and would hopefully distract the attention of the border dogs. The wooded section in which they now traveled used to be a favorite hunting place for the German VIPs, as verified by the number of rabbits and deer they spotted. Finally, Iza sprayed them with some liquid, which was supposed to make them undetectable to canine olfactory senses. She also noted good-humoredly that the aroma of the polluted Elbe which Jerzy and 'D' exuded would make the guard dogs reluctant to pursue them.

So they pushed on, this time with no rest intervals. There was a full moon, a circumstance that Jerzy did not like. Every now and then he would stop them, urging absolute quiet. When they were finally allowed to rest, exhausted and thirsty, Jerzy informed them, trying to control his relief, that according to his calculations they were already within the British zone and had left the border some four miles behind. "I am pretty certain that it is so," he added joyously, and there was spontaneous applause from all of them. Their jubilation was cut short, however, by a sound that to them represented the worst noise imaginable. It was a sound of furious barking, and it came from a place just in front of them. All of them sat as if turned to stone. "What is it?" asked Mrs. Z tremulously. "Is it possible that the British guards use dogs?"

"They don't, not here anyhow," Jerzy answered and they heard despair in his voice. "These must be Soviet dogs and we must still be in the Soviet zone. Oh God, how could I bungle it like this? I was convinced we were moving west, but we must have moved in circles!"

"We did go west," asserted Jozek. "I was watching my compass all the time."

"Then they must have rearranged the border," Jerry was quite wild now. "We cannot go back. The barge will not be there!" He put his head in his arms and sobbed.

As was usual in such moments, the possibility of a tragic mistake was accepted as true by the group. So many things had gone wrong in everyone's past that the coming of a new calamity was almost expected. Terrible possibilities pertaining to their meeting with the Soviet border patrols flashed before their eyes. All were silent with the exception of 'C' who, after excusing himself, rushed into the bushes. ("Nerves affect people in different ways," Jozek noted philosophically.)

Iza knelt close to her husband and embraced him. "Do not take on like this, love," she urged. "Perhaps it is not as bad as it seems. Perhaps it could be straightened out, somehow. What we do now is this: you all stay here and rest, and I will nip quietly a short distance to the west to investigate. Remember, I was here once before, and am somewhat acquainted with this forest. So long for now, be back in a jiffy!" With these words she disappeared and they sat there motionless for several minutes.

The elderly gentleman, 'C,' who had vanished into the bushes before that last scene took place, joined them now and asked where Iza was. Upon hearing what she had done, he burst into old-fashioned indignation. "To let a young woman undertake a dangerous mission while we men stay behind! How could you allow it?" he accosted his son, obviously considering Jerzy beneath his notice. "Well, she did say that she knew the terrain," stammered the youth, "but I admit that it is unfortunate."

"Unfortunate? It is downright shameful," thundered his papa. Nobody said anything for some time. Then Jerzy got up, his face tear-stained. "I am responsible for this terrible fiasco," he said. "I will do my best to take you back safely. It would be suicidal to try to force the border once the dogs sensed us. Soon, we will have to go back." They were spared the rest of this heart rending instruction by Iza's voice coming from afar without any effort at concealment. "It is all right!" In a few minutes she was with them, breathless, in torn clothing, but blissfully happy.

"We are in the British zone," she gasped. "We are some four miles from the border behind us, as Jerzy said. The dogs that made such a racket are owned by a farmer who is part British and lives not far from here. He got them from the Secret State Police men before they surrendered to the Brits!"

"This was the happiest moment of my life," Nina recalled later. "To suddenly ascend from the depths of despair to the pinnacle of happiness. This had never happened to me before and probably never will again."

Elated, but also chastised and timid, Jerzy attempted to make a speech. "I have to ask your forgiveness for my rudeness and for being a lousy, rotten guide," he began. "Not true, the reverse in fact," interrupted his loyal wife. "For being a rotten guide," he repeated, "who by some fantastic stroke of luck got a wonderful wife. Forgive me, if you can," he finished lamely.

After that, nobody felt like blaming him for anything. In fact, they thanked him for his concern. Only 'C's face remained a mask of disapproval.

So now, without bothering to be quiet, they joyfully moved forward. When they got to the road, a truck with some British soldiers drove up to them and stopped. "From the east?" came the friendly inquiry. "Hop on! We'll take you to the Polish Social Agency Center."

They gratefully accepted the offer while the fumes emanating from their clothing became intensified on the crowded lorry, a circumstance that the soldiers tried valiantly to ignore. "Three in our group were wet and reeking," Ala later explained to her uncle who arrived at the Center on the same afternoon. "Jerzy and 'D' reeked from the Elbe refuse, but my brother reeked for a different reason."

New Concerns

After all this came an anti-climax. They bathed, donned clean clothes, ate good nourishing meals. The Center was well equipped to take care of the refugees and spared them questions and inquiries of any kind. The officer who arrived to collect Mrs. Z and her children knew Nina's family. They were at present located in a small town some forty miles from the Center and there was relatively good bus communication with it. The next bus was to leave early the following morning and Nina and Jozek were booked on it. The Center notified the Ilski family about their arrival and, at their urgent request, sent a pre-arranged message to Mrs. Nowak.

Jerzy and Iza were to stay several days at the Center, to rest, and to have their fictitious Serbian papers prepared.[63] The possession of such papers was simply a precaution for, as was explained to Jozek who was to be one of the Serbs, hardly anyone was stopped by the Russian guards on the way east. "Still, it is helpful to be a Serb, in case of emergency," explained Iza. "The Soviets always loved the Serbs and now they love them even more, because of Tito.[64] If we are stopped, we say we are newly released from Nazi camps, volunteers for Tito's army." Jozek wanted to know if his lack of Serbo-Croatian would be a disadvantage. "Not at all," she calmed his fears. "Most Russians do not know the language either. If you say something that is close to Ukrainian/Polish pronunciation, they will think it is the language of Yugoslavia."

That night was the last one for Nina and the young couple to be together. She listened avidly to their plans. Iza had already been admitted to her fourth year of medical school in Poznan, and Jerzy was going to complete his degree in architecture. Both of them had devised ambitious projects for taking care of sick people and building shelters for those who had lost their homes. And Jozek? It was suggested to him that with his linguistic abilities he would be a success in the diplomatic service. "A diplomatic service on behalf of a Moscow-influenced government? No thank you," he rejected the idea with contempt. They learned that he was seriously thinking about becoming a teacher. "After I get my degree, I will become a teacher to tell the students the truth."

"You will not be able to tell them the exact truth," Jerzy commented. "With this new regime, the curriculum is bound to be radically changed. All publications are sure to reflect the censorship they have in the USSR."

---

[63]   At that time, obtaining false papers was not difficult.

[64]   The head of the Yugoslav Communist Partisans.

"Well, there is always a way," the boy responded. "There is no doubt that changes will come, and soon." The three of them made detailed plans to meet at least once every several months or so.

Although those conversations were very interesting, Nina was keenly aware that they no longer concerned her directly. The three of them, Iza, Jerzy, and Jozek, were moving out of the orbit of her immediate interest. She kept reminding herself that her plans were now totally different from theirs. She was to stay abroad to be one of the emigrants, to face an unknown future. The issue of emigration haunted her. She could not imagine the manifold ramifications involved in it. Where and how would she and her family live? Would her parents, both professional people, be able to find suitable work abroad? Would they be in a position to maintain ties with their friends and acquaintances, or would they be forced to settle among strangers, whose past experiences were totally different, in the way Latarnik did (a character in a novel by Henryk Sienkiewicz which describes a lonesome Polish emigrant tormented by nostalgia in the nineteenth century United States), without relations, close friends, people they had known for years and years?

Although Nina's stay on foreign soil had lasted only two days, she already experienced psychological upheavals. The languages used in the Polish Center were mostly English and German. In contrast to the past, those were not the languages imposed by the occupants, resented and considered temporary, but a legitimate way to communicate in a foreign country. She realized that Poles abroad, although much was made of them at the moment, would in fact be on sufferance in somebody else's home. But all these anxieties paled when compared to her feeling of inadequacy in her own family circle. Would she be what they had expected? Her last hazy recollection of Mrs. Ilski and Krysia involved their saying good-bye to her on her sick bed in Rawa. Forced by circumstances not to delay their search for Kinga and Myszka, they parted with her at the moment Father Surman pronounced her to be out of danger. The forthcoming year brought monumental changes to all Poles. To the Ilski family it brought the recovery of a husband and father but the loss of a daughter and sister. Although Nina was telling herself that one year could not make a great change in her relationship with mother and sister, she was not quite sure of it, especially now that Kinga was gone. But it was of her father's attitude toward her that she thought with great anxiety. A period of six years divided them. She remembered him as a laughing man carrying Krysia on his shoulders, or taking her (Nina's) side in some ridiculous discussions. What an obnoxious brat she must have been in her pre-teen years! When she was going through the war, he was either somewhere at the front or, more recently, hospitalized for months and months. How would seeing the war from such a perspective affect a man like her father? Would they have a lot in common?

Nina spent the night examining such questions, one by one. The next morning, she joined the trio of Iza, Jerzy, and Jozek at breakfast, and felt a stranger. She could not eat anything and found it difficult to take part in their lighthearted talk. She was now an outsider, no longer with them, and not yet in the bosom of her long unseen family. An outsider!

The journey by bus was short and when she and Jozek were walking toward the house where Mrs. Ilski lived with the two girls, she was grateful to the boy for his moral support. By keeping silent, but squeezing her arm in a friendly way, he let her know that he understood what she was going through and sympathized.

It was Krysia who spotted them first and rushed out to meet them. Nina saw with amazement the difference that an absence of one year could make in a girl Krysia's age. At thirteen she was much better looking and at the same time more mature and serious. She took charge of the situation and, after embracing each of them, told them that: "Mother and Myszka are waiting in the house. Both have changed physically, Myszka especially, but since you have both changed also, nobody should be shocked. Please be careful what you say to Myszka! She is still not OK and any reference to the war upsets her terribly."

Soon Nina verified the truth of those remarks. Mrs. Ilski's alteration was less in appearance (except for her grey hair) than in a kind of sorrowfulness emanating from her. Hugging her, Nina knew that part of her old mother was gone – her energy, independence of spirit, and humor. Changes in Myszka were shattering. Painfully thin, with a bald head and huge black fearful eyes, she clung to Mrs. Ilski and appeared at first not to recognize Nina at all. After a while, she accepted reluctantly that the newcomer was Kinga's sister and treated her with distant politeness. Nothing remained of their old relationship.

Jozek's meeting with Myszka, the first for both of them, also produced mixed results. After looking at him with shocked surprise, the girl explained that she had seen him dead of cholera together with other inmates of block B. "Was it only a coma?" she cried. "How on earth did you come out of it?" It was useless to try to explain to her that this was a case of mistaken identity, as they had been warned by Mrs. Ilski that efforts to contradict Myszka were ill advised. Jozek's vague explanations that he had come out from 'there' safely and was now alive and kicking were accepted without major problems. However, Myszka's insistent enquiries regarding a boy Zbyszek, whom she had seen lying side by side with Jozek in the camp morgue, were difficult to deal with even for a boy with Jozek's imagination. His clumsy explanations that he was not sure of Zbyszek's fate brought on him Myszka's violent accusations of scandalous indifference towards a fellow inmate. "Perhaps he was also in a coma! If you could get out of the morgue, why couldn't he? Did you leave him there? Oh God, Oh God, what if he was buried alive?" Further embarrassment was fortunately prevented by the approach of a nurse who informed them that the captain was up and had been sitting in his chair since six o'clock this morning waiting for his daughter. He was simply dying to see Nina and to meet Jozek.

Before leaving for the hospital, Mrs. Ilski found an opportunity to look at Nina for a while without speaking, to commiserate with her over past problems, and to exchange with her the latest news. She confirmed that Mr. Ilski was making a good recovery, although his left eye was gone as was his right foot, and that the prognosis for Myszka was also somewhat positive. "All she needs is quiet and care," she said with a beseeching look toward Jozek, who was waiting for them at the door, in an effort to put some distance between himself and the ex-inmate of the Nazi labor camp. "It is mostly psychological, you know, for physically she is doing all right. She spends hours poring over Kinga's poems. Did you know, Nina, that Kinga wrote beautiful verses in that camp, and quite a few of our literary people here are interested in publishing them? I asked to make copies of those sheets, and you will have your own copy of her work."

Krysia reverted to the subject of Myszka, telling Nina that the girl's aunt from Sweden, had written her two letters. However, they did not find favor with the niece. The very first letter she burnt without reading, declaring that she did not like strangers. The other, Krysia managed to save long enough to copy the lady's address. The correspondence was later torn to pieces, without being opened. Mrs. Ilski wrote to the aunt explaining the situation.

"Of course I told her that she is one of us," she said with a trace of her old assertiveness. "If Myszka does not want to go to Sweden, or anywhere else, she should not."

"But mom, this lady is Myszka's close relative, and apparently quite well off, judging from her company's address. It is ridiculous to treat her as a stranger," Krysia argued. Her mother was not convinced. "If she wants to stay with us, she stays with us."

The visit with her father was, for Nina, a heart rending experience. A man still swathed in bandages with a patch on his eye looked at her from his hospital chair. How much he must have suffered during those long months! She was afraid to embrace him, although he laughingly told her that he was not made of feathers. "These bandages will be gone in a month or so and the doctors tell me that you will have your old father back, Nina, minus one eye and a foot," he promised with a smile. He also told her that she had changed for the better in the last six years and that he 'liked what he saw.' She then realized how silly her fears had been. This was her dear old dad. Whether it was one day or six years of his being away, it did not make any difference.

So now they were together again, although without Kinga, and Myszka was temporarily undergoing through some psychological tests. Soon they would also be without Jozek. Because of his forthcoming departure, a lot of time was devoted to the boy. Both parents were keenly interested in his plans for the future and the wellbeing of the orphanage. They asked him to convey their love to the people in Rawa.

During their second visit with the patient late in the afternoon, Jozek confessed that in that one day he had suffered still another episode of mistaken identity. Close to the house where Mrs. Ilski and the two girls lived was a building designed to house newly released concentration camp victims.[65] Passing this institution on his way to the hospital, Jozek, who had separated himself from the others in order to inspect a nearby store, saw two men, or rather two skeletal human beings, warming themselves in the sun on a bench. What happened next shocked him to the core. Upon seeing the boy, the two men (who looked to him extremely old) jumped up and, taking off their caps, bowed to him deeply with a mixture of fear and obsequiousness. "I can hardly get over it," the shaken boy confessed. "They were so old that they could have been my great grandfathers! Why did they behave like this?"

"All the men in that building suffer from post concentration camp delusions," explained Mr. Ilski. "The two you encountered obviously believed that they were still in the camp. I think they come from Dachau where, as in other camps, the inmates were under an obligation to show servility toward any German. Severe beatings or worse were meted out to the reluctant. Your appearance (relatively well-fed and clothed) prevented them from taking you for one of them, so they assigned you to the 'master race.'"

"So they took him for one of the guards? But isn't Jozek too young for camp duty?" asked Nina. "Not at all," replied her mother. "In the last months of the war, youngsters from the Hitlerjugend organization were frequently recruited to fill the positions of adult men needed at the front. As far as I have heard, they were not any better than their predecessors."

Nina's attention was focused on the degrading and vicious camp regulations. "I do not think that I would do it, no matter what the consequences," she cried. "To bow to those murderers? To be humiliated in this way? Not I!"

"There is no humiliation if you do things under duress," her mother argued. "It would have been unwise to oppose those, after all, unimportant rules. All Polish inmates knew that they should try to stay alive as long as possible. There were only two things that they were forbidden to do by our underground government.

---

[65] There was a difference between the Nazi labor camps, where Myszka and Kinga were sent, and concentration camps, which were veritable death factories.

One was taking food by force from another inmate, another was reporting on another prisoner to the Nazi authorities."

"If you thought that you were too weak to withstand the temptation to do one or both of those two things in order to save your own skin," came unexpectedly from Krysia, "you had to kill yourself."

"I thought I knew everything about the war," reflected Nina. Aloud she stammered, "How?"

Her sister informed her calmly that the best way out, under the circumstances was to take a walk toward the electrified barbed wire which had surrounded Nazi camps. If the electricity in the fence did not kill you, the guards who operated search lights night and day would oblige.

"She is only thirteen and she is already well-acquainted with this horror," Nina thought with compassion. "She never even had a childhood!" Deep affection toward her sister, so young and so advanced in her understanding of the world, stirred in her breast.

A nurse, who for a while had been listening to them, related some of her experiences. Two of her female patients had obstinately refused to eat the food supplied by the hospital, despite their urgent need for nourishment. Their argument was that there might be arsenic in the meals. Some of the experiments conducted in the camps allegedly involved arsenic poisoning. As poison-induced deaths were not easy, the two women decided that they preferred death by starvation. No arguments served to convince them that they were no longer under Nazi rule.

"And," asked Jozek in a low voice, "are they still alive?"

"Oh yes," was the cheerful reply. "We devised a routine by which an attendant nurse eats a portion of the dishes served to them. After waiting some time to assess the benignity of the food, they eat it themselves. I would hardly call it eating. They devour it."

Nina's Decision

It was another sleepless night for Nina. She was sharing the room with Krysia, while her mother and Myszka, who suffered from nightmares, slept in another. Jozek was located in the dining room, close to the kitchen, with which he had already become familiar last night. To the delight of the whole family, including a, by now, almost conciliatory Myszka, he produced a pile of pancakes with German manufactured jam from beet roots.

For the first time in her life, Nina was undergoing an emotional upheaval which she did not understand. What was it that was bothering her so? Why couldn't she sleep? An awful urgency to make an all important decision oppressed her, without any awareness of what that decision might be. This by itself was surprising. Hadn't she finally reached the family of whom she had dreamt for months? Shouldn't she feel peaceful and tranquil?

"What is it, Nina?" Krysia whispered from the darkness. "Tell me."

"I hardly know myself," groaned her sister.

"Tell me," persisted Krysia.

"She is good, mature, and very intelligent, far more so than I was at her age," Nina thought. "I had two sisters, both of them wiser and more talented than I." Meanwhile Krysia was talking again.

"Our future abroad, now that we know our parents cannot live in Poland, may not be too bad. I have already learned a lot of the English language and will probably enroll in an English high school. For it is in England that we will be settling.[66] Mother will probably find employment in one of the international libraries and Dad will have his pension. There will be many of his army friends there, so he will not feel abandoned and useless. It will not be bad, Nina, do not worry about us."

"She is already excluding me from the family circle," flashed through Nina's mind, and she did not know if it caused her pain, or relief. Perhaps both?

"Krysia," she asked with a trembling voice. "Would you think me a terrible beast if I were to go back to Poland? That would mean a separation from all of you, perhaps for years and years."

"I would be very sorry if that occurred, but I would not think you a beast," her sister responded after a pause. "I understand that there is an awful lot to do in Poland. Do not worry about them," she added and they both knew that she was referring to the parents. "I'll manage. Myszka will help."

---

[66] Those Poles who were reluctant to return to Poland under the communist regime were allowed to remain abroad by several countries, including Britain and the United States.

"Will you? Will you?" asked Nina full of admiration for this thirteen-year-old sage. She was assured again and again that it would be so.

The next day, Nina went to see her father, accompanied by Mrs. Ilski. In her mind she rehearsed a scene from a week or so ago, when she tried to convince Mrs. Latowicz that there must be people in Poland who would face the reality and make the best of it. She repeated those arguments quite suddenly in front of her parents, just as they were engaged in discussing the English language. "How can any country recover, when its people are not there?" she ended lamely. They did not seem surprised at her outburst. Did they expect it? Her mother embraced her and whispered into her ear. "Go back. You are needed there. Go!" Her father made no such commitment at first. "I always wanted my children to be idealistic," he said. "But idealism must be tempered by prudence. You will be in a Poland ruled by a foreign government.[67] Every effort to rebuild the devastated country may be hampered. It is not enough to be prepared to work hard, to suffer shortages and indignities. It is also necessary to be both upright and canny. Remember the biblical advice to be like a fox in the pursuit of good? It would do nobody any good if they sent you to Siberia."

"She knows. She has had plenty of lessons of the kind you mention," his wife interceded. Reluctantly, he relented after extracting from his daughter her word of honor that she would avoid situations which he vaguely described as 'in any way dangerous.' That she would not open the purse he handed to her before crossing the border. She knew that he wanted to avoid any arguments as to its contents being too much.

"I hope to God that what you are doing is right," he said at their parting. "But I cannot be convinced that it is prudent. However, prudence should not always prevail in life. Other considerations may be more important."

So that was that. Hearing about her decision, Jozek shouted with joy. "Good for you Nina! We managed with the Nazis, we will manage with the commies.[68] Imagine what they, in Rawa, will say when they see you! Mrs. Latowicz and Irena

---

[67] For a comprehensive description of the oppressive Soviet rule in Poland, see Tomasz Balbus, *Major Ludwik Marszalek 'Zbroja,' (1912-1948) Zolnierz Polski Podziemnej*, Wroclaw, Gajt Wydawnictwo, 1999).

[68] "The spontaneous social effort to inculcate the young with the history of the Polish underground resistance during World War II to both the Nazi and the Soviet invaders played an important role... . The more the communist regime maligned that effort, the more attractive its traditions and sacrifices became... This helped to sustain large pockets of... quiet conspiratorial resistance [which] kept open the option of reaching out someday for more ambitious societal self-emancipation," Zbigniew Brzezinski, *The Grand Failure*, (NY: Charles Scribner's Sons, 1989), p. 115.

as well! But what about your precious Marek?" he added with a sidelong glance. "Didn't you make plans for meeting somewhere in Britain, under the gracious auspices of His Majesty?"

"Oh, bah, nothing like that was said," she responded fretfully. "At any rate, it is not important now. Not very important," she corrected herself.

Jozek was dispatched early to Iza and Jerzy to obtain four, rather than three, Serbian identity cards, which originally were to be prepared for the married couple and himself. There was no problem, since skill in document fabrication, which had become a genuine art under the occupation, crossed borders and flourished among the allies as well.

"Whatever happens, I will see you within a year or two," Nina promised Krysia when parting. "I do not know how, but I will. They are bound to start communication between Poland and the western countries, if only because of the refugees."

Krysia was of the same opinion. "What we know about the Soviet Union, the West does not know, or perhaps does not want to know. But being on the same side when fighting Germany makes them inclined toward closer ties. Both the British and the Soviets have common economic interests, and have to deal with each other. Poland is now a Soviet satellite. Tragically."

"It also means," added a physician who visited Myszka, "that Soviet crimes will not be mentioned in the international arena. While the Germans have already paid and will pay for what they have done, the Russians are hailed as 'dear friends' and the fact that they actively collaborated with the Germans in the first two years of the war, as well as their mass execution and deportation of Poles and others, will probably be lost in oblivion. There will be no reparations."[69]

The parting with her parents and Myszka was tearful and there were moments when Nina considered canceling her plans. But those were only moments of weakness. With her parents' blessing, Krysia's assurances, and with Kinga's poems in her backpack, she joined Iza, Jerzy, and Jozek in the Polish Center. All three of them exuded optimism about their personal and national future and congratulated Nina on her decision. As was expected, no problems arose on the border, which this time they crossed legally. On the contrary, the Russian soldiers who inspected their papers, wished them luck and good fortune in the ranks of Tito's communist partisans.

After retrieving their bicycles from the melina, they confirmed the date and place of their future meeting with Iza and Jerzy and said their good-byes. Mounting their bicycles, they rode east. With every turn of the wheels they were coming closer

---

[69]   This remained true until now.

and closer to what to them was dear and familiar, despite the temporary presence of the uninvited and resented guests. There, behind the horizon, lay the challenge. "Why are you tearing along like a demented hawk?" Jozek shouted behind the madly pedaling Nina. "Do you want to break your neck?" But she paid no attention. She was happy that she had made the decision, that she had obtained her family's agreement and understanding. The future she wished for was beckoning to her. Tomorrow she was going to be nineteen! Raising her hand as if in greeting, she called out, "Here I come, Poland!"

Bibliography

Balbus, Thomasz. Doctoral dissertation, *Major 'Zbroja'*, (Wroclaw University Press, 1999).

Bartelski, Lesław W. *Powstanie Warszawskie* [Warsaw Uprising] (Warszawa: Iskry, 1988).

Bartoszewski, Władysław. *The Warsaw Ghetto* (MA: Beacon Press, 1987).

Berstein, Carl. „The Idiot Culture", *New Republic*, 1992.

Bor-Komorowski, T. *The Secret Army* (Nashville: The Battery Press, 1984).

Brzeziński, Zbigniew *Out of Control* (NY: Charles Scribner's Sons, 1993).

Brzeziński Zbigniew, *The Grand Failure* (NY: Charles Scribner's Sons, 1989).

Dadlez, Anna R. *Journey from Innocence* (NY: Columbia University Press, 1998).

Davies, Norman. *Rising '44 The Battle for Warsaw* (NY: Macmillan, 2003).

Davies, Norman. *Heart of Europe* (Cambridge: Oxford University Press, 1966).

Dziewanowski, M.K. *Poland in the Twentieth Century* (NY: Columbia University Press, 1977).

Karski, Jan. *Story of a Secret State* (Boston: Houghton Mifflin Co., 1945).

Korbonski, Stefan. *Fighting Warsaw* (Minerva Press, 1956).

Lane, Arthur Bliss. *I Saw Poland Betrayed: An Ambassador Reports to the American People*, (Indianapolis: Bobbs-Merrill, 1948).

Loewenheim, Francis L. et al., eds. *Roosevelt and Churchill Their Secret Wartime Correspondence* (NY: Dutton & Co. Inc., 1975).

Lukas, Richard C. *The Forgotten Holocaust, the Poles under German Occupation, 1939-1944* (KY: The University Press of Kentucky, 1986).

Nowak, Jan. *The Warsaw Courier* (MI: Wayne State University Press, 1966).

Piotrowski, Tadeusz. *Poland's Holocaust* (NC: McFarland and Co., 1998).

Pontin, Clive. *1940 Myth and Reality, The Truth about Britain's 'Finest Hour'* (Chicago, Ivan R. Dee, 1991).

Seton-Watson, Hugh. *The East European Revolution* (NY: Praeger, 1958).

Szpilman, Władysław. *The Pianist* (NY: Picador 2002).

Tomaszewski, Irene, ed. and trans, *lam First a Human Being: The Prison Letters of Krystyna Wituska* (Montreal, Quebec: Vehicule Press, 1998).

Tworkowski, Alfred. *Polska Walcząca w Oczach CIA* [Fighting Poland in CIA Records] Chicago, Wici, 1994).

Wandycz, Piotr S. *Price of Freedom* (London and New York: Routledge, 1992).

Zawodny, Janusz. *Death in the Forest* (IN: University of Notre Dame Press, 1962).

ISBN 83-7363-412-6

Computer design
MAYA Marcin Ściborek
e-mail: biuro@mayadesign.pl

Cover Design
MAYA Marcin Ściborek

Publisher
The John Paul II Catholic University of Lublin
Al. Racławickie 14, 20-950 Lublin
e-mail: wydawnictwo@kul.lublin.pl

Printing and Binding
MAGIC
ul. Spadochroniarzy 7, 20-043 Lublin
e-mail: info@magic.lublin.pl